1976

INTERNATIONAL SERIES OF MONOGRAPHS IN

PURE AND APPLIED MATHEMATICS

GENERAL EDITORS: I. N. SNEDDON, M. STARK AND S. ULAM

VOLUME 70

LECTURES IN GENERAL ALGEBRA

LECTURES IN
GENERAL ALGEBRA

by

A. G. KUROSH

Translated by
ANN SWINFEN

English translation edited by
P. M. COHN
Reader in Pure Mathematics
University of London

PERGAMON PRESS
OXFORD · LONDON · EDINBURGH · NEW YORK
PARIS · FRANKFURT

Pergamon Press Ltd., Headington Hill Hall Oxford
4 & 5 Fitzroy Square, London W.1
Pergamon Press (Scotland) Ltd., 2 & 3 Teviot Place, Edinburgh 1
Pergamon Press Inc., 122 East 55th St., New York 22, N.Y.
Gauthier-Villars, 55 Quai des Grands-Augustins, Paris 6
Pergamon Press GmbH, Kaiserstrasse 75, Frankfurt-am-Main

First English edition 1965

Library of Congress Catalog Card No. 64–8735

This is an edited translation of the original volume *Лекции по общей
алгебре (Lektsii po obshchei algebre)*, published
in 1962 by Fizmatgiz, Moscow

Printed in Poland
PWN−DRP

CONTENTS

v

PREFACE

IN THE twenties and thirties of this century, general books on mathematics revealed that in algebra, one of the oldest branches of mathematics, a radical revision had taken place. This revision, and in fact the transformation of algebra to a set-theoretical, axiomatic science, having as the fundamental object of study algebraic operations performed on elements of an arbitrary nature, was brought about by all the preceding developments in algebra. It began at the end of the nineteenth century, and continued, gradually growing stronger, during the first decades of the twentieth century, but it was only the appearance in 1930 and 1931 of the two-volume *Modern Algebra* by van der Waerden which made the ideas, results and methods of this "new" algebra accessible to all mathematicians who were not specialists in algebra.

It is well known how important, and sometimes also decisive, the influence of this modern algebra subsequently was on the development of many branches of mathematics, of which we may first mention topology and functional analysis. At the same time, in the last three decades the intensive and even tempestuous development of this algebra has continued, revealing its many new connections with neighbouring branches of science, and as a result the appearance of modern or, as we prefer to call it, general algebra is totally changed from what it was thirty years ago.

During these decades the older branches of general algebra — the theory of fields and the theory of associative and associative-commutative rings — have undergone considerably greater development. It was to these that van der Waerden's book was principally devoted. Even more decisive has been the revision in the theory of groups, the oldest of all branches of general algebra. Together with this the theory of rings, to a considerable extent, has now become the theory of non-associative rings, including as a composite part the theory of Lie rings and algebras. Topological algebra has arisen and come to occupy a very important position, and the theory of ordered algebraic structures has developed parallel to this. The theory of lattices has appeared and developed quickly, and in

very recent years there has arisen, parallel to it, the theory of
categories, which will certainly have a very great future. Within the
framework of the classical divisions of general algebra independent regions have been explored, such as homological algebra,
which has already been found to have many applications in topology and algebraic geometry, projective algebra, which includes the basic contents of projective geometry, and differential
algebra, which applies general algebra directly to the theory
of differential equations. The theories of semigroups and quasi-
groups ceased to be simply theories of "generalized" groups
and have found their own paths of development and their own
fields of application. Finally, there has arisen the general theory
of universal algebras and the theory of models, even more bound
up with mathematical logic.

It would seem that the fundamental ideas and most important
results which have accumulated in general algebra up to the
present time would, in some measure, have become part of the
scientific equipment of every cultured mathematician, as it was
in the thirties that an examination in modern algebra was established for the majority of aspiring mathematicians. In fact,
however, this is far from being the case — the acquaintance of
a vast number of mathematicians with the achievements of general algebra remains now to a remarkable degree on a level with
the beginning of the thirties.

The reasons for this can easily be indicated. The basic text
from which young mathematicians study general algebra is still
van der Waerden's book, although this book, which is quite
remarkable and has played an outstanding part in the history
of twentieth century mathematics, is already so far from the present state of algebra that the author himself, in bringing out
the fourth edition, has called it simply *Algebra*.

In foreign literature there are other books which are more
recent. Some of them, modernizing somewhat the material presented in van der Waerden's book, simply supplement and expand
it in the directions of the author's personal scientific interests.
This has resulted in useful books which, however, do not give
a systematic presentation of the contemporary state of general
algebra. Moreover, these are usually books of considerable
volume, addressed rather to algebraists than to mathematicians
specializing in other subjects. There are books of another type

which are essentially collections of fundamental algebraic concepts and their simplest properties. Useful as reference books, such books do not enable the reader to appreciate all the originality and profundity of modern algebraic investigation — the most profound and remarkable results in it are either omitted altogether or formulated in the exercises.

In order to show mathematicians the contemporary appearance of general algebra, a book must have a rather different character. Not very large in volume, it must be addressed to a reader who is taking a university course in higher algebra and wishes to supplement his algebraic education, but perhaps does not intend to choose algebra as his special subject. This, however, does not exclude the possibility that an algebraist also, in questions far from his own special interests, may find something useful in this book.

Such a book must not and cannot replace the monographs on the separate branches of general algebra. Nor must it be a collection of chapters quoted from these monographs. The purpose of such a book should be to show the fundamental divisions of modern general algebra, for the most part in their relation to each other, where the exposition leads up to the various profound theorems and is aimed at these theorems. The choice of a very small number of such theorems from each of the separate branches of general algebra must necessarily be determined by the personal evaluation of the author. These theorems themselves certainly cannot be explained in the most general form which they have attained at present.

The contents of this book, clearly, are very like a mosaic, and it is sometimes necessary for the reader, following the author, to jump, within the limits of a single paragraph, from one branch of general algebra to another. Breaking down the material into chapters has to be so conventional, that there can be no discussion of the interdependence of chapters.

I had occasion to speak about the desirability that a book of this type should appear in 1951 at the All-union conference on algebra and the theory of numbers (see *Uspekhi mat. nauk* 7, No 3, p. 167 (1952), and I began to write it in 1956. In the four years which have elapsed since then work on the book has been repeatedly interrupted and resumed, the plan of the book has been altered frequently, many paragraphs have been written several times, material which had already been written has been rearranged, altered, rejected. In other words, the work has taken on such a character that I have been reminded more and more often of Balzac's novel *The Unknown Masterpiece.* It was sensible therefore to conclude the work, without trying to bring the book to a state which would correspond with the program outlined above. The reader will detect without difficulty in what ways the book differs from this program.

I might remark that the name of the book is entirely justified by the fact that it is based on three long specialized courses in general algebra given by me in the last ten years at Moscow University.

Here and there in the book there are included the formulations of some results which are not proved or used in the book itself. It is presumed that these formulae, distinguished from the main body of the text by stars, will not be omitted by the reader. It is hardly necessary to emphasize specially that the inclusion in the book of this additional information does not mean that the corresponding parts of the book have been brought up to the very latest results obtained at the present day.

References to articles in journals which occur in the body of the book are in general fairly random and cannot be regarded as material on the history of algebra in the twentieth century. On the other hand, there is appended to the book a fairly full index of books on the various branches of general algebra published in the thirty years. It also includes some outline articles.

Because of the complexity of the plan of the book, which is like a mosaic, it has very often been necessary to refer to preceding material, although it is clear that in most cases the reader will find these references superfluous. The reference V.3.6 means: Chapter V, section 3, subsection 6.

I have had the pleasure of reporting on the original plan of the book and a series of its chapters, as well as some of the various revisions, to the seminar on general algebra at Moscow University. I wish to thank my colleagues in the seminar most sincerely for their interest in my work, their advice and criticism. I also wish to extend my warmest thanks to Oleg Nikolaevich Golovin who took on the great labour of editing the book, carefully reading the manuscript through and making many valuable suggestions.

A. Kurosh

CHAPTER ONE

RELATIONS

§ 1. Sets

1. The concepts and methods of the theory of sets are fundamental to general algebra. A reader who is beginning the study of general algebra does not, of course, need to be reminded of the definitions of such set-theoretical concepts as *subset*, the *complement* of a subset in a set, the *empty set*, the *intersection* and *union* of sets. We note that to denote the intersection and union of sets we will use respectively the symbols ∩ and ∪, to denote the relationship of a subset or an element to a set we will use respectively the symbols ⊂ and ∈, and the complement of the subset A in the set M we will denote by $M \setminus A$. The empty set is denoted by $\emptyset$.

The operations of intersection and union of sets are related to each other by the following mutually dual distributive laws: for any three sets A, B, C

$$A \cap (B \cup C) = (A \cap B) \cup (A \cap C), \qquad (1)$$

$$A \cup (B \cap C) = (A \cup B) \cap (A \cup C). \qquad (2)$$

We will only prove the second of these identities. Because $B \cap C \subseteq B$, then

$$A \cup (B \cap C) \subseteq A \cup B;$$

analogously

$$A \cup (B \cap C) \subseteq A \cup C,$$

and therefore the left-hand side of equation (2) is contained in its right-hand side. On the other hand, if the element x is contained in the right-hand side of equation (2), then simultaneously

$$x \in (A \cup B), \quad x \in (A \cup C). \qquad (3)$$

If $x \in A$, then x is contained in the left-hand side of equation (2). If, however, x does not belong to A, then it follows from (3) that x belongs both to B and to C, i.e. it belongs to the intersec-

1

tion $B \cap C$, and therefore x again belongs to the left side of equation (2). The whole of the right-hand side of equation (2) is thus contained in its left-hand side. Thus equation (2) is proved.

2. The reader will also be familiar with the concept of a *mapping* or *correspondence*, or *single-valued function*. If φ is a mapping of the set A into the set B, i.e. onto the whole of B or onto a subset of it, then we will use the symbol $\varphi : A \to B$, and the image of the element $a \in A$ under the mapping φ we will denote by $a\varphi$.

If $\varphi : A \to B$, $\psi : B \to C$, then the successive application of the mappings φ and ψ leads to a well defined mapping of the set A into the set C, which we will denote by $\varphi\psi$ and which we will call the *product* of the mapping φ by the mapping ψ. Thus, for all a in A

$$a(\varphi\psi) = (a\varphi)\psi. \tag{4}$$

This multiplication of mappings may be called partial: if any two mappings $\varphi : A \to B$ and $\psi : A' \to B'$ are given, then the product $\varphi\psi$ does not always exist; it exists if and only if for all $a \in A$, $a\varphi \in A'$. From this it follows that *for mappings of any set A into itself the product always exists.*

The multiplication of mappings is associative: *if we are given the mappings*

$$\varphi : A \to B, \quad \psi : B \to C, \quad \chi : C \to D, \tag{5}$$

then

$$(\varphi\psi)\chi = \varphi(\psi\chi). \tag{6}$$

In fact, if a is an arbitrary element of A, then in view of (4)

$$a[(\varphi\psi)\chi] = [a(\varphi\psi)]\chi = [(a\varphi)\psi]\chi = (a\varphi)(\psi\chi) = a[\varphi(\psi\chi)].$$

In view of equation (6) the result of the successive application of the mappings (5) can be denoted by $\varphi\psi\chi$.

3. We will agree to denote the *identity mapping* of the set A into itself by ε_A; thus,

$$a\varepsilon_A = a \quad \text{for all} \quad a \in A.$$

In the multiplication of mappings the identity mapping plays the part of a unit element, because for any mappings $\varphi : A \to B$ and $\psi : C \to A$

$$\varepsilon_A\varphi = \varphi, \quad \psi\varepsilon_A = \psi.$$

The reader will be familiar with the concept of a *one–one mapping* of the set A onto the set B (i.e. a one–one correspondence between these sets). It is obvious that the mapping $\varphi: A \to B$ will be a one–one mapping of A into B if and only if [there exists a mapping inverse to it, i.e. a mapping $\varphi^{-1}: B \to A$, satisfying the conditions

$$\varphi\varphi^{-1} = \varepsilon_A, \qquad \varphi^{-1}\varphi = \varepsilon_B.$$

As is well known, if there exists a one–one mapping of the set A onto the set B, then the sets A and B are called *equipotent* or, as one also says, they have the same *power*. Here the power of a finite set coincides with the number of its elements, sets equipotent with the set of all natural numbers are called *countable*, and of sets equipotent with the set of all real numbers one says that they have the *power of the continuum*.

4. In the study of infinite sets it is very often convenient to make use of the following Axiom of Choice:

Given a set M, there exists a function φ which relates every non-empty subset A of M to one definite element $\varphi(A)$ of this subset.

In other words, the function φ *marks out* one element in each of the non-empty subsets of the set M.

The problem of the logical foundations of this axiom and of the validity of using it belongs to a group of very difficult and controversial problems at the basis of the theory of sets. We would not, however, be able to get along without the axiom of choice. For countable sets it can, in fact, be easily proved: if the elements of the set M are numbered by the natural numbers, then we obtain the required function, if in every subset A of M we pick out that element of it which has the smallest number.

In I. 6.3 we will mention some assertions which are equivalent to the axiom of choice.

§ 2. Binary relations

1. If there is given a set M, then its *square* $M \times M$ is the set of all ordered pairs (a, b), where $a, b \in M$. Let R be any subset of $M \times M$. Then, in the following way, R defines a *binary relation* (in the set M) which we will also denote by the symbol R (in concrete cases we will use different special symbols to write down relations): if $a, b \in M$, then we say that the element a is in the

4 LECTURES IN GENERAL ALGEBRA

relation R to the element b, and we denote this by aRb if and only if the pair (a, b) belongs to the subset R; thus the notations

$$aRb \quad \text{and} \quad (a, b) \in R$$

are equivalent.

The study of binary relations in the set M thus does not differ from the study of the subsets of the set $M \times M$. We can speak, in particular, of the *inclusion* of the binary relation R in the binary relation R', $R \subseteq R'$, and also of the *intersection* and *union* of binary relations. The *complement* of the binary relation R is the binary relation $\bar{R}$, defined by the subset $\bar{R} = (M \times M) \setminus R$; in other words, $a\bar{R}b$ if and only if $(a, b) \notin R$.

2. On the other hand, the fact that binary relations are given by sets of ordered pairs of elements of M makes the algebra of binary relations richer than the simple algebra of subsets of an arbitrary set. Thus, suppose that there are given in the set M the arbitrary binary relations R and S. By their *product RS* we understand the binary relation defined in the following way: $a(RS)b$ if and only if there exists in M at least one element c such that aRc and cSb.

The multiplication of binary relations is associative,

$$(RS)T = R(ST),$$

because the element a is in each of the relations $(RS)T$ and $R(ST)$ to the element b if and only if there exist elements c and d such that

$$aRc, \quad cSd, \quad dTb.$$

The multiplication of binary relations is, however, not commutative; the binary relations R and S only sometimes commute

$$RS = SR.$$

If there are given binary relations R_i (i runs through a set of indices I) and S in the set M, then

$$\left(\bigcup_{i \in I} R_i\right) S = \bigcup_{i \in I} R_i S, \quad S\left(\bigcup_{i \in I} R_i\right) = \bigcup_{i \in I} S R_i. \tag{1}$$

In fact, $a[(\bigcup_{i \in I} R_i) S]b$ is equivalent to the existence of an element c such that $a (\bigcup_{i \in I} R_i)c$ and cSb. This, however, is equivalent to the existence of an index i_0 such that $aR_{i_0}c$ and cSb, i.e. $a(R_{i_0}S)b$, and therefore $a(\bigcup_{i \in I} R_i S)b$.

We note that in equations (1) it is not possible to replace the union by the intersection.

From (1) it follows that *if we are given the binary relations R, R' and S, where $R \subseteq R'$, then*

$$RS \subseteq R'S, \qquad SR \subseteq SR'. \tag{2}$$

In fact, the inclusion $R \subseteq R'$ is equivalent to the equation $R \cup R' = R'$ from which follows the equation

$$(R \cup R')S = RS \cup R'S = R'S,$$

which is equivalent to the inclusion $RS \subseteq R'S$.

3. For every binary relation R in the set M there exists an *inverse relation* R^{-1}, defined in the following way: $aR^{-1}b$ if and only if bRa. It is clear that

$$(R^{-1})^{-1} = R$$

and that from $R \subseteq S$ it follows that $R^{-1} \subseteq S^{-1}$.

If we are given the binary relations R_i, $i \in I$, S and T in the set M, then

$$\left(\bigcap_{i \in I} R_i\right)^{-1} = \bigcap_{i \in I} R_i^{-1}, \tag{3}$$

$$\left(\bigcup_{i \in I} R_i\right)^{-1} = \bigcup_{i \in I} R_i^{-1}, \tag{4}$$

$$(ST)^{-1} = T^{-1}S^{-1}. \tag{5}$$

In fact, $a\left(\bigcap_{i \in I} R_i\right)^{-1}b$ means that $b\left(\bigcap_{i \in I} R_i\right)a$, i.e. bR_ia for all $i \in I$, whence $aR_i^{-1}b$ for all $i \in I$, and therefore $a\left(\bigcap_{i \in I} R_i^{-1}\right)b$. Equation (4) is proved analogously. Finally, $a(ST)^{-1}b$ means that $b(ST)a$, i.e. there exists an element c such that bSc and cTa, and therefore $aT^{-1}c$ and $cS^{-1}b$, whence $a(T^{-1}S^{-1})b$.

4. The *identity relation* E is defined in the following way: aEb if and only if $a = b$; in other words, the relation E is given by the set of all pairs of the form (a, a), $a \in M$. It is obvious that $E^{-1} = E$ and that for any binary relation R

$$RE = ER = R.$$

We mention also the *empty relation* 0, defined by the empty subset of the set $M \times M$. It is clear that for any binary relation R in the set M

$$0 \subseteq R \qquad \text{and} \qquad R0 = 0R = 0.$$

5. In the following paragraphs we will encounter binary relations R, given in the set M, which possess some of the following four properties:

Reflexive: aRa for all $a \in M$; in other words, $E \subseteq R$.

Transitive: if aRb and bRc, then aRc; in other words, $RR \subseteq R$.

Symmetric: if aRb, then bRa; in other words, $R^{-1} = R$.

Anti-symmetric: if aRb and bRa, then $a = b$; in other words, $R \cap R^{-1} \subseteq E$.

If the binary relation R possesses any of the four given properties, then the inverse relation R^{-1} possesses the same properties.

In fact, if $E \subseteq R$, then

$$E = E^{-1} \subseteq R^{-1}.$$

If $RR \subseteq R$, then

$$R^{-1}R^{-1} = (RR)^{-1} \subseteq R^{-1}.$$

If $R^{-1} = R$, then

$$(R^{-1})^{-1} = R = R^{-1}.$$

Finally, if $R \cap R^{-1} \subseteq E$, then

$$R^{-1} \cap (R^{-1})^{-1} = R^{-1} \cap R \subseteq E.$$

6. In the set M let us choose the subset N. A binary relation R, given in M, in a natural way *induces* a binary relation R^N in the set N: if a, $b \in N$, then aR^Nb if and only if in M it is true that aRb. In other words, taking into account that $N \times N$ is a subset of the set $M \times M$,

$$R = R \cap (N \times N).$$

It is easy to prove the following equations:

$$(R^N)^{-1} = (R^{-1})^N, \quad (\bigcap_{i \in I} R_i)^N = \bigcap_{i \in I} R_i^N, \quad (\bigcup_{i \in I} R_i)^N = \bigcup_{i \in I} R_i^N.$$

7. The concept of a binary relation has various generalizations. For instance, we consider the *n-th power* M^n of the set M, i.e. the set of all ordered systems $(a_1, a_2, \ldots, a_n)$ of n elements of the set M. Then any subset R of the set M^n defines an *n-ary relation* in the set M (when $n = 3$—a *ternary relation*). Sets in which there are given a certain number of such relations are called *models* and are the object of an independent theory.

§ 3. Equivalence relations

1. An important type of binary relations are the *equivalence relations*, i.e. binary relations possessing the properties of being reflexive, transitive, and symmetric (see I.2.5). Of the numerous concrete examples of such relations with which the reader will be familiar we will mention only the equality of fractions and the congruence of whole numbers with respect to some modulus. To write the relation of equivalence we usually use the symbols $\sim$ and $\equiv$.

2. Equivalence relations, defined on a set M, are very closely related to *the partitions of the set M into non-intersecting classes*. By a partition we understand a choice of a system of non-empty subsets in the set M (the classes of this partition) such that every element of M belongs to one and only one of these subsets.

Every partition π of the set M determines an equivalence relation in M.

In fact, if a, $b \in M$ and if we set $a \sim b$ if and only a and b belong to the same class of the partition π, then we obtain a binary relation in M obviously satisfying all the requirements of the definition of an equivalence relation.

Conversely, *every equivalence relation R given in the set M determines a partition of this set.*

Let us call the set of all those elements x of M for which aRx the *class* of the element a and denote it by K_a. From the fact that the relation R is reflexive follows the inclusion $a \in K_a$, i.e. the system of classes K_a, $a \in M$, covers the whole of the set M. Further, the symmetry of the relation R shows that from $b \in K_a$ it follows that $a \in K_b$, and the transitivity of the relation R leads to the fact that if $b \in K_a$, then from $c \in K_b$ it follows that $c \in K_a$, i.e. $K_b \subseteq K_a$. These last remarks together lead to the fact that if $b \in K_a$, then $K_b = K_a$, i.e. a class is determined by any one of its elements. If, finally, K_a and K_b are two arbitrary classes with non-empty intersection, containing, for instance, the element c, then $K_a = K_c$ and $K_b = K_c$, i.e. the classes K_a and K_b coincide. We have proved that the system of all distinct classes of the form K_a is a partition of the set M.

It is obvious that the transition from a partition π of the set M to the equivalence relation determined by it and then to the partition of the set M determined by the latter leads once again to the partition π. *Between the equivalence relations in the set M and*

*the partitions of the set M into non-intersecting classes there is
thus established a one–one correspondence.*

3. *If the equivalence relations R_i, $i \in I$, are given in the set M,
then their intersection will also be an equivalence relation.*

In fact, from aR_ia for all $i \in I$ it follows that $a(\bigcap_{i \in I} R_i)a$. Further, if $a(\bigcap_{i \in I} R_i)b$ and $b(\bigcap_{i \in I} R_i)c$, then aR_ib and bR_ic for all $i \in I$,
whence aR_ic for all $i \in I$, and therefore $a(\bigcap_{i \in I} R_i)c$. Finally, if
$a(\bigcap_{i \in I} R_i)b$, then aR_ib for all $i \in I$, i.e. bR_ia for all $i \in I$, whence
$b(\bigcap_{i \in I} R_i)a$.

It can be verified without difficulty that if the partitions π_i
of the set M correspond to the equivalence relations R_i, $i \in I$,
then to the equivalence relation $\bigcap_{i \in I} R_i$ corresponds the partition
whose classes are all non-empty intersections of classes, taken
one from each of the partitions π_i, $i \in I$. We call this partition
the *intersection of the partitions* π_i, $i \in I$.

If the equivalence relations R_i, $i \in I$, are given in the set M,
then their union, understood in the sense of the union of the
binary relations, will not necessarily, in general, be an equivalence
relation. *In the set M there exists, however, an equivalence relation
which contains all the relations R_i, $i \in I$* (in the sense of the inclusion of binary relations), *but is itself included in any other equivalence relation containing all the R_i, $i \in I$.* This equivalence relation
will be called the *join* of the equivalence relations R_i, $i \in I$.

To prove this we define a binary relation S in the set M in the
following way: aSb if and only if there is at least one way of
choosing a finite system of elements in M

$$a = c_0, \ c_1, c_2, \ldots, c_{n-1}, c_n = b, \tag{1}$$

such that for $k = 1, 2, \ldots, n$ there exists at least one index $i_k \in I$
for which $c_{k-1} R_{i_k} c_k$. The relation S is obviously reflexive, transitive and symmetric. If, however, T is any equivalence relation
containing all the R_i, $i \in I$, and if aSb, where the system of elements
(1) corresponds to these elements, then from $c_{k-1} R_{i_k} c_k$ it follows
that $c_{k-1} T c_k$, $k = 1, 2, \ldots \ldots n$, and therefore from the transitivity of T it follows that aTb.

* The product RS of two equivalence relations R and S is
an equivalence relation if and only if the relations R and S com-

mute, $RS = SR$. If this is true, then the join of the equivalence relations R and S coincides with their product as binary relations [*Šik, Spisy vyd, přirodovŏde fakult. Masarykovy univ.* No. 3, 97–102 (1954)].*

4. The set of classes of the partition corresponding to a given equivalence relation R in the set M will be denoted by M/R and called the *quotient set* of the set M with respect to the equivalence relation R. The mapping of the set M onto the quotient set M/R, which maps every element $a \in M$ onto that class of the partition corresponding to R in which the element a lies, is called the *natural mapping* of M onto M/R.

Between the equivalence relations existing in a set M and the mappings of this set onto certain other sets there exists a close connection, which is a prototype of the so-called "homomorphism theorems", which we will continually encounter in the subsequent chapters of this book. In fact, if there is given a mapping φ of the set M onto some set N, there exists an equivalence relation R in the set M completely defined by it (i.e. a partition of this set): for the elements a, $b \in M$ we set aRb if and only if $a\varphi = b\varphi$. By relating to every element x of N the class of those elements of M which have x as their image in the mapping φ, *we obtain a one–one mapping ξ of the set N onto the set M/R, where the product $\varphi\xi$ coincides with the natural mapping of M onto M/R.*

§ 4. Partial ordering

1. Other important types of binary relations are the *relations of partial ordering*, i.e. binary relations which possess the properties of being reflexive, transitive and anti-symmetric. A set M with a partial ordering given in it is called *partially ordered*. We shall use the symbol $\leqslant$ to denote a partial ordering; if $a, b \in M$ and $a \leqslant b$, then, depending on the circumstances, we shall say that *a is less than or equal to b, a is contained in b, a precedes b.*

If $a \leqslant b$ and $a \neq b$, we write $a < b$ and we say that *a is less than b, a is strictly contained in b* etc. The binary relation $<$ will not of course be reflexive. By $\geqslant$ and $>$ we denote the relations inverse to the relations $\geqslant$ and $>$, i.e., for instance, $a \geqslant b$ (*a is greater than or equal to b, a contains b, a follows b*) if and only if $b \leqslant a$.

Let there be given a partial ordering in the set M. Elements a and b of this set will be called *comparable* if $a \leqslant b$ or $b \geqslant a$. Certainly not every two elements of M are necessarily comparable—in fact this is the reason why we speak of "partial" ordering. Thus we obtain the *trivial* partial ordering of the set M if we set $a \leqslant b$ only when $a = b$; in this case distinct elements of M will not be comparable. A partially ordered set in which any two elements are comparable is called an *ordered set* or *a linearly ordered set*, or *a chain*.

2. In different branches of mathematics ordered and partially ordered sets are encountered extraordinarily often. As our first examples of ordered sets we may mention the set of natural numbers and the set of points on a straight line (i.e. the set of all real numbers), both of them in their natural ordering. Examples of partially (but not linearly) ordered sets are:

the set $\tilde{N}$ of all subsets of some given set N with the relation of set-theoretical inclusion $\subseteq$ as the relation of partial ordering;

the set of all continuous real functions, defined on the segment $[0, 1]$, if $f \leqslant g$ means that for all x in this segment $f(x) \leqslant g(x)$;

the set of all natural numbers, if $a \leqslant b$ is understood in the sense that b is divisible by a.

* Every partial ordering of a given set M can be extended to a linear ordering of this set, i.e. can be included in a linear ordering (in the sense of the inclusion of binary relations, see I.2.1) [Szpilrajn *Fund. Math.* **16**, 386–389 (1930)].*

3. Let there be given a one–one correspondence φ between the partially ordered sets M and M',

$$a\varphi = a', \quad a \in M, \quad a' \in M'.$$

If from $a \leqslant b$, where $a, b \in M$, it always follows that $a\varphi \leqslant b\varphi$ and conversely, then φ is called an *isomorphism* between M and M', and the sets M and M' themselves are called *isomorphic* partially ordered sets. It is obvious that in the cases when the partial ordering is an independent object of study, and the nature of the elements of which the sets under consideration are composed is of no importance, isomorphic sets can be regarded as identical.

4. We know (see I.2.6) that a partial ordering given in a set M induces some binary relation in every subset of this set; it is easy to see that this will also be a partial ordering. We say that a partially ordered set M is *isomorphically embedded in* a partially ordered set N, if there exists an isomorphic mapping of the set M onto some subset N' of the set N, where N' is considered with the partial ordering induced by the partial ordering of the set N.

5. The following theorem emphasizes the special part played by the first of the examples mentioned in I.4.2 of a partially ordered set.

Every partially ordered set M can be isomorphically embedded in the set $\tilde{N}$ of all subsets of some set N, partially ordered by inclusion. As the set N we can take, for example, M itself.

In fact, we relate to every element a of M the subset A consisting of all elements $x \in M$ such that $x \leqslant a$. Let a, $b \in M$, and let A, B be the subsets corresponding to them. If $A = B$, then $b \leqslant a$, $a \leqslant b$, whence $a = b$. This proves that the correspondence $a \to A$ is a one–one mapping of the set M into the set $\tilde{M}$ of all its subsets. If, further, $a \leqslant b$, then from $x \leqslant a$ it will follow that $x \leqslant b$, i.e. $A \subseteq B$. Conversely, if $A \subseteq B$, then $a \in B$, i.e. $a \leqslant b$. Thus the correspondence $a \to A$ is an isomorphic embedding of M in $\tilde{M}$.

6. It follows from the proof in I.2.5 that *the relation inverse to the relation of a partial ordering will itself be a partial ordering.*

Partially ordered sets M and M' are called *inversely isomorphic* if one of them is isomorphic to the other, taken with the inverse partial ordering, i.e. if there exists between them a one–one correspondence φ,

$$a\varphi = a', \quad a \in M, \quad a' \in M',$$

such that $a \leqslant b$, where $a, b \in M$, if and only if $a\varphi \geqslant b\varphi$.

§ 5. The minimum condition

1. An element a of a partially ordered set M is called a *minimal element* of this set if there is no element x in M satisfying the condition $x < a$. It is clear that M can contain many different minimal elements, but may also have no such element.

Thus the set $\tilde{N}$ of all subsets of some set N possesses a unique minimal element—this will be the empty subset. In the set of all non-empty subsets of a set N the minimal elements are all the subsets consisting of one element. Finally, if the set N is infinite then the set of all its infinite subsets does not have any minimal elements.

The concept of a minimal element will now be used in defining one special class of partially ordered sets, wider than the class of finite partially ordered sets. This is the class of partially ordered sets satisfying the following *conditions, which are equivalent to each other*:

MINIMUM CONDITION. *Every non-empty subset N of the partially ordered set M possesses at least one minimal element* (in N).

DESCENDING CHAIN CONDITION.† *Every strictly descending chain of elements of the partially ordered set M,*

$$a_1 > a_2 > \ldots > a_n > \ldots,$$

breaks off at a finite point. In other words, for every descending chain of elements

$$a_1 \geqslant a_2 \geqslant \ldots \geqslant a_n \geqslant \ldots$$

there exists an index n at which this chain becomes stable, i.e.

$$a_n = a_{n+1} = \ldots$$

THE INDUCTIVE CONDITION. *All the elements of the partially ordered set M possess some property $\mathscr{E}$ if this property is possessed by all the minimal elements of this set (when they exist) and if rom the validity of the property $\mathscr{E}$ for all elements strictly preceding some element a we can deduce the validity of this property for the element a itself.*

2. We will prove the equivalence of the three given conditions. *From the minimum condition follows the inductive condition.*

In fact, let the partially ordered set M satisfy the minimum condition and let the hypothesis of the inductive condition be fulfilled for some property $\mathscr{E}$ in it. If there exist elements in M which do not possess the property $\mathscr{E}$, then let a be minimal among these elements—the existence of the element a follows from the minimum condition. The element a cannot be minimal in the whole of M, by the first premise of the inductive condition, and because all the elements strictly preceding a possess the property $\mathscr{E}$, then, by the second premise of the inductive condition, the element a itself must possess the property $\mathscr{E}$, i.e. we arrive at a contradiction.

From the inductive condition follows the descending chain condition.

---

† The concept of a descending chain which is discussed in this condition is a special case of the general concept, of a chain, introduced in I.4.1.

In fact, let the partially ordered set M satisfy the inductive condition. We apply this condition to the following property: the element a possesses the property $\mathscr{E}$ if every strictly decreasing chain of elements starting with the element a breaks off at a finite point. This property is possessed, obviously, by all the minimal elements of the set M, if any exist. On the other hand, let all the elements strictly preceding the element a possess our property $\mathscr{E}$. In this case the second term of any strictly decreasing chain starting with the element a will possess the property $\mathscr{E}$, and therefore the chain under consideration must break off, i.e. the element a also possesses the property $\mathscr{E}$. From the inductive condition it now follows that our property $\mathscr{E}$ is possessed in general by all the elements of the set M, i.e. in M every strictly decreasing chain breaks off—it begins, clearly, with some element.

From the descending chain condition follows the minimum condition.

To prove this we presuppose that the partially ordered set M does not satisfy the minimum condition, and in fact let a non-empty subset N of it have no minimal elements. Using the axiom of choice (see I.1.4) we mark out one element in every non-empty subset of N, and then we construct a sequence of elements

$$a_n, \quad n = 1, 2, \ldots \tag{1}$$

in the following way. As a_1 we take the element marked out in the subset N itself. If the element a_n has already been constructed and $a_n \in N$, then as a_{n+1} we take the element marked out in the set of elements of N strictly preceding a_n; this set is non-empty because N has no minimal elements. The sequence (1) is obviously an infinite strictly decreasing chain, i.e. the set M cannot satisfy the descending chain condition.

3. The inductive condition enables one to carry out not only proofs by induction but also *constructions by induction*. In fact, let M be a partially ordered set with the minimum condition and suppose that we wish to define on this set a function $\varphi(x)$ mapping every element x of M on some element of an auxiliary set S. We shall assume here that the function $\varphi(x)$ must satisfy some *recurrence relation*, i.e. a relation which uniquely defines a value $\varphi(a)$ for every $a \in M$ by means of the value $\varphi(b)$ for all b strictly less than a. We shall prove that *there exists a function $\varphi(x)$, which is unique, defined on the whole of the set M, satisfying*

*the recurrence relation mentioned and taking arbitrarily given
values at all minimal elements of the set M.*

We begin by proving the uniqueness. Let there exist two
distinct functions $\varphi(x)$ and $\psi(x)$ on M satisfying our conditions.
In the non-empty set of elements x for which $\varphi(x) \neq \psi(x)$, there
exists, by the minimum condition, at least one minimal element
a. This element cannot be minimal in the whole of M, because
on the minimal elements of the set M the functions $\varphi(x)$ and
$\psi(x)$ coincide by hypothesis. Hence there exist elements b such
that $b < a$, where for all these elements $\varphi(b) = \psi(b)$. The recurrence relations, however, uniquely define the values of the functions under consideration for $x = a$ by means of their values for
all $b < a$, and therefore $\varphi(a) = \psi(a)$, i.e. we arrive at a contradiction.

We go on to prove the existence of the desired function $\varphi(x)$,
assuming that on the minimal elements its values are already
given. We will say that the element $a \in M$ possesses the property $\mathscr{E}$
if on the set A of all x such that $x \leqslant a$ we can define a function
$\varphi_a(x)$ satisfying the given recurrence relations and taking the
given values on the minimal elements of M contained in a.

All the minimal elements of M obviously possess the property
$\mathscr{E}$. On the other hand, if a and b possess the property $\mathscr{E}$ and
$b < a$, applying the uniqueness of the desired function proved
above not to M but to the set B of the x for which $x \leqslant b$, we find
that for all these x,

$$\varphi_b(x) = \varphi_a(x).$$

Hence it follows that if all the elements b strictly preceding the
given element a possess the property $\mathscr{E}$, then the element a itself
also possesses this property: we obtain a function $\varphi_a(x)$ satisfying
our requirements, if for every b, $b < a$, we set

$$\varphi_a(b) = \varphi_b(b),$$

and as $\varphi_a(a)$ we take the value which is uniquely determined by
the recurrence relations.

On the basis of the inductive condition, which is satisfied in the
set M, we can now assert that all the elements of this set possess
the property $\mathscr{E}$. By letting, finally, for all $a \in M$

$$\varphi(a) = \varphi_a(a),$$

we define a function $\varphi(x)$ possessing all the required properties
and in this way we complete the proof of the theorem.

4. A linearly ordered set satisfying the minimum condition, and therefore also the other two conditions equivalent to it, is called *well ordered*. An example of a well ordered set is the set of natural numbers in its natural ordering. Every subset of a well-ordered set is itself well ordered. From the definition of a well-ordered set it follows that it possesses a unique minimal element.

In a well-ordered set for every element *a* there exists an element immediately following *a*. The element *a* may, however, not have an element immediately preceding it; in this case it is called a *limit element*.

A partially ordered set satisfies the minimum condition if and only if all its chains (i.e. linearly ordered subsets) are well ordered.

In fact, if a partially ordered set M satisfies the minimum condition, then the same is true of all its subsets, in particular for all chains. The converse assertion follows from the fact that in the formulation of the descending chain condition, equivalent to the minimum condition, one only uses chains of the set M.

5. In a partially ordered set M one can go over to the inverse partial ordering. The minimal elements of this inverse ordering are called *maximal elements* of the set M in its original ordering, and a descending chain in the inverse ordering is called an *ascending chain* of the set M. In general in this way we can obtain a dual concept (or assertion) for every concept (assertion) connected with partial ordering.

Let the partially ordered set M satisfy the minimum condition. Taking the inverse partial ordering in M, we obtain a partially ordered set satisfying the *maximum condition*. Everything stated above for sets with the minimum condition remains true for sets with the maximum condition, after the relation $\leqslant$ has been replaced by $\geqslant$ and conversely.

§ 6. Theorems equivalent to the axiom of choice

1. Let N be a subset of a partially ordered set M. Every element a of M (not necessarily contained in N) satisfying the condition $a \geqslant x$ for all $x \in N$ is called an *upper bound* of the subset N in the set M. The dual of this concept is that of a *lower bound*.

2. In addition, if M is a partially ordered set then the set of all its chains will be partially ordered by set-theoretical inclusion. Maximal elements of this latter set, if they exist, are naturally called *maximal chains* of the set M.

3. These concepts are used in the formulation of two of the following three theorems, *each of which*, as we will now prove, *is equivalent to the axiom of choice* (see I.1.4).

ZERMELO'S THEOREM. *Every set can be well ordered.*

HAUSDORFF'S THEOREM. *Every chain of a partially ordered set is contained in some maximal chain.*

KURATOWSKI-ZORN THEOREM.† *If every chain of a partially ordered set M possesses an upper bound, then every element of the set M is contained in some maximal element.*

4. We will prove the equivalence of these theorems and the axiom of choice.

Zermelo's theorem follows from the axiom of choice.

A *segment* of a well ordered set A is any subset B of it which contains, together with any of its elements b, all elements $x \in A$ such that $x \leqslant b$. The set of elements strictly preceding some element a of A will be a proper segment of the set A (i.e. a segment distinct from A itself), and these are all the proper segments: if B is such a segment then B consists of all the elements strictly preceding a minimal element of the complement $A \backslash B$, i.e. it is *defined* by this element. We will also regard the empty set as a proper segment of the set A; it is defined by a minimal element of this set.

We proceed to the proof of the theorem. Let there be given an arbitrary set M. On the basis of the axiom of choice we select one element $\varphi(N)$ in each of its non-empty subsets N. We will call a non-empty subset A of M *distinguished*, if it can be well ordered and in such a way that for every $a \in A$

$$a = \varphi(M \backslash A'),$$

where A' is the segment of the set A in the given well ordering defined by the element a. Distinguished subsets exist in M; such a subset, for instance, is that consisting of the single element $\varphi(M)$.

Let A and B be two distinguished subsets for which we choose the well orderings possessing the property mentioned in the preceding paragraph. Then both these subsets have $\varphi(M)$ as

---

† This statement is also known as Zorn's Lemma (Ed.).

their first element and therefore possess non-empty coincident segments. The union C of all the coincident segments of these two subsets will obviously be a segment in each of them; this is the greatest of the coincident segments. If the segment C were distinct both from A and from B, then, by the definition of a distinguished subset, the segment C would be defined both in A and in B by the element $\varphi(M \setminus C)$, and then A and B would possess a coincident segment greater than C, consisting of C and the element $\varphi(M \setminus C)$. This, which contradicts the definition of C, shows that one of the two selected subsets A and B is a segment of the other.

From this it follows that the union L of all the distinguished subsets of M will itself be distinguished. In fact, if a and b from L belong respectively to the distinguished subsets A and B, then they both lie in the greater of these subsets, for instance in A. Letting $a > b$ in L, if $a \geqslant b$ in this A, we obtain a linear ordering in L, which will also be a well ordering: every descending chain of elements in L is entirely contained in some distinguished subset A and therefore must break off. Finally, if $a \in L$, then a is contained in some distinguished subset A and defines in L and in A the same segment A', where $a = \varphi(M \setminus A')$. This proves that the set L is distinguished.

To complete the proof it remains to remark that if L were distinct from M, then, in contradiction to the definition of L, we would obtain a distinguished subset greater than L, by adjoining the element $\varphi(M \setminus L)$ to L and assuming that this element follows all the elements of L.

Hausdorff's theorem follows from Zermelo's theorem.

Let us take an arbitrary chain A in the partially ordered set M. If $A = M$, then there is nothing to prove; otherwise we shall assume, on the basis of Zermelo's theorem, that the set $B = M \setminus A$ is well ordered; this well ordering is in no way connected with the partial ordering of B as a subset of the set M.

We will place the first element of the set B in the *first class* if it can be compared in the set M (see I.4.1) with every element of A, and in the *second class* in the opposite case. Now let b be an arbitrary element of B and let each of the elements of the set B, strictly preceding the element b in the sense of the well ordering given in B, be already placed in either the first or the second class. Then we place the element b in the first class if it is comparable in M both with every element of A and also with every one of those elements preceding it in B which has been placed in the first class; in the opposite case the element b will be placed in the second class.

In this way we carry out an inductive construction by means of the well ordering of the set B, and therefore we can assume (see I.5.3) that every element of B is placed in a unique way in the first or second class. The set C, containing all the elements of the chain A and all the elements of the first class from B, will be a chain in the set M, because any two elements from C are comparable with each other in M. This chain will be maximal in M, because any element of the second class from B is not comparable with at least one of the elements of C. The theorem is proved.

The Kuratowski-Zorn theorem follows from Hausdorff's theorem.

For, let there be given a partially ordered set M in which every chain possesses an upper bound, and let $a \in M$. The chain consisting of the single element a is contained in some maximal chain C by Hausdorff's theorem. If the element c is an upper bound of the chain C, then $a \leqslant c$. On the other hand, the element c is maximal in M: if there exists an element b such that $c < b$, then for all $x \in C$, since $x \leqslant c$, it follows that $x < b$, i.e., by adjoining the element b to the chain C, we obtain a larger chain which contradicts the maximality of the chain C. The theorem is proved.

The axiom of choice follows from the Kuratowski-Zorn theorem.

Let there be given an arbitrary set M. We consider systems of non-empty subsets of M on which it is possible to give (in at least one way) functions which mark out in each subset A of the given system one of its elements $\varphi(A)$. Systems of such a type exist—such, for instance, are the systems consisting of one non-empty set. We denote by Φ the set of all functions of the given type, given on all possible systems of subsets on which it is possible to give such functions.

Let φ and ψ be two functions belonging to Φ and given respectively on the systems of sets S and T. We put $\varphi \leqslant \psi$, if $S \subseteq T$ and the functions φ and ψ coincide on the system S. This defines a partial ordering in the set Φ. We take an arbitrary chain Γ in Φ (in the sense of this partial ordering), consisting of the functions φ_α, given respectively on the systems S_α. On the system $T = \bigcup_\alpha S_\alpha$ we can define a function ψ which coincides with the functions φ_α on each of the systems S_α. It is clear that ψ belongs to Φ and is an upper bound for the chain Γ.

The Kuratowski-Zorn theorem is thus applicable to the set Φ, and therefore Φ possesses maximal elements. Let χ be one of these elements. If the system U, on which the function χ is defined, did not contain a non-empty subset A of M, then on the system obtained from U by adjoining A we could define functions strictly greater than χ: such would be every function coinciding with χ on the system U and marking out in the subset A one of its elements. We have obtained a contradiction of the maximality of the function χ, which shows that the system U in fact coincides with the system of all non-empty subsets of the set M. Thus the theorem is proved.

* The assertion that every set can be linearly ordered is weaker than the axiom of choice [Mostowski, *Fund. Math.* 32, 201–252 (1939)].*

CHAPTER TWO

GROUPS AND RINGS

§ 1. Groupoids, semigroups, groups

1. The most fundamental of all the concepts studied in the various branches of algebra is the concept of an *algebraic operation*. We will limit ourselves for the time being to the consideration of *binary* operations. In its widest sense this will be a law by which some ordered pairs of elements of a given set M (i.e. some elements from the square of the set M, see I.2.1) are put into correspondence with elements from M, either one or many at a time. If we call this operation *multiplication* and use the ordinary multiplicative notation for it, then the equation

$$ab = c \qquad (1)$$

will mean that for the pair of elements a, b from M the product is defined and that one of the values of this product is the element c.

The concept of a binary algebraic operation, considered in this wide sense, is equivalent to the concept of a ternary relation given in the set M (see I.2.7).

In fact, if a binary operation is given in M, then we will introduce a ternary relation R in M by letting $R(a, b, c)$ if and only if equation (1) is satisfied. Conversely, if a ternary relation R is given in M, then we will assume that equation (1) is satisfied if and only if it is true that $R(a, b, c)$.

2. In what follows a *binary algebraic operation* will be understood, as a rule, in a narrower sense: the product must be defined for every ordered pair of elements and must be single-valued. Every set in which an algebraic operation of this type is given is called a *groupoid*.

This concept is still too wide. Rather narrower is the concept of a *semigroup*, which has various applications, i.e. a groupoid in which the *associative law* is satisfied: for any elements a, b and c

$$(ab) c = a(bc). \qquad (2)$$

Equation (2) gives a single meaning to the product abc of any three elements of a semigroup. It follows easily from this that for all n the product $a_1 a_2 \ldots a_n$ of any n elements, taken in a given order, will be a uniquely determined element of the semigroup.

3. Even narrower is the concept of a group, one of the most important algebraic concepts. A *group* is a non-empty semigroup in which the inverse operations can be carried out, i.e. for any elements a and b each of the equations

$$ax = b, \quad ya = b \tag{3}$$

has a solution, and it is unique.

We note that the uniqueness of the solutions of each of equations (3) enables one to perform *left or right cancellation* in a group: if

$$ab_1 = ab_2 \quad \text{or} \quad b_1 a = b_2 a,$$

then $b_1 = b_2$.

The solutions x and y of equations (3) will not necessarily coincide in the case of an arbitrary group. This is due to the fact that we have not presupposed that the algebraic operation is commutative, i.e. a product may depend on the order of its factors. A group (or semigroup or groupoid) in which for any two elements a, b the *commutative law*

$$ab = ba$$

is satisfied, is called *commutative* or *Abelian*.

4. *Every group G possesses a uniquely defined element e, satisfying the condition*

$$ae = ea = a$$

for all elements $a \in G$.

In fact, from the definition of a group there follows the existence of an element e_a' in G for any element a, such that $ae_a' = a$, where this element e_a' is uniquely defined. If b is any other element of the group G, and y is an element of the group satisfying the equation $ya = b$, then, by the associative law,

$$be_a' = (ya)e_a' = y(ae_a') = ya = b,$$

whence $e_b' = e_a'$. The element e_a' thus does not depend on the element a; we will denote it by e'. Thus,

$$ae' = a \quad \text{for all} \quad a \in G. \tag{4}$$

In an analogous way we can prove the existence and uniqueness of an element e'' such that

$$e''a = a \quad \text{for all} \quad a \in G. \tag{5}$$

However, by applying equations (4) and (5) to the product $e''e'$, we obtain $e''e' = e''$ and $e''e' = e'$, whence $e'' = e'$. Thus the theorem is proved.

The element e, whose existence and uniqueness are asserted in this theorem, is called the *identity* of the group G and usually denoted by the symbol 1.

For every element a of the group G there exists a uniquely defined element a^{-1} such that

$$aa^{-1} = a^{-1}a = 1.$$

In fact, from the definition of a group follows the existence of uniquely defined elements a' and a'' such that

$$aa' = 1, \quad a''a = 1.$$

However, by applying the associative law, we obtain

$$a''aa' = a''(aa') = a'' \cdot 1 = a'',$$
$$a''aa' = (a''a)a' = 1 \cdot a' = a',$$

whence $a'' = a'$.

The element a^{-1} is called the *inverse element* for a. It is clear that the inverse for a^{-1} is the element a itself and that $1^{-1} = 1$. It is also easy to see that for any elements $a_1, a_2, \ldots, a_n$

$$(a_1 a_2 \ldots a_{n-1} a_n)^{-1} = a_n^{-1} a_{n-1}^{-1} \ldots a_2^{-1} a_1^{-1}.$$

5. The following theorem often makes it easier to prove that a given semigroup is a group:

The semigroup G will be a group if and only if there exists in G at least one right identity e, possessing the property

$$ae = a \text{ for all } a \in G,$$

where this e can be chosen such that for every $a \in G$ there exists at least one right inverse element a^{-1}, satisfying the condition

$$aa^{-1} = e.$$

In one direction this theorem has been proved in the preceding paragraph. Now let there be given a semigroup G satisfying the conditions of the theorem. We will show that the element e will also be a left identity for G. If $a \in G$ and a^{-1} is one of its right inverse elements, then

$$eaa^{-1} = ee = e = aa^{-1}.$$

Multiplying both sides of this equation on the right by one of the elements which are right inverses for a^{-1}, and using the uniqueness of a product in a semigroup, we obtain

$$eae = ae,$$

whence $ea = a$, which we wished to prove.

Now if e' is any right identity for G, and e'' any left identity, then, as in the proof of the first theorem of the preceding paragraph, we obtain that $e'' = e'$, i.e. we prove the existence and uniqueness of the identity e in G.

Further, again let $a \in G$ and let a^{-1} be one of the right inverse elements for a. Multiplying the equation $aa^{-1} = e$ on the left by a^{-1}, we obtain

$$a^{-1}aa^{-1} = a^{-1}.$$

Multiplying this last equation on the right by one of the right inverse elements for a^{-1}, we arrive at the equation

$$a^{-1}ae = e,$$

whence $a^{-1}a = e$. The element a^{-1} is also a left inverse for a.

Now, as in the proof of the second theorem of the preceding paragraph, it is easy to verify that any left inverse element for a is equal to any right inverse element. Hence there follows the existence of a uniquely defined inverse element a^{-1} for every element a in G.

To complete the proof we remark that the solutions of equations (3) are respectively the elements

$$x = a^{-1}b \quad \text{and} \quad y = ba^{-1}.$$

The uniqueness of these solutions follows from the fact that if, for instance, $ax_1 = ax_2$, then, multiplying this equation on the left by a^{-1}, we obtain $x_1 = x_2$.

6. Sometimes, particularly in the study of Abelian groups, one uses not the multiplicative, but the additive notation: the group operation is called *addition*, the sum is written $a + b$, the identity of the group is called the *zero* and is denoted by the

symbol 0, and instead of the inverse element one speaks of the
additive inverse element and denotes it *by* $-a$.

In the additive notation for Abelian groups the inverse operation—in this case it will, of course, be unique—is called *subtraction*. The solution of the equation

$$a + x = b$$

is called a *difference* and is written in the form $b - a$. It is clear
that

$$b - a = b + (-a),$$

and therefore

$$b - (a_1 + a_2) = b - a_1 - a_2.$$

7. The ordinary operations on numbers give us many important
examples of Abelian groups. Thus, by taking all the integers—
positive, zero and negative—and considering the operation of
addition in this set, we obtain an Abelian group called the *additive
group of integers*. All the rational numbers also form an Abelian
group under addition — this is the *additive group of rational
numbers*. One can also speak of the additive groups of all real
and all complex numbers.

If we take only the natural numbers, then they form a semigroup under addition, called the *additive semigroup of natural
numbers*, but not a group, because subtraction is not always
possible here.

In forming groups under multiplication from numbers it is
necessary to bear in mind that none of them† can contain the
number zero, because it is not possible to divide by zero. Multiplicative groups are formed, for instance, by all the rational
numbers distinct from zero, and equally by all the strictly positive rational numbers. On the other hand, semigroups under
multiplication, but not groups, are formed by the systems of
all integers, all non-negative integers and all natural numbers.

As an example of a finite Abelian group we mention the *multiplicative group of n-th roots of unity*. The order of this group—
by the *order* of a finite group is meant the number of its elements—is
equal to n.

8. We go on to some examples of non-commutative groups
and semigroups. A *transformation* of a set M is any mapping of

---

† Except of course the group consisting of zero alone (Ed.).

this set into itself (i.e. onto some subset of it). A special case of a transformation is a *permutation*, i.e. a one–one mapping of the set M onto itself.

In I.1.2 we introduced the multiplication of mappings, regarding this as their successive application, and we proved the associativity of this operation. Applying this to the case of transformations we find that relative to the operation of successive application all the transformations of a given set M form a semigroup; it is called the *symmetric semigroup on the set M*.

Because the successive application of two permutations of a set M is again a permutation, we can also speak of the semigroup of permutations on M. The *identity permutation*, which leaves every element of M unaltered, is the identity of this semigroup. On the other hand, if x is an arbitrary permutation, mapping every element a of M into the element ax, then the inverse transformation mapping ax into a for all $a \in M$ will also be a permutation; it is the *inverse permutation for x*. Thus, in view of II.1.5, under the operation of successive applications all the permutations of a given set M form a group; it is called the *symmetric group on the set M*.

If the set M is finite and consists of n elements, then the symmetric group on M, called the *symmetric group of degree n* and denoted by S_n, will be finite and have order $n!$. The symmetric semigroup on a finite set M will also be finite.

Another example of a non-commutative group is the totality of all non-singular square matrices of order n (where $n \geqslant 2$) with real elements, considered with respect to the operation of multiplication of matrices.

§ 2. Rings, skew fields, fields

1. A second very important algebraic concept, similar to the concept of a group, is the concept of a ring. A *ring* is a set R in which there are given two binary algebraic operations (in the sense of II.1.2)—addition and multiplication, where this is an Abelian group with respect to addition—the *additive group of the ring R*—and the multiplication is connected with the addition by means of the *distributive laws*:

$$a(b+c) = ab+ac, \quad (b+c)a = ba+ca. \tag{1}$$

3*

7 3829

In the general case no restrictions are laid on the multiplication itself, i.e. the ring R is only a groupoid with respect to multiplication—this will be the *multiplicative groupoid of the ring R*. If the multiplication in the ring is associative, then we will call the ring an *associative ring* and we speak of its *multiplicative semigroup*; if the multiplication in the ring is both associative and commutative, then the ring is called *associative-commutative*.

In every ring the distributive laws are satisfied for differences also, i.e.

$$a(b-c) = ab - ac, \quad (b-c)a = ba - ca. \qquad (2)$$

In fact, by II.1.6,

$$c + (b - c) = b.$$

Multiplying both sides of this equation on the left by a, and then applying the first of the distributive laws (1) to the left-hand side of the equation, we obtain

$$ac + a(b-c) = ab,$$

whence, again by II.1.6, follows the first of equations (2).

2. *Every Abelian group G is the additive group of some ring*: it is sufficient to presuppose that the group operation of G is written additively, and then to take *zero multiplication* in G, i.e. to set

$$ab = 0$$

for any a and b in G. The fact that the distributive laws (1) are satisfied is obvious. This *zero ring* with additive group G will, of course, be associative-commutative. In the theory of rings zero rings play a part parallel to the part played in the theory of groups by Abelian groups.

Our first example of a non-zero associative-commutative ring is the *ring of integers*. As an example of an associative but not commutative ring we mention the *ring of square matrices* of order n (where $n \geqslant 2$) with real elements: the operations in this ring are the addition and multiplication of matrices as given in any course in higher algebra.

We mention, finally, one example of a non-associative ring. This is the *ring of vectors of three-dimensional Euclidean space*, where the operations are the usual addition of vectors and the vector multiplication of vectors defined in any course in analytical geometry. It is easy to verify that this multiplication will be neither associative nor commutative, but that it is connected with the addition by the distributive laws (1).

The reader can also verify easily (or find it in a text book on vector algebra) that in the ring which we have constructed for any vectors a, b, c the following equations are satisfied:

$$a^2 = 0 \qquad (3)$$

and the *Jacobi identity*

$$(ab)c + (bc)a + (ca) = 0. \qquad (4)$$

We note that from (3) follows the *anti-commutative law*

$$ba = -ab.$$

In fact, since

$$a^2 = b^2 = (a+b)^2 = 0,$$

we have

$$0 = (a+b)^2 = a^2 + ab + ba + b^2 = ab + ba.$$

3. Every ring satisfying conditions (3) and (4) is called a *Lie ring*. Lie rings form an important class of rings, in general non-associative; to this class belong, as well, all the zero rings.

Between the associative and Lie rings there exists the following remarkable connection:

If R is an arbitrary associative ring, then, by keeping the additive group of this ring, and replacing the operation of multiplication ab by the commutator operation

$$a \circ b = ab - ba,$$

we obtain a Lie ring $R^{(-)}$.

In fact, we verify the validity of the distributive laws; it is sufficient to verify the first of the laws (1):

$$a \circ (b+c) = a(b+c) - (b+c)a = ab + ac - ba - ca =$$
$$(ab - ba) + (ac - ca) = a \circ b + a \circ c.$$

Thus, the set R, considered with the additive and commutator operations, is a ring; we denote it by $R^{(-)}$. It remains to verify the validity of equations (3) and (4):

$$a \circ a = aa - aa = 0,$$
$$(a \circ b) \circ c + (b \circ c) \circ a + (c \circ a) \circ b = (ab - ba)c - c(ab - ba) +$$
$$(bc - cb)a - a(bc - cb) + (ca - ac)b - b(ca - ac) = 0.$$

The ring $R^{(-)}$ is a Lie ring.

4. *If in the associative ring R we keep its additive group, and replace the operation of multiplication ab by the symmetriser operation*

$$a \cdot b = ab + ba,$$

then we obtain a ring $R^{(+)}$, in which for any elements a, b the equations

$$a \cdot b = b \cdot a, \tag{5}$$

$$[(a \cdot a) \cdot b] \cdot a = (a \cdot a) \cdot (b \cdot a) \tag{6}$$

hold.

Again, we need only verify the first to the distributive laws (1):

$$a \cdot (b + c) = a(b + c) + (b + c)a = ab + ac + ba + ca =$$
$$(ab + ba) + (ac + ca) = a \cdot b + a \cdot c.$$

Now we verify the validity of equations (5) and (6):

$$a \cdot b = ab + ba = ba + ab = b \cdot a,$$

$$[(a \cdot a) \cdot b]a = [(aa + aa)b + b(aa + aa)]a +$$
$$a[(aa + aa)b + b(aa + aa)]$$
$$= aaba + aaba + baaa + baaa + aaab + aaab +$$
$$abaa + abaa = (aa + aa)(ba + ab) +$$
$$(ba + ab)(aa + aa) = (a \cdot a) \cdot (b \cdot a).$$

Every ring satisfying the conditions (5) and (6) is called a *Jordan ring*. In the general case it is non-associative; however, the class of Jordan rings includes all the associative-commutative rings.

5. *In every ring R, any product in which at least one of the factors is equal to zero, is itself equal to zero. In other words,*

$$a \cdot 0 = 0 \cdot a = 0 \tag{7}$$

for all elements a from the ring R.

In fact, if x is another arbitrary element of the ring R, then, in view of (2),

$$a \cdot 0 = a(x - x) = ax - ax = 0.$$

If a and b are any elements of an arbitrary ring R, then

$$(-a)b = a(-b) = -ab, \tag{8}$$

$$(-a)(-b) = ab. \tag{9}$$

In fact,

$$ab + (-a)b = [a + (-a)]b = 0 \cdot b = 0.$$

In the same way we can verify the second half of equation (8). On the other hand, using (8), we obtain

$$(-a)(-b) = -[a(-b)] = -(-ab) = ab,$$

which proves (9).

6. We note that the converse of the assertion expressed by equation (7), which is valid for the ring of integers, does not hold in the general case: there exist rings which possess *divisors of zero*, i.e. elements a and b distinct from zero whose product is equal to zero:

$$ab = 0.$$

Examples of such rings, apart from zero rings, are the matrix rings. We have already mentioned the ring of real square matrices. In general, if R is an arbitrary ring, then we can consider all possible square matrices of order n with elements from R. Defining addition and multiplication for them in the usual way, we obtain, as is easy to verify, a ring which is associative if the original ring R is associative. The zero of this ring is the *zero matrix*, consisting of zeros. The ring constructed is called the *total matrix ring* of order n over the ring R and is denoted by R_n.

If $n \geqslant 2$, and the ring R does not consist of zero alone, then the total matrix ring R_n has divisors of zero.

In fact, if a is an element of R distinct from zero, then the matrices

$$\begin{pmatrix} a & 0 & \ldots & 0 \\ 0 & 0 & \ldots & 0 \\ \cdot & \cdot & \cdot & \cdot & \cdot \\ 0 & 0 & \ldots & 0 \end{pmatrix}, \quad \begin{pmatrix} 0 & 0 & \ldots & 0 \\ \cdot & \cdot & \cdot & \cdot & \cdot \\ 0 & \ldots & 0 & 0 \\ 0 & \ldots & 0 & a \end{pmatrix}$$

are distinct from the zero matrix, but their product is equal to zero.

Other examples of rings with divisors of zero are rings of functions. Let there be given an arbitrary set M and an arbitrary ring R. We consider the set of all *functions* on M with values in R, i.e. all mappings f of the set M into the ring R; the image of the element $x \in M$ under the mapping f will be denoted here by $f(x)$. This set of functions becomes a ring if the sum and product of functions are defined, as usual, by the equations

$$(f+g)(x) = f(x) + g(x),$$
$$(fg)(x) = f(x) \cdot g(x),$$

i.e. by means of the addition and multiplication of the values of the given functions for all x from M. It is easy to verify that all the requirements included in the definition of a ring are satisfied, and that the ring obtained is associative and commutative provided only that the original ring R is respectively associative or commutative.

The ring constructed is called the *complete ring of functions* on the set M with values in the ring R. If M is the set of points on the real line, and R is the ring of all real numbers, then our ring will be the ordinary ring of all real functions of a real variable.

Every complete ring of functions on a set M containing not less than two elements, with values in a ring R, not consisting of zero alone, possesses divisors of zero.

In fact, the role of zero in this ring is played by the *zero function* which is identically (i.e. for all x from M) equal to zero. If, however, we divide the set M into two non-empty non-intersecting subsets A and B, then clearly there exist non-zero functions f and g such that f takes zero values on A, and g on B. It is clear that the product fg will be the zero function.

7. An associative-commutative ring without divisors of zero is called an *integral domain*; such, in particular, are all rings of integers. Important examples of integral domains can be obtained by using the following construction.

If R is an arbitrary associative-commutative ring, then we can consider all *polynomials*

$$a_0 + a_1 x + a_2 x^2 + \ldots + a_n x^n, \quad n \geqslant 0,$$

in an *unknown* x with *coefficients* $a_0, a_1, \ldots, a_n$ from R; if $a_n \neq 0$, then n will be the *degree* of this polynomial. By defining the addition and multiplication of polynomials in the same way as this is done in any course in higher algebra, we obtain, as can be verified without difficulty, a ring called the *ring of polynomials* $R[x]$ in an unknown x over a ring R; this ring will also be associative-commutative. The zero of a ring of polynomials is the polynomial all of whose ceofficients are equal to zero.

In an analogous way we define the ring of polynomials $R[x_1, x_2, \ldots, x_n]$ of any finite number of unknowns; it will simply be a ring of polynomials of one unknown x_n over the ring $R[x_1, \ldots, x_{n-1}]$. We can also speak of the ring of polynomials over R in any infinite set of unknowns, by assuming here that each separate polynomial depends on only some finite number of unknowns.

If R is an integral domain, then any ring of polynomials over R will be an integral domain.

The validity of this assertion for the ring of polynomials $R[x]$ in one unknown follows from the fact that if the polynomials f and g are distinct from zero, then the degree of the product fg is equal to the sum of the degrees of the factors, i.e. this product will also be distinct from zero. The transition to the case of any finite number of unknowns is carried out by induction, and in the case of rings of polynomials in an infinite set of unknowns one must take into account that every polynomial depends on a finite number of unknowns.

8. Over an arbitrary associative-commutative ring R one can consider not only polynomials, but also the (formal) *power series*

$$a_0 + a_1 x + a_2 x^2 + \ldots + a_k x^k + \ldots = \sum_{k=0}^{\infty} a_k x^k \qquad (10)$$

in the unknown x. The definitions of the operations with polynomials carry over without any difficulty to power series:

$$\sum_{k=0}^{\infty} a_k x^k + \sum_{k=0}^{\infty} b_k x^k = \sum_{k=0}^{\infty} (a_k + b_k) x^k \,,$$

$$\sum_{k=0}^{\infty} a_k x^k \cdot \sum_{l=0}^{\infty} b_l x^l = \sum_{m=0}^{\infty} c_m x^m \,,$$

where $$c_m = \sum_{k+l=m} a_k b_l \,.$$

As in the case of polynomials, it can be verified that we obtain an associative-commutative ring; it is called the *ring of power series* in the unknown x over the ring R and is denoted by $R\{x\}$.

The transition to rings of power series over R in any finite number, and then in an infinite set of unknowns is carried out in the same way as for rings of polynomials, where in the case of an infinite set of unknowns it is necessary to require that every power series depends on only a finite number of unknowns.

If R is an integral domain, then any ring of power series over R will also be an integral domain.

It is sufficient to consider the case of the ring $R\{x\}$ in one unknown. If we call the number n the *lowest power* of the power series (10) when

$$a_0 = a_1 = \ldots = a_{n-1} = 0, \qquad a_n \neq 0,$$

then every non-zero power series will possess a lowest power. In view of the fact that there are no divisors of zero in R, the lowest power of the product of two power series is equal to the sum of the lowest powers of the factors. Our assertion follows from this.

9. The concept of an *identity*, introduced in II.1.4 for the case of a group, carries over, of course, to the case of any groupoid or ring R: it will be any element 1 such that for all elements a from R

$$a \cdot 1 = 1 \cdot a = a.$$

If an identity exists in a ring R, then it will be the only one. There may, however, be no identity, as the example of the ring of even numbers shows.

Every Lie ring (see II.2.3) *not consisting of zero alone is a ring without identity.*

In fact, let the Lie ring L possess an identity 1. Then, by (3), letting $a = 1$, we obtain $1^2 = 0$. Thus $1 = 0$, from which it follows that the ring L consists of zero alone.

If the ring R possesses an identity, then all rings of matrices over R also possess identities, as do rings of functions with values in R, and, in the associative–commutative case, the rings of polynomials and the rings of power series in any number of unknowns over R.

In fact, the identity of the ring of matrices is the identity matrix, which has 1's along its main diagonal, and all of whose elements not in the diagonal are equal to zero. The identity of the ring of functions is the function identically equal to 1. Finally, the identity of the ring of polynomials |(or the ring of power series) is the polynomial (power series) all of whose coefficients are equal to zero, except a_0, which is equal to 1.

10. Every ring is a groupoid under multiplication, and an associative ring is a semigroup. No ring which does not consist of zero alone can be a group under multiplication, as follows from the multiplicative property of zero (7). It may happen, however, that all the elements of a ring distinct from zero form a group under multiplication. Such a ring—it will necessarily be associative—is called a *skew field*, and the group under multiplication of its non–zero elements is called the *multiplicative group* of this skew field.

A skew field with commutative multiplication is called a *field*. Elementary examples of fields are the field of rational numbers, the field of real numbers and the field of complex numbers. An example of a non-commutative field will be given in V.6.8.

From the definition of a skew field it follows that a *skew field does not possess divisors of zero.* Further, *every skew field possesses an identity*—in fact, the identity of the multiplicative group of this skew field is, in view of (7), the identity for each skew field. Finally, *in every skew field each of the equations*

$$ax = b, \quad ya = b, \quad \text{where} \quad a \neq 0, \tag{11}$$

has a solution, and it is unique.

In fact, if $b \neq 0$, then both the equations (11) have uniquely determined solutions in the multiplicative group of the skew field, and zero cannot satisfy either of these equations. If, however, $b = 0$, then zero is a solution for each of the equations (11) and there are no other solutions in view of the fact that there are no divisors of zero.

Conversely, *an associative ring R will be a skew field if in it every equation of the form* (11), *for any* $a \neq 0$ *and arbitrary* b, *has at least one solution.*

We will show first of all that there are no divisors of zero in R. If $a \neq 0$ and $b \neq 0$, but $ab = 0$, then we denote by e one of the solutions of the equation $ax = a$, and by c one of the solutions of the equation $bx = e$. Then

$$0 = 0 \cdot c = abc = ae = a,$$

which contradicts our hypothesis.

From this it follows that the set of elements of the ring R distinct from zero will be a multiplicative semigroup. It will even be a group, because the equations (11) have solutions in this very set for $a \neq 0$ and $b \neq 0$, and the uniqueness of these solutions follows from the fact that there are no divisors of zero in R: if, for instance, $ax_1 = ax_2$ and $a \neq 0$, then $a(x_1 - x_2) = 0$ and therefore $x_1 = x_2$. Thus the theorem is proved.

We will meet the problem of carrying over the concept of a skew field to the case of non-associative rings in II.6.1.

§ 3. Subgroups, subrings

1. A subset A of a groupoid G is called a *subgroupoid* in G if the product of any two elements in A itself belongs to A. If G is a semigroup the subgroupoid A is naturally called a *subsemigroup*. If, however, G is a group, then a *subgroup* of this group is any subsemigroup A which is itself a group with respect to the operation defined in the group G; for this it is sufficient that the subsemigroup A be non-empty and contain together with each of its elements a its inverse element a^{-1}.

Not every subsemigroup of a group is necessarily a subgroup of this group, as is shown by the example of the additive semigroup of natural numbers, which is a subsemigroup, but not a subgroup, of the additive group of all whole numbers.

We note that it makes sense to speak about the subgroups of any semigroup. Thus the symmetric group on an arbitrary set M (see II.1.8) is a subgroup of the symmetric semigroup on the same set.

2. A *subring* of a ring R is any subset A of this ring which is itself a ring with respect to the operations defined in R. In other words, A must be a subgroup of the additive group of the ring R and a subgroupoid of the multiplicative groupoid of this ring: the distributive laws which are valid in R are satisfied, of course, in A also.

One can speak, in particular, of a subring of a skew field or a field. Thus the ring of whole numbers is a subring of the field of rational numbers.

In an analogous way one defines the concepts of a *skew subfield* and a *subfield*. One can speak here of a skew subfield (subfield) not only of a skew field, but of any ring. Thus in the ring of polynomials $P[x]$ over an arbitrary field P, the polynomials of zero degree, together with zero, form a subfield.

3. Examples of subgroups of every group G are, in particular, this group itself and the *identity subgroup* E which consists of the identity alone. Analogously, examples of subrings of every ring R are this ring itself and the *zero subring* consisting of zero alone.

To obtain more interesting examples of subgroups we introduce the concept of powers of elements. Let G be an arbitrary semigroup and a be an element of G. The associativity of multiplication enables us to define in the usual way the *positive powers* a^n of the element a, $n = 1, 2, \ldots$, where, as usual,

$$a^k \cdot a^l = a^{k+l}, \tag{1}$$

$$(a^k)^l = a^{kl}. \tag{2}$$

From (1) it follows that all the positive powers of an element form an Abelian subsemigroup in the semigroup G, called the *cyclic subsemigroup* of the element a.

If, however, G is a group, then we obtain $a^0 = 1$, and we may introduce *negative powers* of the element a. In fact, if n is any natural number, then it is easy to verify the equation

$$a^n(a^{-1})^n = 1.$$

from which it follows that

$$(a^{-1})^n = (a^n)^{-1}. \tag{3}$$

The element which is equal to both sides of equation (3) we denote by a^{-n}. Equations (1) and (2) remain valid for any powers of the element a of the group G, and therefore all powers of the element a, including the zeroth and the negative powers, form an Abelian subgroup in the group G, called the *cyclic subgroup* of the element a and denoted by $\{a\}$.

In the additive notation for the group operation, instead of powers of an element one must speak of *multiples* of this element.

4. The powers of an element a of a group G with different exponents may not necessarily be distinct elements of this group, as follows already from the existence of finite groups. If all the powers of the element a are in fact distinct, then a is called an *element of infinite order*, and in the opposite case an *element of finite order*. In this second case there exist integers k and l such that $k > l$, but

$$a^k = a^l.$$

Hence $a^{k-l} = 1$, where $k - l > 0$, i.e. there exist powers of a with natural exponent and equal to one. The least of these exponents is called the *order* of the element a.

If a is an element of finite order n, then the powers

$$1 = a^0, \quad a, \quad a^2, \dots, a^{n-1} \tag{4}$$

will, obviously, be distinct elements of the group. Every other power a^k of the element a, positive or negative, is equal to one of the elements (4). In fact, if

$$k = nq + r, \quad 0 \leqslant r < n,$$

then, in view of (1), (2) and the equation $a^n = 1$,

$$a^k = (a^n)^q a^r = a^r.$$

From this it follows that *the order n of an element of finite order a coincides with the order* (see II.1.7) *of its cyclic subgroup* $\{a\}$.

A group, all of whose elements have finite order, not necessarily bounded, is called *periodic*. On the other hand, a group is said to be *torsion free*, if all its elements except 1 are of infinite order.

5. In the case of rings there naturally arises the question of an analogy with cyclic subgroups, i.e. of a minimal subring containing a given element. Let R be an arbitrary (not necessarily associative) ring and a an element of R. Every subring of the ring R containing a also contains all possible products with n factors equal to a ($n = 1, 2, 3, \dots$); these products play the part of the positive powers of the element a. In view of the fact that multiplication may be non-associative, in every such product there must be some distributions of brackets which are such that each time only two elements of the ring are multiplied together. For $n = 3$ there are two such products—$(aa)a$ and $a(aa)$, for $n = 4$ there are five, and so on.

Every subring containing a also contains all possible sums of any finite number of the products mentioned, taken with any integral coefficients. The elements of the ring R which can be written in the form of such sums (possibly not uniquely) themselves form a subring in R; this will be the desired *subring generated by the element a*.

From what has been said it follows that if the ring R is associative, then the subring generated by the element a consists of all those elements of the ring R which, in at least one way, can be written in the form of sums (with integral coefficients) of positive powers of the element a. This subring will thus be commutative.

6. Every subgroup of a group G contains the identity of this group, and every subring of a ring R contains the zero of this ring. The intersection of any system of subgroups of the group G (or any system of subrings of the ring R) will thus be non-empty.

The intersection of any system of subgroups of the group G is a subgroup of this group. Analogously, the intersection of any system of subrings of the ring R will be a subring of this ring, the intersection of any system of subsemigroup of a semigroup, if it is not empty, will be a subsemigroup, and so on.

We will prove the first assertion. Let us take in the group G an arbitrary system of subgroups A_α, where α varies through some index set, and let D be the intersection of these subgroups. If b and c are any elements of D, then their product bc is contained in each of the subgroups A_α, i.e. is contained in D. On the other hand, for any $b \in D$ the element b^{-1} belongs to each of the subgroups A_α, and therefore $b^{-1} \in D$. The set D will thus be a subgroup of the group G.

7. Let G be either a group or a ring or a skew field or a semigroup or an algebraic system of one of the various types which we have met. If M is any subset of G, then there exists a minimal subgroup (respectively, subring, skew subfield, and so on) containing the subset M, which is the *subgroup generated by the set M*; it is denoted by $\{M\}$. In fact, it will be the intersection of all the subgroups of the group G which entirely contain M; at least one such subgroup exists, and that is G itself.

Is is easy to verify, by generalizing the definition of cyclic subgroups given in II.3.3, that *the subgroup $\{M\}$ consists of those elements of the group G, and only those elements, which can be written in at least one way in the form of some product of powers of a finite number of elements from M.*

In an analogous way, by generalizing what was said in II.3.5, we have that *the subring generated in the ring R by the set M consists of all those elements of the ring R which can be written in at least one way in the form of a sum (with integral coefficients) of products of a finite number of elements from M*; in the non-associative case these products are of course considered with some particular distribution of brackets.

8. By applying what we have said above to the case when there is given in the group G some system of subgroups A_i, $i \in I$, and the set M is the union of all the A_i, we arrive at the concept of the *subgroup generated by a given system of subgroups*; it is denoted by $\{A_i, i \in I\}$ in the general case, and by $\{A, B\}$ if we are discussing the union of two subgroups A and B, and so on. The concept of a *subring generated in a ring by a given system of subrings* is analogous.

9. If G is either a group or a ring, and so on, then there exist subsets M in G—G itself, for instance—such that

$$\{M\} = G.$$

Every such subset M is called a *generating system for G*.

If G possesses at least one finite generating system, then we say that G is a *group* (or semigroup or ring) *with a finite number of generators*. A system of generators may consist, in particular, of one element. Groups possessing one generating element, i.e. coinciding with one of their cyclic subgroups, are called *cyclic groups*. A complete survey of cyclic groups will be given in the following section.

§ 4. Isomorphism

1. The concept of an isomorphism can be introduced for each of the types of algebraic systems considered in this chapter, and it plays the same part here as for a partially ordered set (see I.4.3): for instance isomorphic groups can be regarded as identical as two copies of the same group, on all occasions when the group operation itself is being studied, but the nature of the elements of which the groups are composed plays no part.

We go on to the definitions. The groupoids G and G' are called *isomorphic* if there exists a one–one mapping φ of the groupoid G onto the groupoid G', such that for any elements $a, b \in G$

$$(ab)\varphi = a\varphi \cdot b\varphi.$$

The mapping φ itself with these properties is called an *isomorphic mapping*. It is clear that the property of groupoids being isomorphic is symmetric (the mapping inverse to an isomorphism is itself an isomorphism) and transitive; it is also reflexive—it is sufficient to consider the identity mapping of a groupoid onto itself. An isomorphism between the groupoids G and G' is usually denoted by the symbol

$$G \simeq G'.$$

We will also use this symbol to denote isomorphism in the case of other algebraic structures.

It is understood that an isomorphic mapping preserves all the properties of a groupoid which can be formulated in the language of the operation given in this groupoid, in particular those like associativity, commutativity, the existence of an identity and of inverse elements. We will show by means of a simple example how we prove this kind of assertion. Let G be a commutative groupoid, and φ an isomorphic mapping of it onto the groupoid G'. If a' and b' are any elements of G', and a and b are elements of G such that

$$a\varphi = a', \quad b\varphi = b',$$

then

$$(ab)\varphi = a'b', \quad (ba)\varphi = b'a',$$

and from the equation $ab = ba$ and the uniqueness of the mapping follows the equation $a'b' = b'a'$.

From this it follows that *the isomorphic image of a semigroup, group or Abelian group will be respectively a semigroup, group or Abelian group.*

Two rings are called *isomorphic* if a one–one correspondence can be established between them, which is an isomorphism both for the additive groups and for the multiplicative groupoids of these rings. It is clear that an isomorphism preserves the property of a ring being associative, commutative, Lie or Jordan, and also the property of being a skew field.

We will mention one interesting example of an isomorphism of groups: *the multiplicative group of positive real numbers is isomorphic to the additive group of all real numbers.* In fact, by setting up a correspondence between every positive number and its logarithm with respect to a fixed base, we obtain a one–one mapping of the first of the groups mentioned onto the second. The fact that this mapping is an isomorphism follows from the fact that the logarithm of a product is equal to the sum of the logarithms of the factors.

2. We go on to the survey of all cyclic groups promised in II.3.9, and we begin with some examples. The additive group of integers is an example of an infinite cylic group, because every integer is a multiple of the number 1. On the other hand, the multiplicative group of the n-th roots of unity is an example of a finite cyclic group of order n, which follows from the existence of a primitive n-th root of unity.

All infinite cyclic groups are isomorphic to the additive group of integers and therefore are isomorphic to each other. All finite cyclic groups of order n are isomorphic to the multiplicative group of the n-th roots of unity and therefore are isomorphic to each other.

We will prove the first of these assertions. If G is an infinite cyclic group with generating element a, then the correspondence

$$a^k \to k$$

will be a one–one mapping of the group G onto the whole of the additive group of integers. The fact that this mapping is an isomorphism follows from II.3.3, formula (1).

To prove the second assertion it is sufficient to establish a correspondence between the powers (with the same exponent) of the generating element of the given cyclic group and the corresponding primitive root of unity.

By virtue of this theorem, in order to carry out a survey, for instance, of all the subgroups of an infinite cyclic group, it is sufficient to consider the additive group of integers.

All the non-zero subgroups of the additive group of integers are exhausted by the totality of numbers which are multiples of some natural number n.

It is clear, in fact, that all the integers which are multiples of a natural number n form a subgroup, and in fact the cyclic subgroup of the number n, where for different n these subgroups are distinct. On the other hand, if A is any non-zero subgroup of the additive group of integers, then it cannot consist only of negative numbers, because together with every number it must contain the number which is its additive inverse. Let n be the smallest natural number contained in the subgroup A. If a is any number in A, let

$$a = qn + r, \quad 0 \leqslant r < n.$$

Then

$$r = a - qn \in A,$$

and therefore, by the choice of the number n, $r = 0$, i.e. $a = qn$, which is what we were required to prove.

Thus *every subgroup of an infinite cyclic group is itself cyclic.* The same is true for finite cyclic groups.

3. We say that the groupoid G can be *isomorphically embedded* in the groupoid G', if there exists an isomorphic mapping of the groupoid G onto some subgroupoid of the groupoid G'. This concept carries over, of course, to the case of rings.

Every ring R can be isomorphically embedded in the total ring of matrices R_n (see II.2.6).

In fact, *scalar matrices*, i.e. matrices having the same element a along the principal diagonal, and zero everywhere outside this diagonal, form a subring in R_n, isomorphic to the ring R.

Every ring R can be isomorphically embedded in the complete ring of functions on a given set M with values in R (see II.2.6).

In fact, functions which take one value $a \in R$ for all x from M form a subring in the ring of functions, which is isomorphic to the ring R.

For an arbitrary associative-commutative ring R the ring of polynomials $R[x]$ can be isomorphically embedded in the ring of power series $R\{x\}$ (see II.2.8).

In fact, the power series which have only a finite number of coefficients distinct from zero form a subring in $R\{x\}$ which is isomorphic to the ring $R[x]$.

4. The proof of the following theorem requires rather greater effort:

Every ring R can be isomorphically embedded in a ring with identity. If here the ring R is associative or commutative, then it can be embedded respectively in an associative or commutative ring with identity.

Proof. We consider the set of all possible pairs of the form (a, k), where $a \in R$, and k is a whole number. We define the sum and product of such pairs by means of the equations:

$$(a, k) + (b, l) = (a + b, k + l), \tag{1}$$

$$(a, k)(b, l) = (ab + la + kb, kl). \tag{2}$$

We obviously obtain an Abelian group with respect to addition. Because

$$[(a, k) + (b, l)](c, m) = (a+b, k+l)(c, m) =$$
$$((a+b)c + m(a+b) + (k+l)c, (k+l)m) =$$
$$(ac + ma + kc + bc + mb + lc, km + lm) =$$
$$(ac + ma + kc, km) + (bc + mb + lc, lm) =$$
$$(a, k)(c, m) + (b, l)(c, m),$$

and the second distributive law can be verified in the same way, we have constructed a ring. From (2) it follows that

$$(a, k)(0, 1) = (0, 1)(a, k) = (a, k),$$

i.e. the pair $(0, 1)$ is the identity of this ring. Finally, in view of (1) and (2),

$$(a, 0) + (b, 0) = (a+b, 0),$$

$$(a, 0)(b, 0) = (ab, 0),$$

i.e. the pairs of the form $(a, 0)$ form a subring in our ring of pairs which is isomorphic to the ring R.

This proves the first of the assertions of the theorem. The second assertion follows easily from (2).

We note that the ring which we have constructed is in no way the unique (or minimal ring) with identity containing (in the sense of isomorphic embedding) a given ring R—thus the ring R itself may possess an identity.

5. *Every groupoid can be isomorphically embedded in the multiplicative groupoid of some ring, where an associative or commutative groupoid can be embedded in a ring possessing the same property.*

To prove this we consider all sums of the form

$$\sum_{a \in G} k_a a, \tag{3}$$

where a varies through all the elements of the given groupoid G, and the coefficients k_a are integers, and where not more than a finite number of these coefficients are distinct from zero. In the following way we define addition and multiplication of sums of the form (3):

$$\sum_{a \in G} k_a a + \sum_{a \in G} l_a a = \sum_{a \in G} (k_a + l_a)a, \tag{4}$$

$$\sum_{a \in G} k_a a \cdot \sum_{a \in G} l_b b = \sum_{a \in G} m_c c, \tag{5}$$

where m_c is the sum of all products $k_a l_b$ distinct from zero for
a and b such that $ab = c$. It is clear that the right-hand sides of
the equations (4) and (5) are sums of the form (3); thus equation
(5) means that the finite sums included as factors on the left-hand
side of this equation must be multiplied together term by term,
further,

$$k_a a \cdot l_b b = (k_a l_b)(ab),$$

where the product ab must be understood in the sense of the
operation given in the groupoid G, and then like terms are col-
lected.

We obtain, of course, an Abelian group with respect to addition. It is somewhat cumbersome to verify the distributive laws,
and also to prove that from the associativity or commutativity
of multiplication in the groupoid G follows the same property
for the multiplication of sums of the form (3). However, this
presents no serious difficulty, and it is left to the reader to complete
the proofs.

Thus all sums of the form (3) form a ring with respect to the
operations defined by equations (4) and (5). The sums of the form
(3) in which $k_a = 1$ for some one element a from G, and all of
whose remaining coefficients are equal to zero, form, as follows
from (5), a subgroup of the multiplicative groupoid of this ring,
isomorphic to the given groupoid G. Thus the theorem is proved.

The ring which we have constructed is called the *integral
groupoid ring* of the groupoid G. If the groupoid G is a semigroup
or a group, then we speak respectively of the *integral semigroup
ring* or *integral group ring*.

6. *Every group G can be isomorphically embedded in the symmetric group on some set M* (see II.1.8). *As the set M we can take
here the set of elements of the group G itself.*

In fact, we set up a correspondence between each element
a of the group G and the transformation of this group which maps
any element x of G into the element xa. Because from $x \neq y$
it follows that $xa \neq ya$ and, moreover, for any x from G the
equation

$$(xa^{-1})a = x$$

holds, the transformation $x \to xa$ is a one–one mapping of G
onto itself, i.e. it is a permutation. Further, if $a \neq b$, then the

permutations corresponding to these elements will be distinct, because, for instance, $l \cdot a \neq l \cdot b$. Finally, the equation

$$(xa)b = x(ab)$$

shows that the permutation corresponding to the product ab coincides with the result of successively applying the permutations corresponding to the elements a and b.

Every semigroup G can be isomorphically embedded in the symmetric semigroup on some set M (see II.1.8).

To prove this we embed the semigroup G, by using II.4.5, isomorphically in the multiplicative semigroup of some associative ring R, and then embed this ring, by II.4.4, isomorphically in the associative ring $\overline{R}$ with identity and denote by $\overline{G}$ the multiplicative semigroup of this last ring. Because there exists in $\overline{G}$ an element 1 such that from $a \neq b$ it follows that $1 \cdot a \neq 1 \cdot b$, then, by repeating the proof of the previous theorem almost literally, we find that the semigroup $\overline{G}$ can be isomorphically embedded in the symmetric semigroup on the set $\overline{G}$ itself. This proves the desired embedding for the given semigroup G also.

We note that the possibility of embedding any groupoid (and, in particular, any semigroup) in a groupoid (semigroup) with identity can also be proved immediately, without the transition to rings.

§ 5. Embedding semigroups in groups and rings in skew fields

1. Not every semigroup G can be isomorphically embedded in any group—a necessary condition for this is that the *cancellation law* should be satisfied in G (see II.1.3).

From $ac = bc$, and also from $ca = cb$ it follows that $a = b$.

An example of a semigroup which does not satisfy this condition can be constructed very easily.

Analogously, not every associative ring R can be isomorphically embedded in any skew field—for this it is necessary (see II.2.10) that there should be no divisors of zero in R.

The necessary conditions mentioned in the general case are by no means sufficient.

* Necessary and sufficient conditions for the embedding of semigroup in a group can be expressed in the form of an infinite

set of requirements of the form: "from the given system of equations follows such an equation"; they cannot be written down by means of a finite number of such requirements.

[A. I. Mal'cev, *Mat. Sb.* **6**, 331–336 (1939); **8**, 251–264, 1940)].

There exist associative rings without divisors of zero which cannot be embedded in skew fields.

[A. I. Mal'cev, *Math. Ann.* **113**, 686–691 (1937)].*

2. The purpose of this section is to prove that the necessary conditions mentioned above for the embedding of a semigroup in a group and of an associative ring in a skew field will also be sufficient in the commutative case. We begin with the proof of the following auxiliary assertion:

Let us single out the non-empty subsemigroup S in the Abelian semigroup G, where we can carry out cancellation in G by elements of S, i.e. from $ax = bx$, where $x \in S$, a, $b \in G$, it always follows that $a = b$. Then the semigroup G can be isomorphically embedded in an Abelian semigroup $\overline{G}$ with identity such that every element of S possesses an inverse element in $\overline{G}$.

We consider the set of all possible *fractions* of the form a/x, where $a \in G$, $x \in S$, meaning by this simply the ordered pair of elements a, x. The fractions a/x and b/y will be regarded as equal

$$\frac{a}{x} = \frac{b}{y},$$

if and only if $ay = bx$. This relation of equality will obviously be reflexive and symmetric. It is also transitive, because if it is also true that

$$\frac{b}{y} = \frac{c}{z},$$

i.e. $bz = cy$, then

$$ayz = bxz = cyx,$$

from which, after cancellation by $y \in S$, we obtain $az = cx$ or

$$\frac{a}{x} = \frac{c}{z},$$

Thus (see I.3.2) the whole set of fractions can be divided up into non-intersecting classes of equal fractions. The set of these classes we will denote by $\overline{G}$.

We define the *multiplication of fractions* by means of the equation

$$\frac{a}{x} \cdot \frac{b}{y} = \frac{ab}{xy}. \tag{1}$$

This definition has a meaning, because $xy \in S$.

If

$$\frac{a}{x} = \frac{a_1}{x_1}, \qquad \frac{b}{y} = \frac{b_1}{y_1}, \tag{2}$$

i.e.

$$ax_1 = a_1x, \qquad by_1 = b_1y, \tag{3}$$

then

$$abx_1y_1 = a_1b_1xy,$$

whence

$$\frac{ab}{xy} = \frac{a_1b_1}{x_1y_1}.$$

Thus, by replacing the factors on the left-hand side of equation (1) by fractions equal to them, we obtain a product equal to the right-hand side of equation (1).

This enables us to consider equation (1) as the definition of multiplication of classes of equal fractions. The associativity and commutativity of this multiplication are obvious, and therefore we have made $\overline{G}$ into an Abelian semigroup.

All fractions of the form z/z, $z \in S$, are equal to each other. On the other hand, if

$$\frac{a}{x} = \frac{z}{z},$$

then $az = zx$, i.e. after cancellation by z, $a = x$. Fractions of the form z/z thus form a separate class. This class plays the part of the identity in the semigroup $\overline{G}$. In fact, because fractions can be *cancelled* by a common factor belonging to S:

$$\frac{az}{xz} = \frac{a}{x}, \qquad z \in S,$$

in view of the fact that $(az)x = a(xz)$, then

$$\frac{a}{x} \cdot \frac{z}{z} = \frac{az}{xz} = \frac{a}{x}.$$

If a is a fixed element in G, then all fractions of the form ax/x are equal to each other: from

$$(ax)y = (ay)x,$$

it follows that

$$\frac{ax}{x} = \frac{ay}{y}.$$

On the other hand, if

$$\frac{ax}{x} = \frac{b}{y},$$

then $axy = bx$, i.e. $b = ay$. Finally, if

$$\frac{ax}{x} = \frac{by}{y},$$

then $axy = byx$, whence $a = b$. Thus, by setting up a correspondence between every element a of G and the class of fractions ax/x which are equal to each other, we obtain a one–one mapping of the semigroup G into the semigroup $\overline{G}$. The fact that this mapping is an isomorphism follows from the equation

$$\frac{ax}{x} \cdot \frac{by}{y} = \frac{(ab)(xy)}{xy}.$$

To complete the proof we note that the element $z \in S$ corresponds to the class of fractions of the form zy/y. The existence of an inverse element in the semigroup $\overline{G}$ for this class follows from the following remark:

The class of fractions equal to the fraction x/y, where $x, y \in S$, has an inverse element in the semigroup $\overline{G}$. It is the class of fractions equal to the fraction y/x.

In fact,

$$\frac{x}{y} \cdot \frac{y}{x} = \frac{xy}{yx} = \frac{t}{t}, \qquad t \in S.$$

3. From the assertion proved above and the last remark of the previous section follows the theorem (in the case $S = G$):

Every Abelian semigroup with the cancellation law can be isomorphically embedded in an Abelian group.†

---

† In the proof it was assumed that $S \neq \emptyset$, but the theorem clearly holds in any case (Ed.).

Thus, by applying the arguments which we have presented to the additive semigroup of natural numbers, which is an Abelian semigroup with the cancellation law, the reader will obtain the usual embedding of this semigroup in the additive group of integers.

4. *In the associative-commutative ring R let us take a set N of elements which are distinct from zero and are not divisors of zero. Then the ring R can be isomorphically embedded in an associative-commutative ring $\bar{R}$ with identity, such that every element of N has an inverse element in $\bar{R}$.*

We note first that the subsemigroup S of the multiplicative semigroup of the ring R generated by the set N (see II.3.7) also does not contain zero or any divisors of zero. In fact, S consists of all possible products of elements of N. However, if $a \neq 0$, $b \neq 0$ and both these elements are not divisors of zero, then $ab \neq 0$ and from $(ab)c = 0$ it follows that $bc = 0$ and therefore $c = 0$.

Thus, in the multiplicative semigroup of the ring R we can carry out cancellation by elements of S, and therefore by II.5.2 this semigroup can be embedded in a commutative semigroup $\bar{R}$ with identity in which every element of S and, in particular, of N, has an inverse element. We will assume that the semigroup $\bar{R}$ has been obtained by the construction described in II.5.2.

As we wish to make $\bar{R}$ into a ring, we define the *addition of fractions* of the form a/x, $a \in R$, $x \in S$, by means of the equation

$$\frac{a}{x} + \frac{b}{y} = \frac{ay + bx}{xy}. \tag{4}$$

This definition has a meaning, because $xy \in S$.

If equations (2) holds, and thus also equation (3), then

$$(ay + bx)x_1y_1 = ayx_1y_1 + bxx_1y_1 = a_1xyy_1 + b_1yxx_1 =$$
$$(a_1y_1 + b_1x_1)xy,$$

i.e.

$$\frac{ay + bx}{xy} = \frac{a_1y_1 + b_1x_1}{x_1y_1}.$$

Thus equation (4) can be regarded as the definition of the addition of classes of equal fractions, i.e. addition in $\bar{R}$. The commutativity of this addition is obvious, and associativity can easily be verified on the basis of (4).

All fractions of the form $0/z = 0z/z$ are equal to each other and form a complete class of equal fractions. This class plays the part of the zero in $\overline{R}$, because

$$\frac{a}{x} + \frac{0}{z} = \frac{az}{xz} = \frac{a}{x}.$$

Further, every element from $\overline{R}$ has an additive inverse element, because

$$\frac{a}{x} + \frac{(-a)}{x} = \frac{ax + (-a)x}{x} = \frac{0}{x^2}.$$

We thus find that $\overline{R}$ is an Abelian group under addition.

Addition and multiplication in R are connected by the distributive law:

$$\frac{a}{x} \cdot \frac{c}{z} + \frac{b}{y} \cdot \frac{c}{z} = \frac{ac}{xz} + \frac{bc}{yz} = \frac{acyz + bcxz}{xyz^2} = \frac{acy + bcx}{xyz} =$$

$$\frac{ay + bx}{xy} \cdot \frac{c}{z} = \left(\frac{a}{x} + \frac{b}{y} \right) \cdot \frac{c}{z}.$$

Thus $\overline{R}$ turns out to be an associative-commutative ring. As we know, the mapping which carries every element $a \in R$ into the class of fractions of the form ax/x, which are equal to each other, is an isomorphism under multiplication. It is also an isomorphism under addition, as the equation

$$\frac{ax}{x} + \frac{by}{y} = \frac{axy + byx}{xy} = \frac{(a+b)xy}{xy}$$

shows.

The proof of the theorem is thus complete. The ring $\overline{R}$ which we have constructed is called the *quotient ring* of the ring R by the set N of non-divisors of zero (or by the multiplicative semi-group S of non-divisors of zero). As we know from II.5.2, *in the quotient ring $\overline{R}$ not only all the elements of S have inverse elements, but also in general all elements which can be represented as fractions of the form x/y, where $x, y \in S$.*

5. We apply the results obtained to the case when R is an integral domain (see II.2.7). In this case we can set $N = R \setminus 0$, where $S = N$. We arrive at the very important theorem:

Every integral domain R can be isomorphically embedded in a field.

In fact, in this case we can write in the form x/y, where x, $y \in S$ every element of R distinct from zero, i.e. every element of this form has an inverse element in $\overline{R}$. The ring $\overline{R}$ will thus be a field; this is the *quotient field* of the integral domain R.

* Let the associative ring R without divisors of zero satisfy the following condition, which is always fulfilled in the commutative case: for any elements a and b of R, distinct from zero, we can find elements x and y distinct from zero in R such that $ax = by$. Then R can be isomorphically embedded in a skew field [Ore, *Ann. of Math.* **32**, 463–477 (1931)].*

6. The theorem proved above on the existence of a quotient field is supplemented by the following uniqueness theorem:

Let R be an integral domain, $\overline{R}$ its quotient field; suppose also that R is a subring of some field P, where the subfield of P generated by R coincides with P itself. Then there exists an isomorphic mapping φ between $\overline{R}$ and P which maps the ring R identically onto itself, and this mapping φ is uniquely determined.

Let us agree to denote by a' an element a of the ring R, considered as an element of the field P. Thus the correspondence $a \to a'$ is the identity mapping of the ring R onto itself.

We will prove first that if there exists an isomorphic mapping φ of the field $\overline{R}$ onto the field P, which is the identity on R, then it is uniquely determined. In fact, if a/b is an arbitrary fraction, then from

$$b \cdot \frac{a}{b} = a$$

it follows that

$$b\varphi \cdot \left(\frac{a}{b}\right)\varphi = a\varphi,$$

i.e., since $a\varphi = a'$, $b\varphi = b'$,

$$b' \cdot \left(\frac{a}{b}\right)\varphi = a'.$$

Thus the isomorphism φ carries the element a/b of the field $\overline{R}$ into the quotient of the elements a' and b' of the field P and therefore is uniquely determined.

We go on to the proof of the main assertion of the theorem. We let the element a/b of the field $\overline{R}$ correspond to the quotient a'/b' of the elements a' and b' of the field P, thus we set $a'/b' = (a/b)\varphi$. If $a/b = c/d$, i.e. $ad = bc$, then the equation $a'd' = b'c'$ holds in P, and therefore, in view of the equation $b' \cdot (a'/b') = a'$, it will be true that

$$b'd' \cdot \frac{a'}{b'} = a'd' = b'c',$$

whence

$$d' \cdot \frac{a'}{b'} = c',$$

i.e. $a'/b' = c'/d'$. The mapping φ thus does not depend on the way of writing the element of the field $\overline{R}$ in the form of a fraction, i.e. it is a single-valued mapping of the field $\overline{R}$ into the field P. It will even be a one–one mapping, because if the equation $a'b' = c'd'$ holds in the field P, then $a'd' = b'c'$, and therefore it will be true that $ad = bc$ in the ring R, from which the equation $a/b = c/d$ follows in the field $\overline{R}$.

That the mapping φ is an isomorphism follows from the fact that the equations (1) and (4), which define the multiplication and addition of fractions, are known to be valid for quotients in an arbitrary field P.

We have obtained an isomorphic mapping of the quotient field R into the field P. It will be identical on the ring $\overline{R}$, because for any $a \in R$

$$\left(\frac{ab}{b}\right)\varphi = \frac{a'b'}{b'} = a' \in P.$$

Finally, we know that the isomorphic image of a field is always a field. Hence, those elements of the field P which can be written in the form of quotients of elements of R form a subfield in the field P, containing the whole ring R and therefore, by the hypothesis of the theorem, coinciding with P. Thus we have constructed an isomorphic mapping φ of the field $\overline{R}$ onto the whole field P, which is identical on R.

7. The quotient field for the ring of integers is the field of rational numbers.

If P is an arbitrary field, then the ring of polynomials $P[x]$ is an integral domain (see II.2.7) and therefore can be embedded in a quotient field. This field is denoted by $P(x)$ and is called the *field of rational fractions* in the unknown x over the field P. Its elements have the form of fractions $f(x)/g(x)$, where $f(x)$ and $g(x)$ are polynomials from $P[x]$ and where $g(x) \neq 0$, and the equality of these fractions and the operations on them are defined in a way corresponding to II.5.2 and II.5.4.

The concept of a field of rational fractions $P(x_1, x_2, \ldots, x_n)$ in several unknowns is analogous.

*The quotient field for the ring of power series $P\{x\}$ over the field P (see II. 2.8) is isomorphic to the *field of "Laurent" power series* over P, i.e. series of the form

$$a_n x^n + a_{n+1} x^{n+1} + \ldots, \qquad (5)$$

where n may be greater, equal or less than zero, and all the coefficients belong to P; the series (5) in the general case thus contains a finite number of terms with negative powers of the unknown x and infinitely many terms with positive powers of it. The operations on these series are carried out by means of rules which are natural generalizations of the rules for the operations in the ring $P\{x\}$.*

§ 6. Non-associative skew fields, quasi-groups. Isotopy

1. The concept of a skew field can be carried over to the non–associative case in several non-equivalent ways. Thus we can consider rings in which for any elements a and b, where $a \neq 0$, the equations

$$ax = b, \quad ya = b \qquad (1)$$

have solutions which are not necessarily uniquely defined. We will call every such ring a *division ring*; from our definition it follows that a division ring may possess divisors of zero.

A division ring in which the equations (1) have unique solutions is called a *quasi-field*. A quasi-field cannot contain divisors of zero, and therefore the elements of a quasi-field distinct from zero form a groupoid under multiplication. This will be a quasi-group, i.e. a groupoid in which for any elements a and b the equations (1) are uniquely soluble.

Finally, we keep the term *skew field* for quasi-fields which have an identity. The elements of a skew field distinct from zero form a quasi-group with identity under multiplication, i.e. a *loop*.

*Every (not necessarily associative) ring without divisors of zero can be embedded in a quasi–field [B. H. Neumann, *Proc. Lond. math. Soc.* **1**, 241–256 (1951)].*

2. There exist quasi-fields which are not skew fields, and quasi-groups which are not loops. This is due to the fact that, although in the quasi-group G for every element a the equations

$$ax = a, \quad ya = a \tag{2}$$

can be solved uniquely, yet these solutions do not necessarily coincide, nor are they necessarily the right and left identities respectively for other elements of G.

Every subquasi-group A of the loop G with identity e is a subloop with the same identity e.

In fact, for every $a \in A$ the equations (2) have a unique solution e in G, which must thus be contained in the subquasi-group A.

3. A series of results associated with groups carry over to quasi-groups and particularly to loops. We will not touch on this any further and we will introduce only the one generalization of the concept of isomorphism which plays an outstanding part in the theory of quasi-groups.

Let there be given a groupoid G with the multiplication $a \cdot b$ and let φ, ψ and χ be arbitrary one–one mappings of the set G onto itself, not necessarily distinct. We obtain a new groupoid on the set G if for any $a, b \in G$ we set

$$a \circ b = (a\varphi \cdot b\psi)\chi. \tag{3}$$

This new groupoid is not necessarily isomorphic to the old one, but to a certain extent they resemble each other.

Accordingly the groupoid G with multiplication $a \circ b$ is said to be *isotopic* to the groupoid G' with multiplication $a' \cdot b'$, if there exist three one–one mappings φ, ψ and χ^{-1} of G onto G' such that for any $a, b \in G$

$$(a \circ b)\chi^{-1} = a\varphi \cdot b\psi. \tag{4}$$

It is clear that *when $\varphi = \psi = \chi^{-1}$ we obtain an isomorphic mapping of G onto G'.*

It is easy to verify that the relation of isotopy is reflexive, transitive and symmetric.

In many cases it is convenient to assume that the operations
$a \circ b$ and $a \cdot b$ are given in the same set G and that φ, ψ and χ which
occur in (3) or (4) are one–one mappings of this set on itself.

4. *Every groupoid isotopic to a quasi-group is itself a quasi-group.*

In fact, let there be given on the set G a groupoid with multiplication $a \circ b$ and a quasi-group with multiplication $a \cdot b$, where
they are isotopic, i.e. (3) holds. We will prove that, for instance,
the equation

$$a \circ x = b \qquad (5)$$

has a unique solution for any a, $b \in G$. We know that the equation

$$a\varphi \cdot y = b\chi^{-1}$$

has a uniquely determined solution c. We let $x = c\psi^{-1}$. Then

$$a \circ x = a \circ c\psi^{-1} = (a\varphi \cdot c)\chi = (b\chi^{-1})\chi = b.$$

On the other hand, if x' is any solution of equation (5), then

$$a\varphi \cdot x'\psi = b\chi^{-1},$$

whence $x'\psi = c$, i.e. $x' = c\psi^{-1}$.

5. *Every quasi-group is isotopic to a loop* [Albert, *Trans.
Amer. math. Soc.* **54**, 507–519 (1943)].

In fact, we fix an arbitrary element e in the quasi-group G
with multiplication $a \cdot b$. Then there exists in G an element f such
that

$$e \cdot f = e. \qquad (6)$$

Let a be an arbitrary element of G. We denote by $a\varphi$ and $a\psi$ the
uniquely determined elements such that

$$a\varphi \cdot f = a, \qquad e \cdot a\psi = a. \qquad (7)$$

The mappings $a \to a\varphi$ and $a \to a\psi$, where a varies through the
whole set G, will be one-one mappings of G onto itself. Thus,
if $a\varphi = b\varphi$, then $a\varphi \cdot f = b\varphi \cdot f$, i.e. $a = b$. On the other hand,
if c is an arbitrary element of G, then

$$c = (c \cdot f)\varphi.$$

From this it follows that, if we set for all a, $b \in G$

$$a \circ b = a\varphi \cdot b\psi, \qquad (8)$$

we define a new groupoid on G, which is isotopic to the initial quasi-group; the part of χ is played here by the identity mapping, i.e. it will be, as we say, a *principal isotope*. By the proof in the previous section this last groupoid will itself be a quasi-group. It will even be a loop, because the element e will be an identity for it. In fact, because by (6) and (7)

$$e\varphi = e, \quad e\psi = f,$$

then, in view of (8) and (7)

$$a \circ e = a\varphi \cdot f = a,$$
$$e \circ a = e \cdot a\psi = a.$$

Thus the theorem is proved.

6. *If a groupoid with identity is isotopic to a semi-group, then they are isomorphic and therefore are both associative and both have an identity* [Bruck, Trans. Amer. math. Soc. **60**, 245–354 (1946); N. J. S. Hughes, J. Lond. math. Soc. **32**, 510–511 (1957)].

In fact, let there be given on the set G a groupoid with multiplication $a \cdot b$, having an identity e, and a semigroup with multiplication $a \circ b$, where they are isotopic,

$$a \circ b = (a\varphi \cdot b\psi)\chi,$$

where φ, ψ, χ are one–one mappings of the set G onto itself. Because for any a, b, $c \in G$

$$(a \circ b) \circ c = a \circ (b \circ c),$$

then

$$[(a\varphi \cdot b\psi)\chi\varphi \cdot c\psi]\chi = [a\varphi \cdot (b\varphi \cdot c\psi)\chi\psi]\chi,$$

whence

$$(a\varphi \cdot b\psi)\chi\varphi \cdot c\psi = a\varphi \cdot (b\varphi \cdot c\psi)\chi\psi. \tag{9}$$

Letting $a\varphi = c\psi = e$ in this equation, we obtain for all $b \in G$

$$b\psi\chi\varphi = b\varphi\chi\psi. \tag{10}$$

Further, letting $a\varphi = e$ in (9) and using (10), we obtain

$$b\varphi\chi\psi \cdot c\psi = (b\varphi \cdot c\psi)\chi\psi$$

or, replacing $b\varphi$ by a and $c\psi$ by b,

$$a\chi\psi \cdot b = (a \cdot b)\chi\psi \tag{11}$$

for all a, $b \in G$. Finally, letting $c\psi = e$ in (9) and using (10), we obtain

$$(a\varphi \cdot b\psi)\chi\varphi = a\varphi \cdot b\psi\chi\varphi$$

or, replacing $a\varphi$ by a and $b\psi$ by b,

$$(a \cdot b)\chi\varphi = a \cdot b\chi\varphi \tag{12}$$

for all a, $b \in G$.

By using (11), (12) and (10), we arrive at the following equation: for any a, $b \in G$

$$(a \circ b)\psi\chi\varphi = (a\varphi \cdot b\psi)\chi\psi\chi\varphi = (a\varphi\chi\psi \cdot b\psi)\chi\varphi = a\psi\chi\varphi \cdot b\psi\chi\varphi.$$

This equation shows that the product $\psi\chi\varphi$, which is a one–one mapping of the set G onto itself, will be an isomorphism between the given semigroup and the groupoid. Thus the theorem is proved.

From this theorem follows Albert's theorem [*Trans. Amer. math. Soc.* 54, 507–519 (1943)]: *If a loop is isotopic to a group, then they are isomorphic.* From this it follows in particular that isotopic groups are always isomorphic, and therefore there is no reason to apply isotopy in the theory of groups.

7. The concept of isotopy can be carried over to the theory of non-associative rings. In fact, by considering rings with the same additive group G, we define the *isotopy of rings* by means of equation (3), as above, but we will assume that the mappings φ, ψ and χ are isomorphic mappings of the group G onto itself (i.e. automorphisms of it in the sense of III.3.1). From the results obtained above, and the methods used in their proof, there now follow these results:

Every ring which is isotopic to a quasi-field is itself a quasi-field.

In fact, let there be given on the additive Abelian group G a ring with multiplication $a \circ b$ and a quasi-field isotopic to it with the multiplication $a \cdot b$. If $a \circ b = 0$, then

$$(a\varphi \cdot b\psi)\chi = 0,$$

and because the zero of the group G remains fixed under the isomorphism χ, then

$$a\varphi \cdot b\psi = 0.$$

Therefore one of the factors is equal to zero, for instance $a\varphi = 0$, whence $a = 0$, i.e. the given ring does not contain divisors of zero. Thus, there are given a groupoid and a quasi-group on the set $G \setminus 0$, and because the mappings φ, ψ and χ can be regarded as one–one mappings of this set onto itself, it only remains to apply II.6.4.

Every quasi-field is isotopic to a (non-associative) skew field.

In fact, if there is given a quasi-field K with multiplication $a \cdot b$, then, by II.6.5, the multiplicative quasi-group of its elements distinct from zero is isotopic to the loop with multiplication $a \circ b$ by virtue of the equation (8), where the one–one mappings φ and ψ of the set $K \setminus 0$ are defined by the equations (7). In addition we set $0\varphi = 0\psi = 0$, which agrees with (7), and we will prove that φ and ψ are now isomorphic mappings of the additive group of the skew field K onto itself. Thus, from

$$(a\varphi + b\varphi) \cdot f = a\varphi \cdot f + b\varphi \cdot f = a + b$$

it follows that

$$(a + b)\varphi = a\varphi + b\varphi.$$

By setting in addition $a \circ 0 = 0 \circ a = 0$ for all $a \in K$, we define a multiplication $\circ$ for all the elements of K, where the identity e of the loop constructed above will also be the identity for this multiplication. It remains to prove the distributive laws for this multiplication with respect to addition. Thus, by (8),

$$(a + b) \circ c = (a + b)\varphi \cdot c\psi = (a\varphi + b\varphi) \cdot c\psi =$$
$$a\varphi \cdot c\psi + b\varphi \cdot c\psi = a \circ c + b \circ c.$$

Hence the theorem is proved.

If a ring with identity is isotopic to an associative ring, then they are isomorphic.

In fact, let there be given on the additive Abelian group G a ring with multiplication $a \circ b$, having the identity e, and an associative ring with multiplication $a \circ b$, where for any $a, b \in G$ equation (3) holds, where φ, ψ and χ are isomorphic mappings of the group G onto itself. Then the product $\psi\chi\varphi$, which is obviously an isomorphic mapping of the group G onto itself, will, by the proof in II.6.6, be an isomorphism between the given rings.

* An associative ring with identity may have a non-associative isotope. There exist associative rings without identity which are isotopic with each other, but are not isomorphic [Albert, *Ann. of Math.* **43**, 685–707 (1942)].*

§ 7. Normal subgroups, ideals

1. Let there be given a group G and a subgroup H. If a is an arbitrary element of G, then the totality aH of all products of the form ah, where h varies through the subgroup H, is called a *left coset* of the group G with respect to the subgroup H, defined by the element a. It is clear that $a \in aH$, because the subgroup H contains the identity.

If the element b belongs to the coset aH, then $bH = aH$, i.e. *every left coset of the group G with respect to the subgroup H is determined by any one of its elements.* In fact, if $b = ah_0$, $h_0 \in H$, then for any h', $h'' \in H$

$$bh' = a(h_0 h') \quad \text{and} \quad ah'' = b(h_0^{-1} h''),$$

i.e. $bH \subseteq aH$ and $aH \subseteq bH$.

From this it follows that *any two left cosets of the group G with respect to the subgroup H either coincide or else have empty intersection.* We obtain a partition of the group G into non-intersecting left cosets with respect to the subgroup H. It is called the *left-sided partition* of the group G with respect to the subgroup H. One of the cosets of this partition will be the subgroup H itself: if $a \in H$, then $aH = H$.

2. Similarly, we can obtain the *right-sided partition* of the group G with respect to the subgroup H, made up of its *right cosets Ha*, $a \in G$. In the non-commutative case the right-sided partition of G with respect to H may in fact differ from the left-sided partition. Both these partitions, however, consist of the same number of cosets: the mapping which transforms every element a of the group G into the element a^{-1} is a one–one mapping of G onto itself, transforming every left coset aH into the right coset Ha^{-1} and *vice versa.*

The number of cosets in either of the two partitions of the group G with respect to the subgroup H, if it is finite, is called the *index* of the subgroup H in the group G.

3. If G is a finite group of order n, and H is a subgroup of G of order k and index j, then every coset aH consists of exactly k elements, and therefore

$$n = kj.$$

From this follows

LAGRANGE'S THEOREM. *The order and the index of any subgroup of a finite group divide the order of the group itself.*

From this theorem it follows, in view of II.3.4, that *the order of any element of a finite group divides the order of the group.* From Lagrange's theorem it also follows that *every group whose order is a prime number must be cyclic.* In fact, this group must coincide with the cyclic subgroup generated by any of its elements distinct from 1.

4. A subgroup H is called a *normal subgroup* (or *invariant subgroup*) of the group G, if the left-sided partition of the group G with respect to the subgroup H coincides with the right-sided partition, i.e. if for every $a \in G$ the equation

$$aH = Ha \tag{1}$$

holds (understood in the sense that the two subsets coincide in G). Thus we can speak simply of *the partition of the group G with respect to the normal subgroup H.*

We will mention some other definitions of a normal subgroup which are equivalent to that given above.

The elements x and y of the group G are said to be *conjugate* in G, if we can find an element a in G such that

$$y = a^{-1}xa,$$

i.e. y is obtained from x by *transformation* by the element a.

The subgroup H of the group G will be normal in G if and only if H contains, together with any element, all its conjugates in G.

In fact, if H is a normal subgroup in G, h any element of H, and a any element of G, then, by (1), there exists in H an element h' such that

$$ah' = ha, \tag{2}$$

whence

$$a^{-1}ha = h' \in H. \tag{3}$$

Conversely, if for any $h \in H$ and $a \in G$ there exists in H an element h' in H, satisfying equation (3) and therefore (2), then $Ha \subseteq aH$. This inclusion is valid for all a, in particular for a^{-1}, i.e. $Ha^{-1} \subseteq a^{-1}H$, from which it follows that $aH \subseteq Ha$, and therefore equation (1) in fact holds.

The subgroups U and V of the group G are said to be *conjugate* in G, if there exists in G an element a which transforms the subgroup U into V, i.e.

$$a^{-1}Ua = V.$$

We note that the set $a^{-1}Ua$ for any subgroup U and any $a \in G$ will be a subgroup, which is isomorphic to U. In fact, if $u_1, u_2 \in U$, then

$$(a^{-1}u_1a)(a^{-1}u_2a) = a^{-1}(u_1u_2)a;$$

on the other hand, from

$$a^{-1}u_1a = a^{-1}u_2a$$

it follows that $u_1 = u_2$, and therefore the mapping $u \to a^{-1}\,ua$, $u \in U$, will be an isomorphic mapping of U onto $a^{-1}Ua$ and hence $a^{-1}Ua$ is a subgroup.

Every normal subgroup of the group G coincides with every subgroup conjugate to it in G. Conversely, if the subgroup H of the group G coincides with all the subgroups conjugate to it in G, then it will be a normal subgroup.

In fact, from (1) follows the equation

$$a^{-1}Ha = H, \tag{4}$$

which proves the first assertion of the theorem. On the other hand, if

$$a^{-1}Ha \subset H,$$

where the inclusion is a strict one, then

$$H \subset aHa^{-1} = (a^{-1})^{-1}Ha^{-1}.$$

Thus, if the subgroup H contains *all* the subgroups conjugate to it, then it must necessarily coincide with them, i.e. for any $a \in G$ equation (4) holds, and therefore also equation (1), which follows from this.

5. *The intersection of any set of normal subgroups of the group G is itself a normal subgroup in G.*

In fact, if D is the intersection of the normal subgroups A_i, $i \in I$, then D will be a subgroup in G (see II.3.6), and, moreover, every element conjugate to an element of D is contained in each of the normal subgroups A_i and therefore belongs to D.

The subgroup generated by any system of normal subgroups of the group G (see II.3.8) will itself be normal in G.

In fact, let there be given the normal subgroups A_i, $i \in I$, and let B be the subgroup generated by them. As we mentioned in II.3.7, every element b of B can be written in the form

$$b = a_1a_2 \ldots a_n,$$

where $a_j \in A_{i_j}, j = 1, 2, \ldots, n$. If g is any element of G, then

$$g^{-1}bg = (g^{-1}a_1 g)(g^{-1}a_2 g) \ldots (g^{-1}a_n g),$$

and because

$$g^{-1}a_j g \in A_{i_j}, \quad j = 1, 2, \ldots, n,$$

it follows that

$$g^{-1}bg \in B.$$

6. All the subgroups of an Abelian group will, of course, be normal. On the other hand, for every group G the identity subgroup E and the group G itself will be normal. A group which has no normal subgroups other than itself and E is called *simple*.

The simple Abelian groups are the finite cyclic groups of prime order and there are no others.

In fact, if the Abelian group G is simple, then in general it does not contain non-trivial subgroups, and because there must be cyclic subgroups in it, it will itself be cyclic. Infinite cyclic groups, however, possess non-trivial subgroups—the additive group of whole numbers contains as a proper subgroup the group of even numbers. Further, if the group $G = \{a\}$ is cyclic of finite order n, then if the number n has factors, $n = kl$, the subgroup $\{a^k\}$ will have order l, i.e. it will be distinct from G and from E. If, however, the group $G = \{a\}$ has prime order p, then it cannot have non-trivial subgroups, which follows from Lagrange's theorem.

7. There also exist non-commutative simple groups, both finite ones and infinite ones. For instance, we consider in the symmetric group of the n-th degree S_n (see II.1.8) the subset A_n of even permutations. As is proved in text books on higher algebra, the parity of a permutation of degree n coincides with the parity of the number of factors of any decomposition of this permutation into the product of transpositions. From this it follows that the product of even permutations of degree n is always even, and because the permutation inverse to an even permutation is itself even, we see that A_n will be a *subgroup of the group S_n*.

The group A_n is called the *alternating group of degree n* and has order $n!/2$. We note that it will not only be a subgroup in S_n, but also a normal subgroup: the index of A_n in S_n is equal to two, and both the partitions of the group S_n with respect to the subgroup A_n coincide, and consist of two cosets—the subgroup A_n itself and the coset of odd permutations.

The group A_3 has order 3 and is therefore a cyclic group of prime order, i.e. it is simple. The group A_4 will not be simple— it is easy to verify that the even permutations†

$$(12)(34), \quad (13)(24), \quad (14)(23)$$

together with the identity, form a normal subgroup of this group. *The alternating group of degree n, A_n is simple when $n \geqslant 5$.*

We will show first that the cycles (ijk) of length 3, which are, as it is easy to see, even permutations, form a system of generators for the group A_n (see II.3.9). In fact, every even permutation can be decomposed into the product of an even number of transpositions, and therefore also into the product of cycles of length 3, because

$$(ij)(ik) = (ijk),$$

$$(ij)(kl) = (ijk)(ilk).$$

We will prove, further, that every normal subgroup H of the group A_n containing at least one cycle (ijk) of length 3 also contains any other cycle $(i'j'k')$ of length 3 and therefore, as we proved above, coincides with A_n. In fact, if the symbols l and m are distinct from i, j and k, then the permutation of the n-th degree

$$\alpha = \begin{pmatrix} i & j & k & l & m & ... \\ i' & j' & k' & l' & m' & ... \end{pmatrix},$$

† We recall that in writing a permutation in terms of cycles we write after every symbol the symbol into which it is carried by the permutation under consideration. The cycle is closed when we reach the symbol which is carried into the first symbol of the cycle. Symbols which are left fixed by our permutation are omitted in the decomposition into cycles. Thus,

$$\begin{pmatrix} 1 & 2 & 3 & 4 & 5 & 6 \\ 4 & 6 & 1 & 3 & 5 & 2 \end{pmatrix} = (143)(26).$$

On the other hand,

$$(12)(34) = \begin{pmatrix} 1 & 2 & 3 & 4 \\ 2 & 1 & 4 & 3 \end{pmatrix}.$$

if, of course, it is known that this permutation is of degree 4. We note also that the parity of the permutation coincides with the parity of the difference between the number of the symbols actually permuted by this permutation, and the number of cycles in its decomposition.

which can be made even by transposing, if necessary, the symbols l' and m' in the lower row, is such that

$$\alpha^{-1}(ijk)\alpha = (i'j'k').$$

It remains to prove that every normal subgroup H of the group A_n, $n \geqslant 5$, distinct from E, contains at least one cycle of length 3. We take an element α in H distinct from 1, which leaves fixed as many symbols as possible. If the permutation α is not a cycle of length 3, then it will have one of the following two forms:

(1) The decomposition of α into cycles contains at least one cycle whose length is not less than three:

$$\alpha = (ijk \ldots) \ldots$$

Here α, being an even permutation, cannot be a cycle $(ijkl)$ of length 4, and therefore α permutes at least two symbols distinct from i, j, and k; let these be l and m.

(2) The permutation α can be decomposed into the product of independent cycles of length 2, which will not be less than two in number:

$$\alpha = (ij)(kl) \ldots$$

In this case, because $n \geqslant 5$, we denote by m any symbol distinct from i, j, k and l.

Let $\beta = (klm)$. Then $\beta^{-1}\alpha\beta \in H$, because $\beta \in A_n$, and therefore

$$\gamma = \beta^{-1}\alpha\beta\alpha^{-1} \in H.$$

The permutation γ is distinct from 1, because in case (1) the permutation $\beta^{-1}\alpha\beta$ carries the symbol j not into the symbol k, as α does, but into the symbol l; in case (2) the permutation $\beta^{-1}\alpha\beta$ carries the symbol l into the symbol m, and not into the symbol k, as is done by the permutation α.

On the other hand, the permutation γ leaves fixed, in the first case, all the symbols left fixed by the permutation α, because all these are distinct from k, l and m, and in the second case, all the symbols left fixed by α, except, perhaps, the symbol m. It is easy to verify, however, that in the first case the permutation γ also leaves the symbol i fixed, and in the second case the symbols i and j. Thus, in both cases γ leaves fixed more symbols than α. This contradicts the choice of the permutation α, and shows that α must be a cycle of length 3, i.e. the theorem is proved.

We note that the alternating groups A_n, $n \geqslant 5$, by no means exhaust all the finite non-commutative simple groups.

8. In the following chapter we will prove that the part which is played in the theory of groups by the concept of a normal subgroup, belongs in the theory of rings to the concept of an ideal.

A subset A of an arbitrary ring R is called an *ideal* in R, if it is a subgroup of the additive group of the ring R—for this it is sufficient that A be non-empty and that the difference of any two elements of A should belong to A—and if, in addition, for any elements $a \in A$ and $r \in R$ both of the products ar and ra are contained in A.

From this definition it follows that every ideal of the ring R will be a subring in R. It is easy to see, further, that the intersection of any system of ideals of a ring R will itself be an ideal. On the other hand, *the subgroup of the additive group of the ring R generated by a given system of ideals A_i, $i \in I$, will also be an ideal*: this subgroup consists of all finite sums of elements from the ideals A_i, but the multiplication of such a sum on the left or on the right by any element of the ring R again reduces to a sum of this form.

In II.4.2 we described all the subgroups of the additive group of whole numbers. *All these subgroups* (including the zero) *and, of course, only these, are ideals in the ring of whole numbers*, because the product of a number which is a multiple of n by any whole number is itself a multiple of n.

9. Every ring R has the ideals R itself and the *null ideal* 0, consisting of the zero alone. A ring which does not contain any other ideals except these two is called *simple*.

Every skew field and in general every division ring (see II.6.1) *is a simple ring.*

In fact, let there be given a division ring K. If there is given an ideal A distinct from 0 in it, and if $a \in A$, $a \neq 0$, then, in view of the fact that the equations (1) from II.6.1 can be solved in K, any element b of K will belong to A, i.e. $A = K$.

The total matrix ring K_n of any order n over any division ring K is a simple ring.

In fact, let there be given in the ring K a non-null ideal A. If $\alpha = (a_{ij})$ is a non-zero matrix belonging to A, then let, for instance, $a_{kl} \neq 0$. Let us agree to denote by $\bar{x}_{ij}$ the matrix from

K_n which has the element x from K in its (i,j)-th position, and all of whose remaining positions are filled with zeros. We suppose, further, that b is an arbitrary element from K, and s and t are arbitrary indices, $1 \leqslant s$, $t \leqslant n$. In view of the fact that equations (1) from II.6.1 can be solved in K, there exist elements x and y in K such that

$$y(a_{kl}x) = b.$$

By applying the rule for the multiplication of matrices, we see that

$$\bar{y}_{sk}(\alpha \bar{x}_{lt}) = \bar{b}_{st}.$$

Thus, all the matrices of the form $\bar{b}_{st}$ belong to the ideal A, and because every matrix from K_n can be represented in the form of a sum of matrices of this form, $A = K_n$, which was what we wished to prove.

10. If, in the definition of an ideal, we omit the requirement that for any a from the ideal A and any r from the ring R both the products ar and ra should belong to A, and require this only for the product ar or the product ra, then we arrive at the concept of a *one-sided ideal*, or in fact a *right ideal*, if $ar \in A$ for all $a \in A$ and $r \in R$, and a *left ideal*, if $ra \in A$. In the commutative case, and equally in the anticommutative case, in particular in Lie and Jordan rings (see II.2.3 and II.2.4), every one-sided ideal will of course be an ideal (or, as one sometimes says, a *two-sided ideal*).

Because in the proof given above of the simplicity of any division ring it was sufficient to use the solvability of only one of the equations (1) from II.6.1, we can assert that *no division ring K contains any one-sided ideals distinct from K and 0.*

If an associative ring R does not contain any one-sided ideals except R and 0, and is not a ring with zero multiplication (see II.2.2), then it will be a skew field.

In fact, we will call *a left annihilator* of the ring R any element a such that $ar = 0$ for all $r \in R$. The left annihilators form an ideal in the associative ring R, even a two-sided ideal. In our present case this ideal will be equal to zero—if it were equal to R, then R would be a zero ring. Thus for any non-zero element a the set aR of all possible products of the form ar, $r \in R$, which is a right ideal in the associative ring, will be distinct from 0 and therefore $aR = R$. From this it follows that for any element $b \in R$ the equation $ax = b$ can be solved in R. In an analogous way we can prove that every equation of the form $ya = b$, $a \neq 0$, can be solved in R, and therefore, by II.2.10, the ring R will be a skew field.

From what has been said it follows easily that *a non-zero associative-commutative ring will be simple if and only if it is a field*. On the other hand, because every subgroup of the additive group in a zero ring is an ideal, then, in view of II.7.6, *the simple zero rings are exhausted by the zero rings on cyclic additive groups of prime order*.

11. The definitions of an ideal and a one-sided ideal can easily be carried over to the case of any groupoid—it is sufficient to exclude from these definitions any mention of the additive group. All the ideals, and also the left and right ideals of a ring will obviously be, respectively, ideals, left and right ideals of the multiplicative groupoid of this ring. The converse, however, is not true: in the ring of integers the totality of numbers which are multiples of at least one of the numbers 2 and 3 will not be an ideal, although it will be an ideal of the multiplicative semigroup of this ring.

§ 8. Gaussian semigroups

1. As is well known, in the ring of integers C and in the ring of polynomials $P[x]$ over any field P there are exactly parallel theories of divisibility. In the present and subsequent paragraphs we will establish the reasons for this parallelism.

Let there be given an Abelian semigroup G with identity 1, satisfying the cancellation law (see II.5.1). *The units (divisors of the identity) of this semigroup*, i.e. those elements ε for which there exists an inverse element ε^{-1},

$$\varepsilon\varepsilon^{-1} = 1,$$

form a subgroup, because the product of units, and the element inverse to a unit, will themselves be units. On the other hand, *if the product of the elements a_1, a_2, ..., $a_n \in G$ is a unit*,

$$a_1 a_2 \ldots a_n = \varepsilon,$$

then each of the elements a_i, $i = 1, 2, ..., n$, will itself be a unit. In fact,

$$a_i^{-1} = a_1 \ldots a_{i-1} a_{i+1} \ldots a_n \varepsilon^{-1}, \quad i = 1, 2, \ldots, n.$$

2. If the elements a, $b \in G$ are such that $a = bc$, then the element b is called a *divisor* of the element a; one also says that a is *divisible* by b. The elements a and b are called *associates* if each of them is a divisor of the other,

$$a = bc, \quad b = ad. \tag{1}$$

Because from (1) it follows that

$$a = a(cd),$$

i.e., in view of the cancellation law,

$$cd = 1,$$

then both c and d will be units. On the other hand, for any unit ε *the elements a and εa are associates,* because

$$a = \varepsilon^{-1}(\varepsilon a).$$

From this it follows that *every unit is a divisor of any element of the semigroup G.*

The relation of associativity is obviously an equivalence relation, and therefore the whole semigroup G can be decomposed into *classes of associated elements*; one of these classes will be the group of units. On the other hand, the relation "b is a divisor of a" is reflexive and transitive. At the same time, for any units ε_1 and ε_2, from

$$a = bc$$

it follows that

$$\varepsilon_1 a = (\varepsilon_2 b)(\varepsilon_1 \varepsilon_2^{-1} c),$$

i.e. $\varepsilon_2 b$ is a divisor of $\varepsilon_1 a$. In this way we obtain a *partial ordering* in the set of classes of associated elements of the semigroup G, if for the classes A, B we set $B \leqslant A$ in the case when at least one (and hence every) element of B is a divisor of at least one (and hence every) element of A. The class of units will be a minimal element of this set (see I.5.1), and it will be unique.

3. An element $p \in G$, which is not a unit, is called *irreducible* if its only divisors, apart from units, are elements associated with it, i.e. if from

$$p = ab$$

it always follows that one of the elements a, b is a unit, and therefore the other is an associate of p. *Together with p, obviously,*

all elements which are associates of p will be irreducible. The classes
of associated irreducible elements, if such elements exist in general
in the semigroup G, will be exactly the minimal elements of the
partially ordered set of classes of associated elements distinct
from the class of units.

An element $p \in G$, which is not a unit, is called *prime* if the
product ab can be divided by p only in the case when one of the
elements a, b is divisible by p. *Every element which is associated
with a prime element p will obviously be prime.* By simple induction
with respect to n we can also prove that *if the product $a_1a_2 \ldots a_n$
is divisible by the prime element p, then at least one of the elements
a_i, $i = 1, 2, \ldots, n$ is divisible by p.*

Every prime element p is irreducible.

In fact, if

$$p = ab,$$

then, in view of the fact that p is prime, at least one of the factors,
for instance a, is divisible by p. However, p is divisible in its turn
by a, i.e. p and a are associates, and therefore b will be a unit.

We note that the converse assertion does not hold in the
general case.

4. If $a, b \in G$, then the element $d \in G$ is called a *greatest common
divisor* of the elements a and b and is denoted by

$$d = (a, b), \tag{2}$$

if d is a common divisor for a and b and if d itself is divisible
by any other common divisor of the elements a and b.

If also $d' = (a, b)$, then d and d' must be divisible by each
other, i.e. they are associates. On the other hand, if $d = (a, b)$
and ε_1, ε_2, ε_3 are arbitrary units, then also

$$\varepsilon_1 d = (\varepsilon_2 a, \varepsilon_3 b),$$

i.e. the replacement in equation (2) of all the elements included
in it by any elements which are associated with them does not
violate this equation. In other words, if A, B, D are respectively
the classes of the elements associated with a, b and d, then equation (2) can be rewritten in the form

$$D = (A, B).$$

The class D will be the unique maximal element (see I.5.5)
in the partially ordered set of all classes X such that $X \leqslant A$ and

$X \leqslant B$, and the symbol (A, B) may be regarded as the notation for this class.

Of course, generally speaking, the elements $a, b \in G$ may not have a greatest common divisor. However, *if a is divisible by b, then* (a, b) *exists*, and in fact

$$(a, b) = b.$$

5. *If a greatest common divisor exists for any pair of elements* $a, b \in G$, *then every irreducible element of the semigroup* G *will be prime.*

We will prove first that with our hypotheses, for any $a, b, c \in G$

$$(ac, bc) = (a, b)c. \tag{3}$$

In fact, because a is divisible by (a, b), ac is divisible by $(a, b)c$. Analogously, bc is divisible by $(a, b)c$, and therefore the left-hand side of equation (3) is divisible by the right,

$$(ac, bc) = (a, b)cd. \tag{4}$$

Hence

$$ac = (ac, bc)u = (a, b)cdu,$$

i.e., by virtue of the cancellation law,

$$a = (a, b)du. \tag{5}$$

Analogously,

$$b = (a, b)dv. \tag{6}$$

From (5) and (6) it follows that the element $(a, b)d$ is a common divisor for a and b, and because it is itself divisible by (a, b), the element d must be a unit. This proves that from equation (4) one can derive equation (3).

Now we will show that for any three elements $a, b, c \in G$

$$((a, b), c) = (a, (b, c)). \tag{7}$$

In fact, the element $((a, b), c)$ is a common divisor of (a, b) and c, and therefore also a common divisor of the elements a, b, c. On the other hand, every common divisor of these three elements is a common divisor of (a, b) and c, and therefore it will be a divisor also of $((a, b), c)$. The same assertion can be made with respect to the element $(a, (b, c))$, and therefore the left and right-hand sides of equation (7) are associates, which is essentially also expressed by equation (7).

We shall say, further, that the elements a, $b \in G$ are *mutually prime*, if their only common divisors are units; this can be expressed by the equation

$$(a, b) = 1.$$

If $(a, b) = 1$ and $(a, c) = 1$, then $(a, bc) = 1$.
In fact, because a is a divisor of ac, then

$$(a, ac) = a.$$

Further, from $(a, b) = 1$ it follows, in view of (3), that

$$(ac, bc) = c.$$

Therefore, in view of (7),

$$(a, bc) = ((a, ac), bc) = (a, (ac, bc)) = (a, c) = 1.$$

We go on to the proof of the theorem itself. Let p be an irreducible element of the semigroup G and let the product ab be divisible by p. If neither a nor b were divisible by p, then in view of the fact that p is irreducible, the common divisors of a and p (and also of b and p) could only be units, i.e. a and p (and also b and p) would be mutually prime,

$$(a, p) = 1, \quad (b, p) = 1.$$

But then, as we proved above, we would also have

$$(ab, p) = 1,$$

although by hypothesis ab is divisible by p, and p is not a unit. This contradiction proves that the element p is prime.

6. Let G be, as before, an Abelian semigroup with 1, satisfying the cancellation law. If

$$a = b_1 b_2 \ldots b_k \tag{8}$$

and if the elements ε_1, ε_2, ..., ε_k are such that

$$\varepsilon_1 \varepsilon_2 \ldots \varepsilon_k = 1$$

—all these elements will, thus, be units—then the equation

$$a = (\varepsilon_1 b_1)(\varepsilon_2 b_2) \ldots (\varepsilon_k b_k) \tag{9}$$

also holds.

Two factorizations of the element a into the product of several elements, (8) and

$$a = c_1 c_2 \ldots c_l, \tag{10}$$

will be called *associated factorizations*, if $l = k$ and if after, perhaps, a change in the numbering of the factors of the second of these factorizations, the elements b_i and c_i are associates, $i = 1, 2, ..., k$, i.e. (10) has the form (9).

An Abelian semigroup G with identity, satisfying the cancellation law, is called a *Gaussian semigroup* if each of its elements a, which is not a unit, can be factorized into the product of irreducible elements, where any two such factorizations of the element a are associated with each other.

Amongst the Gaussian semigroups are found all Abelian groups—they do not contain any elements which are not units. The multiplicative semigroup of integers distinct from zero will also be Gaussian. The units in this semigroup are the numbers 1 and -1, and the irreducible elements are all the prime numbers, taken with the sign $+$ or $-$. The multiplicative semigroup of polynomials distinct from zero in the unknown x with coefficients in a field F is also one of the Gaussian semigroups. Its units are all the elements of the field F which are distinct from zero, and its irreducible elements coincide with the irreducible polynomials.

7. *An Abelian semigroup G with identity, satisfying the cancellation law, will be Gaussian if and only if it satisfies one of the following sets of conditions, which are equivalent to each other:* (α, β'), (α, β''), *where the conditions* α, β' *and* β'' *are as follows:*

(α) *the partially ordered set of classes of associated elements of the semigroup G (see II.8.2) satisfies the minimum condition (see I.5.1);*

(β') *any two elements of the semigroup G have a greatest common divisor;*

(β'') *every irreducible element of the semigroup G is prime.*

Because, by II.8.5, (β'') follows from (β'), this theorem reduces to the two assertions proved below.

8. *Every Gaussian semigroup G satisfies the conditions* (α) *and* (β').

In fact, we shall define the *length* of the element a of the Gaussian semigroup G as the number of factors in any factorization of the element a into the product of irreducible factors. If $a = bc$, where b is a proper divisor of a, i.e. neither b nor c is a unit, then we obtain a factorization of the element a into the product of irreducible factors, by multiplying together factorizations of this kind for the elements b and c. Thus, the length of the element

a is equal to the sum of the lengths of the elements b and c, and therefore the length of a proper divisor of the element a is strictly less than the length of a itself. From this it follows that every sequence

$$a_1, a_2, \ldots, a_n, \ldots$$

of elements of the semigroup G such that a_{n+1} is a proper divisor of a_n, $n = 1, 2, \ldots$, breaks off after a finite number of terms. This proves the validity of condition (α).

On the other hand, let $a, b \in G$ and let

$$p_1, p_2, \ldots, p_n \qquad (11)$$

be a collection of irreducible elements such that every irreducible divisor both of the element a, and of the element b, is associated with one and only one element from (11); from this it follows that no two of the elements (11) are associated. The elements a and b can now be written in the form

$$a = \varepsilon p_1^{k_1} p_2^{k_2} \ldots p_n^{k_n}, \qquad b = \varepsilon' p_1^{l_1} p_2^{l_2} \ldots p_n^{l_n},$$

where ε, ε' are units, and some of the exponents $k_1, k_2, \ldots, k_n$, $l_1, l_2, \ldots, l_n$ may be equal to zero. Because any divisor c of the element a can be written in the form

$$c = \varepsilon'' p_1^{s_1} p_2^{s_2} \ldots p_n^{s_n},$$

where ε'' is a unit and $0 \leqslant s_i \leqslant k_i$, $i = 1, 2, \ldots, n$, and an analogous assertion is true for divisors of the element b, then the greatest common divisor of the elements a and b will be the element

$$\alpha = p_1^{m_1} p_2^{m_2} \ldots p_n^{m_n},$$

where $m_i = \min(k_i, l_i)$, $i = 1, 2, \ldots, n$. Thus condition (β') is also satisfied.

9. *Every Abelian semigroup G with identity, satisfying the cancellation law and conditions (α) and (β''), is Gaussian.*

We must prove that every element $a \in G$ which is not a unit has a factorization into the product of irreducible elements and that this factorization is determined uniquely to within associated ones. First we note that if this assertion is satisfied for a, then it is also satisfied for any element which is associated with a. This enables us, in view of (α) and I.5.1, to prove our assertion by induction with respect to the partially ordered set of classes of associated elements of the semigroup G.

This assertion is known to be satisfied for the irreducible elements, i.e. for elements from the minimal classes distinct from the class of units. We will therefore assume that everything has been proved for all the proper divisors of the element a. If a is not an irreducible element, then

$$a = bc,$$

where b and c are proper divisors of a. By the induction hypothesis

$$b = p_1 p_2 \dots p_k, \quad c = p_{k+1} p_{k+2} \dots p_n,$$

where all the p_i, $i = 1, 2, \dots, n$, are irreducible. Hence

$$a = p_1 p_2 \dots p_k p_{k+1} p_{k+2} \dots p_n. \tag{12}$$

Further, let

$$a = q_1 q_2 \dots q_s \tag{13}$$

be any other factorization of the element a into the product of irreducible factors. Because, by (β''), the irreducible element q_1 is prime, then, by II.8.3, at least one of the elements p_i, $i = 1$, $2, \dots, n$, must be divisible by q_1. Let this be the element p_1. However, it is irreducible, and therefore the elements p_1 and q_1 are associates,

$$p_1 = \varepsilon q_1. \tag{14}$$

Hence, in view of the cancellation law,

$$(\varepsilon p_2) p_3 \dots p_n = q_2 q_3 \dots q_s. \tag{15}$$

The left and right-hand sides of equation (15) are factorizations into irreducible factors for a proper divisor of the element a, and therefore, by the induction hypothesis, they are associated. From this and from (14) it also follows, however, that the factorizations (12) and (13) of the element a are associated—indeed, from the fact that the element εp_2 is associated with the element q_2, for instance, it follows that the elements p_2 and q_2 are associated.

§ 9. Gaussian rings

1. We recall that if R is an integral domain (see II.2.7), then the set $R \backslash 0$ will be an Abelian semigroup under multiplication, satisfying the cancellation law.

An integral domain R with identity is called a *Gaussian ring*†
if the multiplicative semigroup of the elements of R distinct
from zero is a Gaussian semigroup.

Amongst the Gaussian rings are included, trivially, all fields.
However, not every integral domain with identity will be a Gaussian ring.

* The totality of complex numbers of the form $a + b\sqrt{-3}$,
where a and b are any whole numbers, will be an integral domain
with identity, but not a Gaussian ring. Thus,

$$4 = 2 \cdot 2 = (1 + \sqrt{-3})(1 - \sqrt{-3})$$

will be two non-associated factorizations of the number 4 in
this ring into the product of irreducible factors.*

2. Let there be given an integral domain R with identity.
If $a \in R$, then the set

$$(a) = aR,$$

i.e. the totality of elements of the form ar, $r \in R$, will be an ideal
in R (see II.7.8). This is the *principal ideal* generated by the element
a. It is clear that a is contained in the ideal (a), because $a = a \cdot 1$.
If all the ideals in R are principal, i.e. if every ideal of R is generated by some element, then R is called a *principal ideal domain*.

Every principal ideal domain R is a Gaussian ring.

In view of II.8.7 it is sufficient to prove that in the multiplicative semigroup of the elements of R distinct from zero the
conditions (α) and (β') are satisfied.

If the element a is divisible by the element b, $a = bc$, then
$a \in (b)$ and therefore $(a) \subseteq (b)$; the converse is also true. Thus,
if, in the sequence of non-zero elements

$$a_1, a_2, \ldots, a_n, \ldots \tag{1}$$

every element a_n is divisible by a_{n+1}, $n = 1, 2, \ldots$, then the corresponding principal ideals will form an increasing sequence,

$$(a_1) \subseteq (a_2) \subseteq \ldots \subseteq (a_n) \subseteq \ldots \tag{2}$$

It is easy to verify that the set-theoretical union of this increasing
sequence of ideals will itself be an ideal in R, i.e., by our hypothesis
on R, some principal ideal; we denote it by (b). The element b,
which belongs to the union of the increasing sequence (2), must

---

† A Gaussian ring is also called a *unique factorization domain* (Ed.).

be contained in some ideal (a_n) and therefore in all the ideals (a_i) where $i > n$. For all these i it will thus be true that $(b) \subseteq (a_i)$, which together with $(a_i) \subseteq (b)$ gives $(a_i) = (b)$. Thus, the elements a_i and b are divisors of one another, i.e. they are associates. This proves that in the sequence (1) all the elements a_i where $i > n$ are associated with each other, i.e. condition (α) is satisfied.

On the other hand, if a, $b \in R$, then the totality of elements of the form $ar + bs$, where r and s vary independently through the whole ring R, will be an ideal and, hence, a principal ideal; we denote it by (d). Then

$$(d) \supseteq (a), \qquad (d) \supseteq (b),$$

because

$$a = a \cdot 1 + b \cdot 0 \in (d), \qquad b = a \cdot 0 + b \cdot 1 \in (d),$$

and therefore the element d is a common divisor of a and b. If however c is any common divisor of a and b, then

$$(c) \supseteq (a), \qquad (c) \supseteq (b),$$

and therefore the ideal (c) contains every element which has the form $ar + bs$, i.e. $(c) \supseteq (d)$, from which it follows that c is also a divisor of d. We obtain that d is the greatest common divisor of a and b. This proves that the condition (β') is also satisfied.

3. An integral domain R with identity is called a *Euclidean ring* if every element $a \in R$ distinct from zero can be related to a non-negative integer $n(a)$, where the following requirement is fulfilled: for any elements a, $b \in R$, where $b \neq 0$, it is possible to select elements q and r in the ring R such that

$$a = bq + r,$$

where either $r = 0$, or else $n(r) < n(b)$.

Every Euclidean ring is a principal ideal domain and, hence, a Gaussian ring.

In fact, let us take an ideal A in the Euclidean ring R. If $A = 0$, then $A = (0)$. If, however, $A \neq 0$, then let a_0 be one of the non-zero elements of A such that $n(a_0) \leqslant n(a)$ for all non-zero elements $a \in A$. Then for arbitrary $a \in A$ we can find, by hypothesis, elements q and r in R such that

$$a = a_0 q + r,$$

where if $r \neq 0$, then $n(r) < n(a_0)$. However

$$r = a - a_0 q \in A,$$

and we arrive at a contradiction to the choice of the element a_0. Therefore $r = 0$, i.e. $a = a_0 q$, which proves that A is a principal ideal, generated by the element a_0.

Amongst the Euclidean ring are the ring of integers Z—the part of $n(a)$ is played here by the absolute value $|a|$ of the number a,— *and also the ring of polynomials $F[x]$ over the field F—*here the part of $n(a)$ is played by the degree of the polynomial. *The rings Z and $F[x]$ will thus be principal ideal domains and Gaussian rings.*

* In every Euclidean ring to find the greatest common denominator of two elements one can apply Euclid's algorithm, which will be familiar to the reader.

There exist principal ideal domains which are not Euclidean rings [Motzkin, *Bull. Amer. Math. Soc.* **55**, 1142–1146 (1949)].*

4. We complete this section with the proof of the following theorem:

If R is a Gaussian ring, then the ring of polynomials $R[x]$ will also be Gaussian.

We know from II.2.7 that the ring $R[x]$ in our present case will be an integral domain with identity. We have to prove, in view of II.8.7, that in the multiplicative semigroup of the elements of $R[x]$ distinct from zero the conditions (α) and (β'') from II.8.7 are satisfied.

We begin with the remark that the units *in the ring $R[x]$ are precisely the units in the ring R*. We note, further, that because condition (β') from II.8.7 is fulfilled for the non-zero elements of the Gaussian ring R, then, in view of (7) from II.8.5, *we can speak of the greatest common divisor of any finite system of non-zero elements of R, and it will be defined uniquely to within associated elements.* It is clear that this remains true in the case when we add several elements equal to zero to the system under consideration.

A polynomial $\varphi(x)$ is called *primitive* if the greatest common divisor of the system of its coefficients is a unit and therefore can be taken equal to 1. A polynomial which is associated with a primitive polynomial is itself, obviously, primitive. Amongst the polynomials of zero degree those which are primitive will be the units and nothing else.

If $f(x)$ is an arbitrary non-zero polynomial and a is the greatest common divisor of its coefficients, then

$$f(x) = a\varphi(x), \qquad (3)$$

where the polynomial $\varphi(x)$ is primitive. If the equation

$$f(x) = b\psi(x)$$

also holds, where $b \in R$, and $\psi(x)$ is a primitive polynomial, then b, which is a divisor of all the coefficients of the polynomial $f(x)$, will also be a divisor of a,

$$a = bc.$$

Therefore, since there are no divisors of zero in $R[x]$,

$$\psi(x) = c\varphi(x),$$

whence, in view of the fact that $\psi(x)$ is primitive, the element c must be a unit.

This proves that *in the expression* (3) *for the polynomial* $f(x)$ both the element a from R, and the primitive polynomial $\varphi(x)$, are *determined to within factors which are units, i.e. to within associated elements*. We will call a factorization of the form (3) a *canonical factorization* of the polynomial $f(x)$.

5. GAUSS'S LEMMA. *The product of primitive polynomials is itself primitive.*

In fact, let there be given the primitive polynomials

$$f(x) = a_0 x^k + a_1 x^{k-1} + \ldots + a_i x^{k-i} + \ldots + a_k,$$
$$g(x) = b_0 x^l + b_1 x^{l-1} + \ldots + b_j x^{l-j} + \ldots + b_l$$

and let their product

$$f(x)g(x) = c_0 x^{k+l} + c_1 x^{k+l-1} + \ldots + c_{i+j} x^{(k+l)-(i+j)} + \ldots + c_{k+l}$$

not be primitive. From this it follows, because the ring R is Gaussian, that the coefficients $c_0, c_1, \ldots, c_{k+l}$ have a common irreducible divisor p. Because the polynomials $f(x)$ and $g(x)$ are primitive, neither one of them can have its coefficients all divisible by p. Let a_i and b_j be the coefficients of these polynomials with the smallest indices which are not divisible by p. However,

$$c_{i+j} = a_i b_j + a_{i-1} b_{j+1} + a_{i-2} b_{j+2} + \ldots$$
$$\ldots + a_{i+1} b_{j-1} + a_{i+2} b_{j-2} + \ldots \qquad (4)$$

Because, by hypothesis, all the coefficients a_{i-1}, a_{i-2} ..., and b_{j-1}, b_{j-2}, ... are divisible by p, the left-hand side of equation (4) is also divisible by p, as are all the summands on the right-hand side, except the first. From this it follows that the product $a_i b_j$ is also divisible by p, and because the irreducible element p in the Gaussian ring R is prime (see II.8.7), at least one of the elements a_i, b_j must be divisible by p, which contradicts the choice of these elements. Thus the lemma is proved.

From this it follows that *if we are given the polynomials* $f_i(x)$, $i = 1, 2, \ldots n$, *with the canonical factorizations*

$$f_i(x) = a_i \varphi_i(x), \quad i = 1, 2, \ldots, n,$$

and if

$$f(x) = \prod_{i=1}^{n} f_i(x), \quad a = \prod_{i=1}^{n} a_i, \quad \varphi(x) = \prod_{i=1}^{n} \varphi_i(x),$$

then

$$f(x) = a\varphi(x)$$

will be a canonical factorization of the polynomial $f(x)$. From this it follows that *if the product of several polynomials is equal to a primitive polynomial, then each of the factors will be a primitive polynomial.* We note also that *if we are given the polynomials* $f(x)$ *and* $g(x)$ *with the canonical factorizations*

$$f(x) = a\varphi(x), \quad g(x) = b\psi(x)$$

and if $f(x)$ *is divisible by* $g(x)$, *then* a *is divisible by* b, *and* $\varphi(x)$ *is divisible by* $\psi(x)$.

6. Let there be given in the ring $R[x]$ a sequence of non-zero polynomials

$$f_1(x), f_2(x), \ldots, f_n(x), \ldots, \tag{5}$$

such that $f_n(x)$ is divisible by $f_{n+1}(x)$, $n = 1, 2, \ldots$ If

$$f_n(x) = a_n \varphi_n(x), \quad n = 1, 2, \ldots,$$

are canonical factorizations of these polynomials, then in each of the sequences

$$a_1, a_2, \ldots, a_n, \ldots, \tag{6}$$

$$\varphi_1(x), \varphi_2(x), \ldots, \varphi_n(x), \ldots, \tag{7}$$

each element is divisible by the one following it.

Because the ring R is Gaussian and because, on the other hand, the degrees of the polynomials in the sequence (7) are non-increasing, we can find a natural number N with the following properties: (1) all the elements $a_n \in R$ are associates when $n \geqslant N$; (2) all the polynomials $\varphi_n(x)$ have the same degree when $n \geqslant N$, i.e. they differ from each other by factors in R which, in view of the fact that the polynomials $\varphi_n(x)$ are primitive, must be units. From this it follows that all the polynomials $f_n(x)$ from (5) will be associates when $n \geqslant N$, and therefore for polynomials of $R[x]$ distinct from zero, the condition (α) is satisfied.

7. Now let the irreducible polynomial $p(x)$ be a divisor of the product $f(x)g(x)$. If

$$f(x) = a\varphi(x), \qquad g(x) = b\psi(x)$$

are canonical factorizations of the polynomials $f(x)$ and $g(x)$, then

$$f(x)g(x) = (ab)[\varphi(x)\psi(x)]$$

will be a canonical factorization of the product $f(x)g(x)$. On the other hand, there also exists a canonical factorization for the polynomial $p(x)$, and therefore, in view of the fact that it is irreducible, $p(x)$ will be either an irreducible element p of the ring R, or else an irreducible primitive polynomial $\pi(x)$.

In the first case the element p is a divisor of the product ab, and therefore, since the ring R is Gaussian, p will be a divisor of at least one of the elements a, b, for instance of a. In this case the element p will also be a divisor of the polynomial $a\varphi(x) = f(x)$.

8. There remains the more difficult second case. Here the polynomial $\pi(x)$ will be a divisor of the product of primitive polynomials $\varphi(x)\psi(x)$.

As we know from II.5.5, the integral domain R can be embedded in a quotient field; we will denote it by Q. Every polynomial from the ring $R[x]$ will, of course, be a polynomial from the ring $Q[x]$ also. On the other hand, if $q(x)$ is an arbitrary non-zero polynomial from $Q[x]$, then, by reducing the fractions which are its coefficients to a common denominator and taking this denominator outside the brackets, and then doing the same with the greatest common divisor of the numerator, we arrive at the expression

$$q(x) = \frac{a}{b}\varphi(x), \tag{8}$$

where $\varphi(x)$ is a primitive polynomial from $R[x]$.
If

$$q(x) = \frac{c}{d}\,\psi(x)$$

is another expression of the form (8) for $q(x)$, i.e. the polynomial
$\psi(x)$ belongs to $R[x]$ and is primitive, then

$$(ad)\varphi(x) = (bc)\psi(x), \tag{9}$$

and therefore the left and right sides of the equation (9) will be
canonical factorizations of the same polynomial from the ring
$R[x]$, i.e. they are associates. Thus, *the primitive polynomial
$\varphi(x)$ is determined for the polynomial $q(x)$ uniquely to within
associated elements.* We will call an expression of the form (8)
a *canonical factorization* of the polynomial $q(x)$ from $Q[x]$.

*If we are given the non-zero polynomials $q_1(x)$, $q_2(x)$ from
$Q[x]$ with the canonical factorizations*

$$q_i(x) = \frac{a_i}{b_i}\,\varphi_i(x), \quad i = 1, 2, \tag{10}$$

then

$$q_1(x)q_2(x) = \frac{a_1 a_2}{b_1 b_2}\,[\varphi_1(x)\varphi_2(x)] \tag{11}$$

will, by Gauss's lemma, be a canonical factorization of the product
$q_1(x)q_2(x)$.

*The irreducible primitive polynomial $\pi(x)$ remains irreducible in
the ring $Q[x]$.* In fact, if

$$\pi(x) = q_1(x)q_2(x),$$

where $q_1(x)$, $q_2(x) \in Q[x]$ and have the canonical factorizations (10),
then, by (11), $\pi(x)$ is associated with the product $\varphi_1(x)\varphi_2(x)$.
Therefore one of the polynomials $\varphi_i(x)$, $i = 1, 2$, must have
degree 0; this is true for the corresponding $q_i(x)$.

We know from II.9.3 that the ring $Q[x]$ is Gaussian. From
this it follows, because $\pi(x)$ is a divisor of the product $\varphi(x)\psi(x)$,
that one of these factors, for instance $\varphi(x)$, is divisible by $\pi(x)$
in the ring $Q[x]$,

$$\varphi(x) = \pi(x)q(x), \quad q(x) \in Q[x].$$

If $q(x)$ has the canonical factorization

$$q(x) = \frac{c}{d}\,\chi(x),$$

then from the fact that the polynomials $\varphi(x)$ and $\pi(x)$ are primitive it follows that $\varphi(x)$ is associated with the product $\pi(x)\chi(x)$, and therefore $\varphi(x)$ is divisible by $\pi(x)$ in the ring $R[x]$. Hence the polynomial $f(x) = a\varphi(x)$ is also divisible by $\pi(x)$.

. Thus, the condition (β'') is also satisfied in the ring $R[x]$, and the theorem in II.9.4 is proved.

9. From this theorem it follows immediately that *the ring of polynomials $R[x_1, x_2, \ldots, x_n]$ in any finite number of unknowns over any Gaussian ring R will itself be Gaussian.* In particular, the ring of polynomials $F[x_1, x_2, \ldots, x_n]$ over any field F is Gaussian.

Now it is easy to show that *there exist Gaussian rings which are not principal ideal domains.* Thus, in the ring of polynomials $R = F[x, y]$ over the field F the set A of polynomials without constant terms will be an ideal distinct from R. This ideal is not, however, principal, because the only common divisors of the polynomials x and y included in it are the elements of F distinct from zero.

§ 10. Dedekind rings

1. As in the preceding paragraph we will consider an integral domain R with identity. We recall (see II.5.5 and II.5.6) that an integral domain R is contained in a uniquely determined quotient field.

If A and B are ideals of R, then their *product AB* is the ideal generated by all possible products of the form ab, where $a \in A$, $b \in B$. It is easy to see that the ideal AB consists of those, and only those, elements of the ring R which can, in at least one way, be written in the form

$$\sum_{i=1}^{n} a_i b_i, \qquad a_i \in A, \qquad b_i \in B. \tag{1}$$

From the fact that the operations in R are associative it follows that the multiplication of ideals is associative. We can speak thus of the *semigroup of ideals* of the ring R; the commutativity of this semigroup is obvious.

Because every element of the form (1) also belongs to the intersection of the ideals A and B, then

$$AB \subseteq A \cap B.$$

On the other hand, from $B \subseteq B'$ it follows, obviously, that

$$AB \subseteq AB'. \tag{2}$$

2. An ideal C is called *prime* if from the inclusion $xy \in C$, $x, y \in R$, it always follows that at least one of the elements x, y is contained in C. This definition is obviously satisfied by the ideals R and 0. In what follows, in speaking of prime ideals, we will exclude these two ideals from our considerations.

The ideal C will be prime if and only if for any ideals A, B it follows from $AB \subseteq C$ that either $A \subseteq C$ or $B \subseteq C$.

In fact, let $AB \subseteq C$, but $A \nsubseteq C, B \nsubseteq C$. Thus there exist $a \in A, b \in B$ which are not contained in C, although $ab \in C$. The ideal C is thus not prime. Conversely, if the ideal C is not prime, then there exist a and b which lie outside C, but $ab \in C$. Going over to the principal ideals, we obtain that $(a) \nsubseteq C$, $(b) \nsubseteq C$, but $(a)(b) \subseteq C$.

Below, by a *maximal ideal* we shall mean any maximal proper ideal (i.e. distinct from R) of our ring R.

Every maximal ideal M is prime.

In fact, let $a \notin M$, $b \notin M$, but

$$ab \in M. \tag{3}$$

The ideal (M, a), generated by the ideal M and the element a, coincides with R. It consists, however, of elements which can be written in the form $m + xa$, $m \in M$, $x \in R$, and therefore can be written in the form $M + Ra$. Analogously, $(M, b) = R$ and this ideal can be written in the form $M + Rb$. Therefore, in view of (3), we arrive at the contradiction:

$$R = RR = (M + Ra)(M + Rb) \subseteq M.$$

3. *In a principal ideal domain* (see II.9.2) *the prime ideals coincide with ideals of the form* (p), *where p is a prime element* (see II.8.3).

In fact, if $xy \in (p)$, then

$$xy = pz, \quad z \in R,$$

and therefore, by the definition of a prime element, at least one of the elements x, y is divisible by p, i.e. is contained in the ideal

(p). If however the element q is not prime, then, by II.8.7, we can write it $q = ab$, where neither a nor b is a unit. Hence $ab \in (q)$; however, if, for instance, $a \in (q)$, then

$$a = qc = abc,$$

from which, in view of the fact that there are no divisors of zero, $bc = 1$, i.e. b would be a unit.

In a principal ideal domain every ideal which is distinc from the whole ring and from zero is the product of a finite number of prime ideals.

In fact, if the element a is not a unit and is not equal to zero, then there exists a factorization of a into the product of prime factors,

$$a = p_1 p_2 \dots p_n,$$

and then

$$(a) = (p_1)(p_2) \dots (p_n).$$

An integral domain R with identity is called a *Dedekind ring* if every ideal of R, distinct from R itself and from 0, can be represented in the form of a product of a finite number of prime ideals. Below we shall mention some of the characterizations of Dedekind rings.

4. Let R be an integral domain with identity 1, and F its quotient field. A subgroup A of the additive group of the field F is called a *fractional ideal* of the ring R if the following two conditions are satisfied: (1) if $a \in A$, $x \in R$, then $ax \in A$; (2) all the elements of A can be written in the form of fractions with a common denominator, i.e.

$$A = \frac{1}{d} A_0, \quad A_0 \subseteq R, \quad d \in R, \quad d \neq 0. \tag{4}$$

It is clear that A_0 will be an ideal in R and that here the conditions of equation (4) can be regarded as the definition of a fractional ideal.

Amongst the fractional ideals there are the ideals of the ring R itself or, as we shall now call them, its *integral ideals*. On the other hand, a *principal fractional ideal* is a fractional ideal of the form $(1/b)(a)$, where (a) is a principal integral ideal. This principal fractional ideal contains, in particular, the element a/b of the field F and is generated by this element, and therefore it can be written in the form (a/b).

In general, because the intersection of any set of fractional ideals is a fractional ideal, we can speak of the fractional ideal *generated* by a given finite set of elements of F: because all these elements can be written in the form of fractions with a common denominator d, they all lie in the fractional ideal $1/dR$, and therefore we can speak of the intersection of all the fractional ideals containing the given elements.

5. The definition of the product of ideals also carries over to fractional ideals, where if

$$A = \frac{1}{c} A_0, \qquad B = \frac{1}{d} B_0,$$

then

$$AC = \frac{1}{cd} A_0 B_0,$$

i.e. *this product is itself a fractional ideal.* Because multiplication remains associative (and commutative) and because the product of non-zero quotient ideals is itself distinct from zero, we can speak of the *semigroup of non-zero fractional ideals* of the ring R. The identity of this semigroup is R itself.

Our aim is to prove the following theorem:

An integral domain R with identity will be a Dedekind ring if and only if its semigroup of non-zero fractional ideals is a group.

6. Let R be once again an integral domain with identity. A quotient ideal A of R is called *invertible* if there exists a fractional ideal A^{-1} such that

$$AA^{-1} = R.$$

Every non-zero principal fractional ideal is invertible, because

$$\left(\frac{a}{b} \right)^{-1} = \left(\frac{b}{a} \right).$$

Every invertible fractional ideal is generated by a finite number of elements.

In fact, if $AA^{-1} = R$, then for the identity there exists an expression of the form

$$1 = \sum_{i=1}^{n} a_i a_i' \qquad a_i \in A, \qquad a_i' \in A^{-1}, \qquad i = 1, 2. \ldots, n.$$

Hence for any $a \in A$ it will be true that

$$a = \sum_{i=1}^{n} a_i(a_i'a),$$

and because $a_i'a \in R,\ i = 1, 2, \ldots, n,$ then

$$A = (a_1, a_2, \ldots, a_n).$$

If

$$B = A_1 A_2 \ldots A_n,$$

and if the fractional ideal B is invertible, then each of the fractional ideals $A_i,\ i = 1, 2, \ldots, n$, will also be invertible, because

$$A_i \left[\left(\prod_{j \neq i} A_j \right) B^{-1} \right] = R.$$

7. *If the prime ideals $C_1, C_2, \ldots, C_n$, considered as fractional ideals, are invertible, then*

$$A = C_1 C_2 \ldots C_n \qquad (5)$$

will be a unique representation of the integral ideal A as a product of prime ideals.

We will prove this by induction with respect to n. If $n = 1$, we show that the representation of the ideal C_1 in the form of the product to two integral ideals, distinct from R,

$$C_1 = B_1 B_2,$$

is in general impossible. In fact, because the ideal C_1 is prime, then, by II.10.2, it will be true, for instance, that $B_1 \subseteq C_1$. Hence, because, by hypothesis, the ideal C_1 is invertible, and the inclusion (2) also holds in the case of a fractional ideal A,

$$B_2 = RB_2 = C_1^{-1} C_1 B_2 \supseteq C_1^{-1} B_1 B_2 = C_1^{-1} C_1 = R,$$

which is impossible.

We go on to the general case. Let the ideal A have both the representation (5) and the representation

$$A = D_1 D_2 \ldots D_k \qquad (6)$$

where the ideals $D_j,\ j = 1, 2, \ldots, k$, are prime. Let C_1 be a minimal ideal amongst the ideals $C_i,\ i = 1, 2, \ldots, n$. Because A is contained in the prime ideal C_1, then, in view of (6) and II.10.2, it will be true, for instance, that $D_1 \subseteq C_1$. Analogously, there exists an i such that $C_i \subseteq D_1$. From this, in view of the fact that C_1 is minimal, it follows that

$$C_i = D_1 = C_1.$$

Now by equating the right sides of equations (5) and (6), multiplied by C_1^{-1}, we obtain

$$C_2 \dots C_n = D_2 \dots D_k,$$

whence, by the induction hypothesis, $n = k$ and, after renumbering, $C_i = D_i$, $i = 2, \dots, n$.

8. *In a Dedekind ring R every prime ideal is maximal and invertible.*

We suppose first that the prime ideal C is invertible, and we shall prove that it is maximal. Let there exist an element $a \in R$, lying outside C, such that the ideal $(C, a) = C+Ra$ is distinct from R. Then *a fortiori*, the ideal $C+Ra^2$ will be distinct from R, because $C+Ra^2 \subseteq C+Ra$, and, since the ring is Dedekind, there exist factorizations for these two ideals as the products are prime ideals,

$$C + Ra = \prod_{i=1}^{n} C_i, \qquad C + Ra^2 = \prod_{j=1}^{k} D_j. \qquad (7)$$

Now we need to construct a ring, which in III.2.6 will be called the factor-ring of the ring R with respect to the ideal C. We divide up the additive group of the ring R into cosets with respect to the subgroup C. If $C+x$ and $C+y$ are any two cosets, then, by multiplying any element of the first coset by any element of the second, we obtain (because C is an ideal) an element of the coset $C+xy$. This enables us to speak of the multiplication of cosets. We can also speak of the addition of cosets, because the sum of any element from $C+x$ and any element from $C+y$ lies in the coset $C+(x+y)$. It is easy to verify that the set of cosets with respect to C forms a ring R under these operations; its zero will be C, and its identity $C+1$.

In our present case the ring $\overline{R}$ has no divisors of zero, because from $x \notin C$, $y \notin C$ and

$$(C + x)(C + y) = C$$

it would follow that $xy \notin C$, which contradicts the fact that the ideal C is prime. Thus, the results of the preceding section are applicable in the ring $\overline{R}$.

Because, by (7), $C \subseteq C_1, i = 1, 2, ..., n$, then the prime ideal C_1 can be decomposed into cosets with respect to C, which, as it is easy to verify, form a prime ideal $\overline{C}_i$ in $\overline{R}$; in an analogous way we can introduce the prime ideals $\overline{D}_j, j = 1, 2, ..., k$. If we set $\overline{a} = C + a$, then from (7) for the principal ideal Ra there follows the expansion

$$\overline{Ra} = \prod_{i=1}^{n} \overline{C}_i,$$

and therefore

$$(\overline{Ra})^2 = \overline{Ra^2} = \prod_{i=1}^{n} \overline{C}_i^2 = \prod_{j=1}^{k} \overline{D}_j. \qquad (8)$$

All the prime factors, included in the expansion (8) for the principal and therefore, by II.10.6, invertible ideal $\overline{Ra^2}$, are themselves invertible, and, hence, by II.10.7, the expansions (8) coincide. From this it follows that $k = 2n$ and, after renumbering,

$$C_i = D_{2i-1} = D_{2i}, i = 1, 2, ..., n.$$

Thus,

$$C + Ra^2 = (C + Ra)^2,$$

whence

$$C \subset (C + Ra)^2 \subset C^2 + Ra.$$

For every $x \in C$ there thus exist $y \in C^2$ and $z \in R$ such that

$$x = y + za.$$

Hence $za \in C$, and because the ideal C is prime and $a \notin C$ then $z \in C$. Thus,

$$C \subseteq C^2 + Ca,$$

and because the inverse inclusion is obvious, then

$$C = C^2 + Ca.$$

Multiplying both sides by the ideal C^{-1}, which exists because C is invertible, we obtain

$$R = C + Ra,$$

which contradicts our hypothesis. We have proved that the ideal C is maximal.

Now we will prove that every prime ideal C is invertible. Let $x \in C, x \neq 0$. Then

$$Rx = \prod_{i=1}^{n} C_i,$$

where the ideals $C_i, i = 1, 2, \ldots, n$, are prime and, by II.10.6, invertible (because the ideal Rx is principal and therefore invertible), i.e., by what we proved above, they are maximal. Because, however, $Rx \subseteq C$ and the ideal C is prime, then at least for one i it will be true that $C_i \subseteq C$, i.e., because C_i is maximal, $C_i = C$, and therefore the ideal C is invertible.

9. From the results of the two preceding sections follows this important assertion:

In a Dedekind ring every ideal distinct from R and 0 has a unique expression as a product of prime ideals.

10. Now we shall prove that *every non-zero fractional ideal A of a Dedekind ring R can be expressed as the product of positive or negative powers of prime ideals and is therefore invertible.*

In fact, let $A = \dfrac{1}{d} A_0$. Then

$$A_0 = \prod_{i=1}^{n} C_i, \qquad Rd = \prod_{j=1}^{k} D_j,$$

where all the C_i and D_j are prime, and because all the prime ideals $D_j, j = 1, 2, \ldots, k$, are invertible, then

$$A = A_0(Rd)^{-1} = \prod_{i=1}^{n} C_i \cdot \prod_{j=1}^{k} D_j^{-1}.$$

This proves one half of the fundamental theorem in II.10.5.

11. Let us now prove the converse assertion of this theorem. If the non-zero fractional ideals of the integral domain with identity R form a group under multiplication and therefore are invertible, then, by II.10.6, every (integral) ideal of R is generated by a finite number of elements. From this it follows that *in R the maximal condition for ideals is satisfied*: the union B of the ascending chain of ideals

$$A_1 \subseteq A_2 \subseteq \ldots \subseteq A_n \subseteq \ldots$$

will itself be an ideal and is therefore generated by a finite number of elements. We can find an n such that all these elements lie in A_n, and then

$$B = A_n = A_{n+1} = \ldots$$

The assertion that the ring R is Dedekind will be proved, in view of II.10.2, if we show that *every integral ideal of R, distinct from R and 0, is the product of maximal ideals.* If this is not so, then let A be a maximal one of those ideals which cannot be so represented. It will not be a maximal ideal of the ring R, but, because of the maximal condition, there exists a maximal ideal M containing it. Because $A \subseteq M$ and $M^{-1}M = R$, then $M^{-1}A \subseteq R$, i.e. $M^{-1}A$ is an integral ideal. From

$$A = RA = M(M^{-1}A) \tag{9}$$

it follows that

$$A \subseteq M^{-1}A.$$

If this inclusion were strict, then the ideal $M^{-1}A$ could be expressed as the product of maximal ideals, and then, by (9), such a representation would also exist for A, contrary to the hypothesis. Therefore $M^{-1}A = A$, i.e.

$$A = MA. \tag{10}$$

We will reduce this to a contradiction by showing that there exists an element $z \in M$ such that the product of the element $1 - z$ by any element from A will be equal to zero, although $z \neq 1$, and there do not exist any divisors of zero in R.

Let the ideal A be generated by the elements $x_1, x_2, \ldots, x_n$,

$$A = (x_1, x_2, \ldots, x_n).$$

We set

$$A_i = (x_i, x_{i+1}, \ldots, x_n), \quad i = 1, 2, \ldots, n,$$

and $A_{n+1} = 0$, and we will prove the existence of $z_i \in M$, $i = 1, 2, \ldots, n+1$, such that

$$(1 - z_i)A \subseteq A_i. \tag{11}$$

Because $A_1 = A$, we can take $z_1 = 0$. Suppose that z_i has been found with the property (11). Then, because of (10),

$$(1 - z_i)A = (1 - z_i)MA \subseteq MA_i,$$

and because every element of the ideal MA_i can be represented in the form of a sum of products of the elements $x_i, x_{i+1}, \ldots, x_n$ by certain elements of M, then

$$(1 - z_i)x_i = \sum_{j=i}^{n} z_{ij}x_j, \qquad z_{ij} \in M.$$

Hence

$$(1 - z_i - z_{ii})x_i \in A_{i+1}$$

and therefore

$$(1 - z_{i+1})A \subseteq A_{i+1},$$

where

$$1 - z_{i+1} = (1 - z_i)(1 - z_i - z_{ii});$$

it is clear that $z_{i+1} \in M$. The element z_{n+1} will also be the desired element z. Thus the theorem is proved.

* An integral domain R with identity will be a Dedekind ring if and only if the following conditions are satisfied: (1) the maximal condition for ideals; (2) every prime ideal is maximal; (3) the ring R is integrally *closed* in its quotient field F, i.e. every element from F which is the root of an equation with coefficients in R and with leading coefficient 1 itself belongs to R.*

CHAPTER THREE

UNIVERSAL ALGEBRAS
GROUPS WITH MULTI-OPERATORS

§ 1. Universal algebras. Homomorphisms

1. The parallel between the theory of groups and the theory of rings, which was illustrated repeatedly in the previous chapter, is also revealed in many other branches of these theories. In many cases it turns out to be convenient not to consider groups and rings separately, but to construct a single theory, from which the results associated with groups and rings follow as simple corollaries. In fact it was for this purpose that there was initiated the study of algebraic structures with an arbitrary number of algebraic operations, which are not necessarily binary.

2. Let there be given a set G. We will say that in G an n-ary *algebraic operation* ω is defined (where n is a non-negative integer), if with any ordered system of n elements $a_1, a_2, \ldots, a_n$ of the set G there is associated a uniquely determined element of this same set; this result of applying the operation ω to the given system of elements will be denoted by $a_1 a_2 \ldots a_n \omega$. In some cases it is necessary to omit from our requirements that the n-ary operation should be defined for every ordered system of n elements, i.e. this operation will only be *partial*. The requirement that the operation be unique will, however, usually be retained, and therefore the concept of an n-ary operation is only a special case of the concept of an $(n+1)$-ary relation (cf. II.1.1).

When $n = 2$, we arrive at the concept of a binary operation with which we are familiar (see II.1.2), when $n = 3$, we obtain *a ternary* operation, and so on. On the other hand, when $n = 1$ we will speak of a *unary operation*. This operation relates every element $a \in G$ to a uniquely defined element $a\omega \in G$, i.e. it is a single-valued mapping of the set G into itself. Finally, the case $n = 0$, i.e. the case of a *nullary operation*, means that in the set G there is fixed some definite element which does not depend on the choice of any elements or system of elements in G. Thus, by taking the identity of a group, we arrive at a nullary operation in this group; in the case of a ring, taking its zero and identity (if the latter exists) will be nullary operations.

3. A set G is called a *universal algebra*, if there is given in it some system Ω of n-ary algebraic operations, where for different operations $\omega \in \Omega$ the number n may either be different or the same. This system of operations may also be infinite—an example of universal algebras of this type are the vector spaces over infinite fields: here there is one binary operation, namely addition, and an infinite set of unary operations, the multiplciations by elements of the ground field.

In the preceding chapter we met many different types of universal algebras — groupoids, groups, quasigroups, rings and so on. We note that we have two ways of considering a group as a universal algebra: on the one hand, it is a set with three binary operations—multiplication and left and right division; on the other hand, it is a set with one binary operation—multiplication, with one unary operation—taking the inverse of an element, and with one nullary operation—taking the identity. In III.6.6 we will return to the problem of the different ways of regarding the same algebraic system as a universal algebra.

We note also that a skew field can be regarded as a universal algebra only in the case when the algebraic operations under consideration are assumed to be partial, because in fact this is the case with both left and right division in a skew field, and with taking the inverse of an element.

4. Let there be given a universal algebra G with a system of operations Ω. A subset $A \subseteq G$ will be called a *subalgebra* of the universal algebra G if, for any n-ary operation $\omega \in \Omega$ from $a_1, a_2, \ldots, a_n \in A$ it always follows that

$$a_1 a_2 \ldots a_n \omega \in A.$$

Special cases of this concept are, obviously, a subgroupoid of a groupoid, a subgroup of a group, a subring of a ring. We note, however, that if the ring R has an identity and if it is regarded as a universal algebra, amongst whose operations is included the nullary operation of taking the identity, then the subalgebras will only be those subrings of the ring R (see II.3.2) which contain the identity of the ring R, and not any subring, even if it contains its own identity.

In the same way as in II.3.6, we can prove that *the intersection of any system of subalgebras of a universal algebra G, if it is not empty, will be a subalgebra of this algebra.*

From this it follows that *if in the universal algebra G we take an arbitrary non-empty subset M, then there exists a uniquely determined subalgebra $\{M\}$, which is the least subalgebra containing M.* This will be the intersection of all the subalgebras of G containing M,—one such subalgebra will be G itself. If $\{M\} = G$, then M will be a *system of generators* for G.|

5. The universal algebras G and G', in which there are given respectively the systems of operations Ω and Ω', are said to be *of the same type* if it is possible to establish a one–one correspondence between the systems Ω and Ω', in which any operation $\omega \in \Omega$ and the operation $\omega' \in \Omega'$ corresponding to it will be n-ary with the same n. We can thus assume that in universal algebras of the same type the same system of operations Ω is given.

Universal algebras G and G' of the same type with the same system of operations Ω are said to be *isomorphic* if there exists a one–one mapping φ of the algebra G onto the algebra G', such that for any n-ary operation $\omega \in \Omega$ and any elements $a_1, a_2, \ldots, a_n \in G$

$$(a_1 a_2 \ldots a_n \omega)\varphi = (a_1\varphi)(a_2\varphi) \ldots (a_n\varphi)\omega. \tag{1}$$

The concept of an isomorphism of universal algebras plays exactly the same part as it played for groups, rings or partially ordered sets. Now we will introduce a generalization, namely the concept of a homomorphism, which is very important in all the subsequent theory. In fact, by keeping the requirement (1), but assuming that φ is only a single-valued (and not necessarily one–one) mapping of the algebra G into the algebra G' (i.e. not necessarily onto the whole of this algebra), we arrive at the definition of a *homomorphic mapping* of one universal algebra into another, which is of the same type.

From the definition of a homomorphism it follows easily that *the product of homomorphisms* (in the sense of I.1.2) *will itself be a homomorphism.* In fact, if we are given the algebras G, G', G'' of the same type with the same system of operations Ω and the homomorphisms $\varphi: G \to G'$ and $\psi: G' \to G''$, then for any *n*-ary operation $\omega \in \Omega$ and any elements $a_1, a_2, \ldots, a_n \in G$ it will be true that

$$(a_1 a_2 \ldots a_n \omega)(\varphi\psi) = [(a_1 a_2 \ldots a_n \omega)\varphi]\psi =$$
$$[(a_1\varphi)(a_2\varphi) \ldots (a_n\varphi)\omega]\psi = [(a_1\varphi)\psi][(a_2\varphi)\psi] \ldots [(a_n\varphi)\psi]\omega =$$
$$[a_1(\varphi\psi)][a_2(\varphi\psi)] \ldots [a_n(\varphi\psi)]\omega,$$

which proves that the product $\varphi\psi$ will be a homomorphism of the algebra G into the algebra G''.

From (1) it also follows that if $G\varphi$ is the image of the algebra G under the homomorphic mapping φ into the algebra G', then $G\varphi$ *will be a subalgebra of the algebra* G'.

If $G\varphi = G'$, then we speak of the homomorphic mapping *onto* G' and we say that G' is the *homomorphic image* of the algebra G.

6. We will apply the concept of a homomorphism to the case of groupoids and rings. It is clear that in the case of binary multiplication the equation (1) reduces to the equation

$$(ab)\varphi = a\varphi \cdot b\varphi \qquad (2)$$

and that a universal algebra of the same type as a groupoid will itself be a groupoid. It is easy to verify, as in the case of an isomorphism (see II.4.1) that under a homomorphic mapping of the groupoid G onto the groupoid G' properties of the operation given in G, such as commutativity and associativity, are preserved.

Let φ be *a homomorphic mapping of the groupoid G onto the groupoid G'. If G has an identity e, then $e\varphi$ will be the identity in G'. If, in addition, the element $b \in G$ is one of the (right) inverse elements of $a \in G$ then $b\varphi$ will be one of the right inverse elements of $a\varphi$.*

In fact, for $a \in G$ it follows from $ae = ea = a$ and (2) that $a\varphi \cdot e\varphi = e\varphi \cdot a\varphi = a\varphi$, and because the element $a\varphi$ runs through the whole groupoid G', while a runs through the groupoid G, then $e\varphi$ will in fact be the identity in G'. On the other hand, it follows from $ab = e$ and (2) that $a\varphi \cdot b\varphi = e\varphi$.

Thus, *the homomorphic image of a semigroup or group is a semigroup or group respectively.*

Now we consider the homomorphic mapping φ of the ring R onto a universal algebra R' of the same type. From what has been said above it follows that R' will be an Abelian group with respect to addition and a groupoid with respect to multiplication. We will prove that the distributive laws are satisfied in R'. If a', b', $c' \in R'$, and the elements $a, b, c \in R$ are such that $a\varphi = a'$, $b\varphi = b'$, $c\varphi = c'$, then from the equation

$$(a + b)c = ac + bc,$$

which is valid in the ring R, follows the equation

$$(a' + b')c' = a'c' + b'c'.$$

The second distributive law can be verified in the same way.

Thus, *the homomorphic image of a ring is a ring.* From what has been said above it follows that under a homomorphism of rings the zero goes into the zero and that the homomorphic image of an associative or commutative ring will be a ring with the same properties.

7. There are several ways of surveying all the homomorphic mappings of a given universal algebra G. First we shall introduce the following concept.

We consider the universal algebra G with the system of operations Ω. An equivalence relation π (see I.3.1), given in G, is called a *congruence* in G if for any n-ary operation $\omega \in \Omega$ and any elements

$$a_i, a_i' \in G, \quad i = 1, 2, ..., n,$$

from

$$a_i \pi a_i', \quad i = 1, 2, ..., n,$$

it follows that

$$(a_1 a_2 ... a_n \omega) \pi (a_1' a_2' ... a_n' \omega).$$

In other words, if we take arbitrary classes $A_1, A_2, ..., A_n$ of the partition defined by the equivalence relation π (see I.3.2), then the class B containing the element $a_1 a_2 ... a_n \omega$, where $a_i \in A_i$, $i = 1, 2, ..., n$, does not depend on the choice of the elements a_i from the classes A_i, $i = 1, 2, ..., n$. This enables us to define an n-ary operation ω in the factor set G/π (see I.3.4), by setting

$$A_1 A_2 ... A_n \omega = B. \tag{3}$$

Because this is true for all the operations $\omega \in \Omega$, it follows that G/π becomes a universal algebra with the same system of operations Ω as the original algebra G. This algebra G/π is called the *factor algebra* of the universal algebra G with respect to the congruence π.

The definition (3) of the operations in the factor algebra G/π and the definition of a homomorphism (1) show that the natural mapping of the algebra G onto the factor algebra G/π (see I.3.4) will be a homomorphism. It is called the *natural homomorphism* of G onto G/π.

From the existence of a natural homomorphism of G onto G/π and what has been said in the previous section it follows that *the factor algebras of groupoids, groups, rings will themselves be respectively groupoids, groups, rings*. Thus we can speak of the *factor groupoid* (or *factor group*, or *factor ring*) G/π of a groupoid (group, ring) G with respect to some congruence π.

8. A converse of what was said in the previous section is the following homomorphism theorem, which gives a survey of all the homomorphic mappings of a universal algebra.

If G is a universal algebra with a system of operations Ω, and φ is a homomorphic mapping of it onto a universal algebra G' of the same type, $G\varphi = G'$, then there exists a congruence π in G such that the algebra G' is isomorphic to the factor algebra $G\pi$. Moreover, there exists an isomorphic mapping ψ of the algebra G' onto the factor algebra G/π such that the product $\varphi\psi$ coincides with the natural homomorphism of G onto G/π.

In fact, we obtain a partition of the algebra G into non-intersecting classes by placing in one class those elements of G whose images under the homomorphism φ coincide. The equivalence relation π, defined by this partition, will be a congruence in the algebra G. In fact, for any n–ary operation $\omega \in \Omega$ from

$$a_i\varphi = \bar{a}_i\varphi, \quad i = 1, 2, \ldots, n,$$

it follows, by (1), that

$$(a_1a_2 \ldots a_n\omega)\,\varphi = (a_1\varphi)(a_2\varphi) \ldots (a_n\varphi)\,\omega =$$
$$(\bar{a}_1\varphi)(\bar{a}_2\varphi) \ldots (\bar{a}_n\varphi)\,\omega = (\bar{a}_1\bar{a}_2 \ldots \bar{a}_n\omega)\varphi,$$

i.e. the elements $a_1a_2 \ldots a_n\omega$ and $\bar{a}_1\bar{a}_2 \ldots \bar{a}_n\omega$ also belong to one class of the partition π.

Hence there exists a factor algebra G/π. By setting up a correspondence between every element $a' \in G'$ and the class A of the partition π consisting of all the inverse images of the element a' under the homomorphism φ, we obtain a one–one mapping ψ of the algebra G' onto the factor algebra G/π. We will prove that ψ is an isomorphism.

Let the n-ary operation ω be any operation from Ω, and a_i, $i = 1, 2, \ldots, n$, be any elements of G'. By setting

$$a_i'\psi = A_i, \quad i = 1, 2, \ldots n,$$

and by choosing the elements $a_i \in A_i$, $i = 1, 2, \ldots, n$, whence

$$a_i\varphi = a_i', \quad i = 1, 2, \ldots, n,$$

we obtain, by (1),

$$(a_1 a_2 \ldots a_n \omega)\varphi = a_1' a_2' \ldots a_n' \omega. \tag{4}$$

Because, by (3),

$$a_1 a_2 \ldots a_n \omega \in A_1 A_2 \ldots A_n \omega,$$

it follows from (4) that

$$(a_1' a_2' \ldots a_n' \omega)\psi = A_1 A_2 \ldots A_n \omega = (a_1'\psi)(a_2'\psi) \ldots (a_n'\psi)\omega,$$

which proves that the mapping ψ is an isomorphism.

Finally, if a is an arbitrary element of the algebra G and if

$$a\varphi = a', \quad a'\psi = A,$$

then, by the definition of the mapping ψ, $a \in A$. This proves that the product $\varphi\psi$ coincides with the natural homomorphism of G onto G/π. Hence the homomorphism theorem is proved.

§ 2. Groups with multi-operators

1. As we shall see below, there exists a very close connection between congruences and, hence, homomorphisms of groups and rings, on the one hand, and normal subgroups of groups and ideals of rings, on the other hand. This connection cannot be completely extended to the case of all universal algebras, in particular to the case of groupoids or semigroups. It is preserved in its entirety, however, for one special class of universal algebras, recently introduced by Higgins [*Proc. Lond. math. Soc.* **6**, 366–416 (1956)], which is a very successful union of the classes of groups and rings.

Let there be given a group G. This group need not be commutative, but we shall find it convenient to use an addititive notation for it; in particular, the zero element of this group will, as usual, be denoted by the symbol 0. The group G will be called *a group with a system of multi-operators* Ω or, more concisely, an Ω-*group*, if besides addition there is given in G some system of n-ary algebraic operations Ω (for certain n satisfying the condition $n \geqslant 1$), such that for all $\omega \in \Omega$ the condition

$$00 \ldots 0\omega = 0 \qquad (1)$$

is satisfied, where on the left the element 0 occurs n times, if the operation ω is n-ary.

It is clear that with an empty system of operations Ω we obtain the concept of a group. On the other hand, the concept of an Ω-group reduces to the concept of a ring if the *additive group* of this Ω-group—this is what we shall agree to call the group with respect to addition — is commutative and if the system of operations consists of one binary multiplication, connected with addition by the distributive laws; as we know, condition (1) follows from this.

2. An Ω-group G can be regarded as a universal algebra with respect to the operations of the additive group and the operations of Ω. Every subalgebra of this algebra (see III.1.4) will be a subgroup of the additive group and therefore contains 0, condition (1) continues to be satisfied, and therefore it is itself an Ω-group. Therefore we shall not speak of subalgebras, but of Ω-*subgroups* of the Ω-group G.

From this, in view of III.1.4, it follows that *the intersection of any system of* Ω-*subgroups of an* Ω-*group G will itself be an* Ω-*subgroup* and, in particular, will contain the element 0. In addition, *the subalgebra* $\{M\}$, generated by a non-empty subset M of the Ω-group G, *will also be an* Ω-*subgroup*.

We note that, in view of (1), the zero subgroup of the additive group will be an Ω-subgroup.

3. If the Ω-group G is mapped by the homomorphism φ (see III.1.5) onto the universal algebra G' of the same type, then it will be, in particular, a homomorphism for the additive group of the Ω-group G, and therefore the algebra G' will itself be a group with respect to the operations corresponding to the operations of the additive group of the Ω-group G. We will assume that this group is written additively and that its zero is denoted by $0'$. Because φ is a homomorphism, and $0\varphi = 0'$, then for any operation $\omega \in \Omega$ it will be true, because of (1), that

$$0'0' \ldots 0'\omega = 0'.$$

Thus, *every homomorphic image of an* Ω-*group will itself be an* Ω-*group*. In particular, *the factor algebras of* Ω-*groups* (see

III.1.7) *are themselves* Ω-*groups*. We can therefore speak of the Ω-*factor-group* G/π of the Ω-group G with respect to the congruence π.

4. A non-empty subset A of the Ω-group G is called an *ideal* in G if the following two conditions are satisfied:

(1) A is a normal subgroup of the additive group;

(2) for every *n*-ary operation $\omega \in \Omega$, any element $a \in A$ and any elements $x_1, x_2, \ldots, x_n \in G$ the inclusion

$$-(x_1 x_2 \ldots x_n \omega) + x_1 \ldots x_{i-1}(a + x_i)x_{i+1} \ldots x_n \omega \in A \qquad (2)$$

must hold for $i = 1, 2, \ldots, n$.

For groups the concept of an ideal just defined coincides with the concept of a normal subgroup, because, since the system of operations is empty, condition (2) is omitted.

For rings our new concept of an ideal coincides with the concept of a (*two-sided*) *ideal introduced in* II.7.8.

In fact, in this case condition (1) requires that A should be a subgroup of the additive group of the ring, while condition (2) for the operation of multiplication and any $a \in A$, x_1, $x_2 \in G$ when $i = 1$ reduces to

$$-x_1 x_2 + (a + x_1)x_2 = -x_1 x_2 + a x_2 + x_1 x_2 = a x_2 \in A,$$

and when $i = 2$ to

$$-x_1 x_2 + x_1(a + x_2) = -x_1 x_2 + x_1 a + x_1 x_2 = x_1 a \in A,$$

which is what we were required to prove.

We note that the inclusion (2) can be rewritten in the form

$$x_1 \ldots x_{i-1}(a + x_i)x_{i+1} \ldots x_n \omega \in x_1 x_2 \ldots x_n \omega + A,$$

$$i = 1, 2, \ldots, n, \qquad (3)$$

where on the right we have the coset with respect to the normal subgroup A, containing the element $x_1 x_2 \ldots x_n \omega$. By applying the inclusion (3) repeatedly, we arrive at the following assertion:

For any ideal A of the Ω-group G, any n-ary operation $\omega \in \Omega$ any elements $a_1, a_2, \ldots, a_n \in A$ and any elements $x_1, x_2, \ldots, x_n \in G$ the inclusion

$$(a_1 + x_1)(a_2 + x_2) \ldots (a_n + x_n) \omega \in x_1 x_2 \ldots x_n \omega + A. \qquad (4)$$

holds.

From this it follows that *every ideal A of the Ω-group G is an Ω-subgroup of G*. In fact, A will be a subgroup of the additive group by virtue of condition (1), and from (4) for any n-ary operation $\omega \in \Omega$ and any $a_1, a_2, \ldots, a_n \in A$ it follows, when $x_1 = x_2 = \ldots = x_n = 0$ because of equation (1), that

$$a_1 a_2 \ldots a_n \omega \in A.$$

It is clear that the Ω-group G will have, in particular, the ideals G itself and the zero subgroup 0. If there are no other ideals in G, then it will be a *simple* Ω-group.

Without any difficulty we can verify that *the intersection of any system of ideals of the Ω-group G will itself be an ideal*, and therefore we can also speak of the ideal *generated* by any system of elements M.

We note that *the ideal generated by a system of ideals A_i, $i \in I$, of the Ω-group G coincides with the subgroup B of the additive group generated by these ideals*.

In fact, from II.7.5 we know that $B = \{A_i, i \in I\}$ is a normal subgroup of the additive group and that every element of B can be written in the form

$$b = a_1 + a_2 + \ldots + a_k, \qquad a_j \in A_{i_j}, \qquad j = 1, 2, \ldots, k. \qquad (5)$$

Now let there be given the n-ary operation $\omega \in \Omega$, the element $b \in B$ with the expansion (5) and the elements $x_1, x_2, \ldots, x_n \in G$. Because $A_{i_1}, A_{i_2}, \ldots, A_{i_k}$ are ideals, then, by using (3) and (5), we obtain

$$x_1 \ldots x_{i-1}(b + x_i)x_{i+1} \ldots x_n \omega \in x_1 x_2 \ldots x_n \omega + B,$$

which is what we were required to prove.

The ideal $B = \{A_i, i \in I\}$ will be called the *sum* of the ideals $A_i, i \in I$.

5. Now we will prove a theorem which clarifies the role of the concept of an ideal in the theory of Ω-groups. We note that, in speaking of *a decomposition of the Ω-group G with respect to the ideal A*, we mean by this the decomposition of the additive group of this Ω-group with respect to A, as with respect to a normal subgroup.

All the congruences in an arbitrary Ω-group G may be obtained by its decompositions with respect to the different ideals.

In fact, let A be an arbitrary ideal of the Ω-group G. For any $a_1, a_2 \in A$ and $x_1, x_2 \in G$ there exists, by virtue of the definition of a normal subgroup, an element $a_3 \in A$ such that

$$a_1 + x_2 = x_2 + a_3,$$

and therefore

$$(x_1 + a_1) + (x_2 + a_2) = (x_1 + x_2) + (a_3 + a_2) \in (x_1 + x_2) + A.$$

On the other hand, for any n-ary operation $\omega \in \Omega$, any elements $a_1, a_2, \ldots, a_n \in A$ and $x_1, x_2, \ldots, x_n \in G$ the inclusion (4) holds. These inclusions show that the decomposition of G into cosets with respect to A is in fact a congruence in the Ω-group G.

Now let there be given in G an arbitrary congruence π. We denote by A the class of the partition π which contains the zero of the additive group; the elements $a \in A$ are thus characterized by the fact that $a \pi 0$. If $a_1, a_2 \in A$, then $a_1 \pi 0$, $a_2 \pi 0$, and therefore, by the definition of a congruence,

$$(a_1 + a_2) \pi (0 + 0), \quad \text{i.e.} \quad (a_1 + a_2) \pi 0,$$

whence $a_1 + a_2 \in A$. Further, if $a \in A$, then

$$[0 + (-a)] \pi [a + (-a)],$$

.e. $-a \pi 0$, whence $-a \in A$. Finally, if $a \in A$, $x \in G$, then

$$(-x + a + x) \pi (-x + 0 + x),$$

i.e. $(-x + a + x) \pi 0$, whence $-x + a + x \in A$. This proves that A is a normal subgroup of the additive group.

If now we are given the n-ary operation $\omega \in \Omega$, the element $a \in A$ and the elements $x_1, x_2, \ldots, x_n \in G$, then

$$(a + x_i) \pi (0 + x_i), \quad \text{i.e.} \quad (a + x_i) \pi x_i,$$

whence

$$[x_1 \ldots x_{i-1}(a + x_i) x_{i+1} \ldots x_n \omega] \pi (x_1 x_2 \ldots x_n \omega),$$

and therefore

$$-x_1 x_2 \ldots x_n \omega + x_1 \ldots x_{i-1}(a + x_i) x_{i+1} \ldots x_n \omega \in A,$$
$$i = 1, 2, \ldots, n.$$

Thus we find that the class A is an ideal of the Ω-group G.

We consider, finally, an arbitrary class B of the partition π. If $b \in B$, $a \in A$, i.e. $a \pi 0$, then

$$(b + a) \pi (b + 0), \quad \text{i.e.} \quad (b + a) \pi b,$$

whence, for the coset $b + A$, there follows the inclusion

$$b + A \subseteq B.$$

On the other hand, if b' is an arbitrary element of the class B, then from $b' \pi b$ it follows that $(-b + b') \pi 0$ or

$$-b + b' \in A, \quad \text{i.e.} \quad b' \in b + A.$$

This proves the equation $B = b + A$, i.e. it proves that every class of the partition π is a coset with respect to the ideal A. Thus the theorem has been proved.

6. By virtue of this theorem we will speak in future not of the Ω-factor-group G/π of the Ω-group G with respect to some congruence π, but of *the Ω-factor-group with respect to the ideal A* and we will denote it by G/A. The ideal A will obviously be the zero of this Ω-factor-group.

By applying all that has been said to the case of groups, we find that *all the congruences in the group G are obtained by its decompositions with respect to the different normal subgroups. Hence we can speak of the factor group of the group G with respect to the normal subgroup A* and we will denote it by G/A.

On the other hand, *all the congruences in the ring R are obtained by its decompositions with respect to the different (two-sided) ideals*, and therefore we will speak of *the factor ring of the ring R with respect to the ideal A* and we will denote it by R/A.

From the theorem proved above there follows one other remark. If φ is a homomorphic mapping of the Ω-group G onto the Ω-group G', then the *kernel* of the homomorphism φ is the set of those elements of G which are mapped by φ into the zero of the Ω-group G'. From the theorem in III.2.5 and from the theorem on homomorphism in III.1.8 it follows that:

The kernels of the homomorphisms of an Ω-group are its ideals and only these. A homomorphic image of an Ω-group is determined to within isomorphism by the kernel of the homomorphism under consideration.

7. We will consider some very simple but important examples.

Every homomorphic image of a cyclic group is itself a cyclic group.

In fact, if G' is the image of a cyclic group $G = \{a\}$ under the homomorphism φ, where $a\varphi = a'$, then for any element $g' \in G'$ we can find an inverse image $a^k \in G$, and therefore

$$g' = a^k\varphi = (a\varphi)^k = a'^k,$$

i.e. $G' = \{a'\}$.

Now we will find all the homomorphic images of an infinite cyclic group, which, by II.4.2, we can take as the additive group of integers.

In II.4.2 we gave a survey of the subgroups of this group, and all of them will, of course, be normal. If $\{n\}$ is the subgroup consisting of the numbers which are multiples of the natural number n, then two numbers will belong to one coset with respect to this subgroup if and only if their difference is exactly divisible by n, i.e. if these numbers when divided by n give the same remainder. Because the only remainders after the division of integers by n are the numbers $0, 1, 2, \ldots, n-1$, the factor group of the additive group of integers with respect to the subgroup $\{n\}$ will be a finite group of order n, which, as we proved above, will be cyclic. The number n was arbitrary, and therefore, taking into account the description of cyclic groups given in II.4.2, we arrive at the following result:

The homomorphic images of an infinite cyclic group are all possible cyclic groups and these are the only ones.

8. Now we will find all the homomorphic images of the ring of integers C. As we noted in II.7.8, all the subgroups of the additive group of this ring are ideals, and therefore it remains for us to consider the factor rings with respect to these ideals.

The factor ring with respect to the zero ideal is isomorphic, of course, to the ring C itself. The factor ring of the ring C with respect to the ideal of numbers, which are multiples of the natural number n, we denote by C_n and call *the ring of residues modulo n*. From what was said in the previous section, it follows that this ring is finite and consists of n elements, that its additive group is cyclic and that in the cosets forming this ring we can take as representatives the numbers $0, 1, 2, \ldots, n-1$. Corresponding with this the actual elements of the ring C_n can be denoted by $\overline{0}, \overline{1}, \overline{2}, \ldots, \overline{n-1}$.

From the definition of operations in a factor ring (cf. III.1.7) there follows this rule for the operations in the ring C_n: if $0 \leqslant k$, $l < n$ and $k + l = nq_1 + r_1$, $kl = nq_2 + r_2$, where $0 \leqslant r_1, r_2 < n$, then

$$\overline{k} + \overline{l} = \overline{r}_1, \quad \overline{k} \cdot \overline{l} = \overline{r}_2.$$

In particular, the element 0 will be the zero of the ring C_n, the element $\bar{1}$ its identity.

The ring C_n has divisors of zero if the number n is composite, but is a field if the number n is prime.

In fact, if $n = kl$, $1 < k$, $l < n$, then the elements $\bar{k}$ and $\bar{l}$ of the ring C_n are distinct from the zero $\bar{0}$ of this ring, but $\bar{k} \cdot \bar{l} = 0$. If, however, the number n is prime, $n = p \geqslant 2$, then every number k which satisfies the inequalities $1 \leqslant k \leqslant p - 1$ will be prime to p. Hence there exist whole numbers l and m such that the equation

$$kl + pm = 1$$

holds, where the number l can be taken so that $1 \leqslant l \leqslant p - 1$. From this it follows that in the ring of residues C_p the equation

$$\bar{k} \cdot \bar{l} = \bar{1}$$

is satisfied, i.e. every element of C_p, distinct from zero, has an inverse element in the ring C_p, and therefore this ring will be a field.

The rings of residues C_p with respect to prime moduli p, $p = 2, 3, 5, \ldots$, are our first examples of finite fields, and they play a very important part in the theory of fields and skew fields, as we shall now show.

9. Let there be given a skew field K, not necessarily associative (see II.6.1). The intersection of all the skew subfields of the skew field K will itself be a skew subfield, which we shall temporarily call the prime skew subfield of the skew field K. Our purpose is to describe the structure of this skew subfield.

The *centre* of an arbitrary ring R is what we shall call the totality of elements a of R which commute with every element of the ring R, i.e.

$$ax = xa \tag{6}$$

for all $x \in R$, and, moreover, satisfy for all x, $y \in R$ the conditions

$$(ax)y = a\,(xy), \quad (xy)a = x(ya), \tag{7}$$

and therefore also the condition

$$(xa)y = x(ay),$$

because, by (6) and (7),

$$(xa)y = (ax)y = a(xy) = (xy)a = x(ya) = x(ay).$$

The zero of the ring R, and also its identity, if it exists, obviously belong to the centre of this ring.

The centre of the ring R is an associative-commutative subring. The centre of a skew field is a subfield.

In fact, if the elements a and b are contained in the centre of the ring R, then for any $x, y \in R$

$$(a \pm b)x = ax \pm bx = xa \pm xb = x(a \pm b),$$

$$[(a \pm b)x]y = (ax \pm bx)y = (ax)y \pm (bx)y =$$

$$a(xy) \pm b(xy) = (a \pm b)(xy);$$

the second of the conditions (7) can also be verified in this way. On the other hand,

$$(ab)x = a(bx) = a(xb) = (ax)b = (xa)b = x(ab),$$

$$[(ab)x]y = [a(bx)]y = a[(bx)y] = a[b(xy)] = (ab)(xy).$$

Thus the centre of the ring R is a subring, which is obviously associative-commutative.

If, moreover, R is a skew field with identity e and a is an element of its centre, where $a \neq 0$, then, by solving the equations $ax = e$ and $ya = e$ and taking into account that a is contained in the centre, we find a uniquely defined inverse element a^{-1}, which is both the left and right inverse. Then for any $x, y \in R$

$$a^{-1}x = (a^{-1}x)(aa^{-1}) = [(a^{-1}x)a]a^{-1} = [a^{-1}(xa)]a^{-1} =$$

$$[a^{-1}(ax)]a^{-1} = [(a^{-1}a)x]a^{-1} = xa^{-1},$$

$$(a^{-1}x)y = (a^{-1}a)[(a^{-1}x)y] = a^{-1}\{a[(a^{-1}x)y]\} =$$

$$a^{-1}\{[a(a^{-1}x)]y\} = a^{-1}\{[(aa^{-1})x]y\} = a^{-1}(xy);$$

the second of the conditions (7) can also be verified in this way. This proves that the element a^{-1} belongs to the centre of the skew field R, and therefore the centre will be a field.

10. Generally speaking, the centre of a ring may consist of zero alone. If, however, K is a skew field with identity e, then its centre necessarily contains e, and also all multiples ne, where n is any whole number. All these multiples form an associative-commutative subring $C^{(K)}$ in K, which is contained in all skew subfields of the skew field K, and therefore also in its prime skew subfield. On the other hand, the prime skew subfield must be contained in the centre of the skew field K, because the centre is a subfield, and therefore *the prime skew subfield is associative and commutative*. In future, therefore, we can speak not of the prime skew subfield, but of *the prime subfield* of the skew field K.

The prime subfield of a skew field K is isomorphic either to the field of rational numbers, or else to one of the fields of residues C_p modulo a prime p.

To prove this we consider the mapping $n \to ne$ of the ring of integers C onto the ring $C^{(K)}$. This mapping will be a homomorphism, and therefore, as we proved in III.2.8, the ring $C^{(K)}$ is isomorphic either to the ring of integers C, or else to some ring of residues C_n, in fact some field of residues C_p modulo prime p, because there are no divisors of zero in K. In the latter case the field C_p will also be the desired prime subfield of the skew field K. If, however, we have the first case, then the centre of the skew field K, which is a field and contains the subring $C^{(K)}$, isomorphic to the ring of integers will also contain the quotient field of this subring, isomorphic (see II.5.7) to the field of rational numbers. This field will also be the prime subfield of the skew field K.

11. If the prime subfield of the skew field K is isomorphic to the field of rational numbers, then we say that the skew field K has *characteristic* zero (or that it is without *characteristic*); such, in particular, are all the number fields. If, however, the prime subfield of the skew field K is isomorphic to the field of residues C_p modulo a prime p, then K is called a skew field of *finite characteristic* or of *prime characteristic*, and in fact of *characteristic* p.

Every non-zero element of the skew field K of characteristic zero (of characteristic p) has infinite order (order p) in the additive group of this skew field.

In fact, if the skew field K is of characteristic zero and $a \in K$, $a \neq 0$, then from $na = 0$ it would follow that $(ne) \cdot a = 0$, i.e. $ne = 0$, because there are no divisors of zero in K, whence $n = 0$. If, however, the characteristic of the skew field K is equal to p, then for any a from K it will be true that

$$pa = (pe)\, a = 0 \cdot a = 0,$$

and therefore, if $a \neq 0$, the order of this element will be equal to the prime number p.

12. We now return to consider an arbitrary Ω-group G. We take an ideal A in G and the Ω-factor-group $G' = G/A$. Let B' be an arbitrary Ω-subgroup of the Ω-group G', and B its complete inverse image in G under the natural homomorphism of G onto G', i.e. the totality of those elements of G which lie in the cosets forming B'. We will prove that B is *an Ω-subgroup in G.*

In fact, if x, $y \in B$, i.e. $x + A$, $y + A \in B'$, then

$$(x + y) + A = (x + A) + (y + A) \in B',$$
$$- x + A = - (x + A) \in B',$$

i.e. $x + y \in B$, $- x \in B$. On the other hand, for the n-ary operation $\omega \in \Omega$ and the elements x_1, x_2, ..., $x_n \in B$ from the inclusions $x_i + A \in B'$, the equations $x_i + A = A + x_i$, $i = 1, 2, ..., n$, and the inclusion (4) follows the equation

$$x_1 x_2 \ldots x_n \omega + A = (x_1 + A)(x_2 + A) \ldots (x_n + A) \omega \in B',$$

and therefore $x_1 x_2 \ldots x_n \omega \in B$.

The Ω-subgroup B which we have constructed obviously contains the ideal A. Conversely, *given an arbitrary Ω-subgroup B of the Ω-group G, containing the ideal A, then its image B' under the natural homomorphism of the Ω-group G onto the Ω-group $G' = G/A$ will be an Ω-subgroup, and B will be the complete inverse image of B'.*

In fact, the natural homomorphism of G onto G' induces a homomorphism of B into G, and therefore, by what we said in III.1.5, B' will be an Ω-subgroup in G'. On the other hand, from $B \supseteq A$ it follows that every element of G, contained in a coset with respect to A which belongs to B', will be contained in B.

We have therefore proved the following theorem:

By setting up a correspondence between every Ω-subgroup of the Ω-factor-group $G' = G/A$ and its complete inverse image under the natural homomorphism of G onto G', we obtain a one–one correspondence, preserving the inclusion relation, between all the Ω-subgroups of the Ω-group G' and all those Ω-subgroups of the Ω-group G which contain the ideal A.

13. We supplement this result with the following theorem:

Under the correspondence mentioned in the preceding theorem, an ideal in one of the Ω-groups G, G' corresponds to an ideal in the other Ω-group, and the Ω-factor-groups with respect to corresponding ideals are isomorphic to one another.

In fact, if B' is an ideal of the Ω-group $G' = G/A$, and B is its complete inverse image in G, then the successive application of the natural homomorphisms of G onto G' and of G' onto

$G'' = G'/B'$ will be a homomorphism of G onto G'', which follows from what we said in III.1.5. The kernel of this homomorphism (see III.2.6) consists of those elements of G which are mapped into B' under the mapping of G onto G', i.e. the elements which form the Ω-subgroup B. From this it follows, in view of III.2.6, III.2.5 and III.1.8, that B is an ideal of the Ω-group G and that the Ω-factor-groups G/B and G'/B' are isomorphic.

Now let B be an ideal of the Ω-group G, and B' its image under the natural homomorphism of G onto G'. If $b \in B$, $x \in G$, then $b + A \in B'$, $x + A \in G'$. Because

$$-x + b + x \in B,$$

then

$$-(x + A) + (b + A) + (x + A) = (-x + b + x) + A \in B',$$

i.e. B' is a normal subgroup of the additive group of G'. If, however, we are given an n-ary operation $\omega \in \Omega$ and arbitrary elements $b \in B$ and $x_1, x_2, \ldots, x_n \in G$, i.e. $b + A \in B'$, $x_i + A \in G'$, $i = 1, 2, \ldots, n$, then from

$$-x_1 x_2 \ldots x_n \omega + x_1 \ldots x_{i-1}(b + x_i)x_{i+1} \ldots x_n \omega = b_0 \in B,$$

$$i = 1, 2, \ldots, n,$$

it follows that

$$-(x + A)(x_2 + A) \ldots (x_n + A)\omega +$$

$$(x_1 + A) \ldots (x_{i-1} + A)[(b + A) + (x_i + A)](x_{i+1} + A) \ldots (x_n + A)\omega =$$

$$b_0 + A \in B', \quad i = 1, 2, \ldots, n.$$

This proves that B' is an ideal in G'.

We note that in the last part of the proof we did not make use of the hypothesis that $B \supseteq A$.

§ 3. Automorphisms, endomorphisms. The field of p-adic numbers

1. Let G be a universal algebra. Every isomorphic mapping of the algebra G onto itself is called an *automorphism*. Thus, G always has the *identity automorphism*—this will be the identity mapping of G onto itself. Examples of non-trivial automorphisms are the automorphism of the additive group of whole numbers which carries every whole number k into the number $-k$, and also the automorphism of the field of complex numbers which carries every complex number $a + bi$ into the number $a - bi$.

The result of the successive application of automorphisms of an algebra G will again be an automorphism. Under this multiplication, which is associative in view of I.1.2, all the automorphisms of the algebra G form a group; thus its identity will be the identity automorphism, and the inverse mapping for any automorphism will also be an automorphism; this group is called *the group of automorphisms* of the universal algebra G.

* Every group is isomorphic to the group of all automorphisms of some universal algebra [Birkhoff, *Revista Unione Mat. Argentina* **11**, 155–157 (1946)].

Every group can be isomorphically embedded in the group of automorphisms of some Abelian group.*

2. Let there be given a non-commutative semigroup G, which has an identity, and choose in it a *unit* ε, i.e. an element for which there exists in G an inverse element ε^{-1}, which is both a left and a right inverse (cf. II.8.1). By transforming the semigroup G by the element ε, i.e. by mapping every element x of G into the element $\varepsilon^{-1}x\varepsilon$, we obtain an automorphism of the semigroup G, called an *inner automorphism* of G. In fact, from

$$\varepsilon^{-1}x\varepsilon = \varepsilon^{-1}y\varepsilon$$

it follows that $x = y$, i.e. the mapping under consideration is oneone. Further, from

$$x = \varepsilon^{-1}(\varepsilon x \varepsilon^{-1})\varepsilon$$

it follows that this will be a mapping onto the whole semigroup G. Finally, the equation

$$\varepsilon^{-1}(xy)\varepsilon = \varepsilon^{-1}x\varepsilon \cdot \varepsilon^{-1}y\varepsilon$$

proves that this mapping is an isomorphism.

It is clear that a commutative semigroup with identity, in particular every Abelian group, has a unique inner automorphism, namely the identity automorphism.

It is easy to verify that the product of the transformations of a semigroup with identity by the elements ε and δ coincides with the transformation by the element $\varepsilon\delta$, and the inverse of the transformation by the element ε is the transformation by the element ε^{-1}. From this it follows that *the inner automorphisms of a semigroup with identity form a subgroup in the group of all automorphisms of this semigroup.*

The subgroup of inner automorphisms will in fact be a normal subgroup in the group of all automorphisms of the semigroup G under consideration. In fact, let there be given an arbitrary automorphism φ of the semigroup G and an inner automorphism α of G, induced by the unit ε. Then for any $x \in G$

$$x(\varphi^{-1}\alpha\varphi) = [\varepsilon^{-1}(x\varphi^{-1})\varepsilon]\varphi =$$
$$(\varepsilon^{-1})\varphi \cdot (x\varphi^{-1})\varphi \cdot (\varepsilon\varphi) = (\varepsilon\varphi)^{-1}x(\varepsilon\varphi),$$

i.e. the automorphism $\varphi^{-1}\alpha\varphi$ is an inner automorphism and is induced by the unit $\varepsilon\varphi$.

On the other hand, if G is a group and, hence, all the elements of G are units, then we obtain a homomorphic mapping of the whole group G onto the group of its inner automorphisms, by setting up a correspondence between every element of G and the inner automorphism induced by it. The kernel of this homomorphism (see III.2.6) is the totality of elements of G which commute with every element of this group; it is called the *centre* of the group G. From the theorem on homomorphisms it follows that *the centre of the group G is a normal subgroup and the group of inner automorphisms of the group G is isomorphic to the factor group of the group G with respect to its centre.*

3. The concept of an inner automorphism carries over to the case of any associative ring with identity. In fact, *every inner automorphism of the multiplicative semigroup of the associative ring R with identity will be an automorphism of this ring itself,* because

$$\varepsilon^{-1}(x+y)\varepsilon = \varepsilon^{-1}x\varepsilon + \varepsilon^{-1}y\varepsilon.$$

Such an automorphism is naturally called an *inner automorphism* of the ring R.

4. Every homomorphic mapping of a universal algebra G into itself is called an *endomorphism* of G. Amongst the endomorphisms are found, in particular, all the automorphisms, and also all the isomorphic mappings of G into itself and all the homomorphic mappings of G onto itself.

The result of the successive application of endomorphisms will again be an endomorphism, and therefore all the endomorphisms, with respect to this multiplication, associative in view of I.1.2, form a semigroup, called the *semigroup of endomorphisms* of the universal algebra *G*.

This semigroup of endomorphisms has an identity—it is the identity automorphism. The units in the semigroup of endomorphisms are the automorphisms and only these because only in the case of automorphisms is it possible to have a single-valued inverse mapping.

It is useful to note that the identity automorphism of the universal algebra *G* plays the part of the identity not only for the endomorphisms of this algebra: it is obviously a left identity for all homomorphic mappings of the algebra *G* into any other algebra, and is also a right identity for all homomorphisms of algebras into the algebra *G*.

5. Now we shall consider homomorphic mappings of Ω-groups. If φ and ψ are two homomorphisms of the Ω-group *G* into the Ω-group *G'*, then the mapping

$$a(\varphi + \psi) = a\varphi + a\psi, \quad a \in G, \tag{1}$$

in the general case is not a homomorphism. It will be a homomorphism (see III.1.5) if and only if for any $a, b \in G$

$$(a + b)(\varphi + \psi) = a(\varphi + \psi) + b(\varphi + \psi),$$

i.e. if

$$b\varphi + a\psi = a\psi + b\varphi, \tag{2}$$

and if for any *n*-ary operation $\omega \in \Omega$ and any $a_1, a_2, \ldots, a_n \in G$

$$(a_1 a_2 \ldots a_n \omega)(\varphi + \psi) = [a_1(\varphi + \psi)][a_2(\varphi + \psi)] \ldots [a_n(\varphi + \psi)]\omega,$$

i.e. if

$$(a_1\varphi)(a_2\varphi) \ldots (a_n\varphi)\omega + (a_1\psi)(a_2\psi) \ldots (a_n\psi)\omega =$$
$$(a_1\varphi + a_1\psi)(a_2\varphi + a_2\psi) \ldots (a_n\varphi + a_n\psi)\omega. \tag{3}$$

If the conditions (2) and (3) are satisfied, then the homomorphisms φ and ψ are called *summable*, and the homomorphism $\varphi + \psi$ is called their *sum*.

Condition (2) shows, for the case of groups without multi-operators, that *the homomorphisms φ and ψ of the group G into the group G' are summable if and only if the subgroups $G\varphi$ and $G\psi$ of the group G' commute elementwise.* If, however, we are considering homomorphisms φ and ψ of the ring *R* into the ring *R'*, then condition (2) is satisfied automatically, and condition (3) is altered to the condition: for any $a, b \in R$

$$a\varphi \cdot b\varphi + a\psi \cdot b\psi = (a\varphi + a\psi)(b\varphi + b\psi),$$

i.e.

$$a\varphi \cdot b\psi + a\psi \cdot b\varphi = 0.$$

6. We have defined a partial addition of homomorphisms of the Ω-group G into the Ω-group G'. This addition is commutative, because from (2) for all $a \in G$ it follows that

$$a\varphi + a\psi = a\psi + a\varphi,$$

i.e., in view of (1), $\varphi + \psi = \psi + \varphi$. It is also associative, because for all $a \in G$

$$a[(\varphi + \psi) + \chi] = a[\varphi + (\psi + \chi)] = a\varphi + a\psi + a\chi.$$

From this it follows that if the sum $\sum_{i=1}^{n} \varphi_i$ of the homomorphisms $\varphi_i : G \to G'$, $i = 1, 2, \ldots, n$, is a homomorphism, then it is defined uniquely. We note that we can also speak of *the sum of an infinite family of homomorphisms* $\varphi_i ; G \to G'$, $i \in I$, if we presuppose in addition that for any $a \in G$ only a finite number of the elements $a\varphi_i$, $i \in I$, are distinct from zero.

If the homomorphisms φ and ψ of the Ω-group G into the Ω-group G' are summable, then for any Ω-groups H and F and any homomorphisms $\sigma : H \to G$ and $\tau : G' \to F$ the homomorphisms $\sigma\varphi$ and $\sigma\psi$, and also $\varphi\tau$ and $\psi\tau$ (see III.1.5) will be summable and

$$\sigma(\varphi + \psi) = \sigma\varphi + \sigma\psi, \quad (\varphi + \psi)\tau = \varphi\tau + \psi\tau. \qquad (4)$$

In fact, if $a \in H$, then

$$a[\sigma(\varphi + \psi)] = (a\sigma)(\varphi + \psi) = (a\sigma)\varphi + (a\sigma)\psi =$$
$$a(\sigma\varphi) + a(\sigma\psi) = a(\sigma\varphi + \sigma\psi),$$

i.e. the mapping $\sigma\varphi + \sigma\psi$ will be a homomorphism and the first of the equations (4) holds. It is just as simple to prove the second assertion of the theorem. We note that from the existence of the sums on the right-hand sides of equations (4) does not follow the existence of the sums on their left-hand sides.

7. Because of the equation $0 + 0 = 0$, where 0 is the zero of the Ω-group, and equation (1) from III.2.1, the mapping which carries every element of the Ω-group G into the zero of the Ω-group

G' will be a homomorphism; it is the *zero homomorphism* of G into G'.

The following assertions can be verified immediately: every homomorphism $\varphi:G \to G'$ is summable with the zero homomorphism, and the sum is equal to φ; if the homomorphisms φ, ψ: $G \to G'$ are summable and

$$\varphi + \psi = \varphi,$$

then the homomorphism ψ is the zero homomorphism; finally, for any Ω-groups H and F and any homomorphisms $\sigma:H \to G$ and $\tau:G' \to F$ the product of σ by the zero homomorphism of G into G' is equal to the zero homomorphism of H into G', and the product of the zero homomorphism of G into G' by τ is equal to the zero homomorphism of G into F.

8. We will consider the homomorphisms of some group G (without multi-operators) into the Abelian group G'; we will assume that the first group is written multiplicatively, and the second additively. In this case, in view of (2), any two homomorphisms are summable. On the other hand, for any homomorphism $\varphi:G \to G'$ the mapping $-\varphi$ defined by the equation

$$a(-\varphi) = -a\varphi, \qquad a \in G,$$

will, in this case, be a homomorphism, because for any $a, b \in G$

$$(ab)(-\varphi) = -(ab)\varphi = -(a\varphi + b\varphi) = (-a\varphi) + (-b\varphi) =$$
$$a(-\varphi) + b(-\varphi).$$

This homomorphism will be the additive inverse of φ, because for $a \in G$

$$a[\varphi + (-\varphi)] = a\varphi + a(-\varphi) = a\varphi - a\varphi = 0$$

i.e. $\varphi + (-\varphi)$ is equal to the zero homomorphism.

Thus, *the homomorphisms of any group G into an Abelian group G' form an Abelian group under addition.*

We consider, in particular, the endomorphisms of an Abelian group G. They form an Abelian group under addition, and a semigroup with identity under multiplication (see III.3.4), and the distributive laws (4) are satisfied. We thus find that *the endomorphisms of an Abelian group G form an associative ring with identity with respect to the operations of addition and multipli-*

cation of endomorphisms. This ring is called the *ring of endomorphisms of* the Abelian group *G.*

Every associative ring can be isomorphically embedded in the ring of endomorphisms of some Abelian group.

In view of II.4.4 we can assume that the associative ring *R* under consideration has an identity 1. If *a* is any element of *R*, then the mapping which carries every element *x* of *R* into the element *xa* will be an endomorphism of the additive group of the ring *R*, because

$$(x + y)a = xa + ya.$$

The sum and product of elements of *R* correspond to the sum and product of the corresponding endomorphisms, as the equations

$$x(a + b) = xa + xb,$$

$$x(ab) = (xa)b$$

show. Finally, to different elements of *R* correspond different endomorphisms, because from $a \neq b$ it follows that $1 \cdot a \neq 1 \cdot b$.

9. *The ring of endomorphisms of an infinite cyclic group is isomorphic to the ring of integers C.*

In fact, if *a* is the generating element of the given group, written additively, and if the endomorphism φ carries the element *a* into the element *ka*, where *k* is some integer then

$$(na)\varphi = nka, \tag{5}$$

i.e. the endomorphism φ is completely defined by the given integer *k*. Conversely, a mapping φ of our group, defined by equation (5), will in fact be an endomorphism. Thus, we have established a one–one correspondence between the endomorphisms of the infinite cyclic group $\{a\}$ and the integers. The fact that this correspondence is an isomorphism follows from the fact that if

$$a\varphi = ka, \qquad a\psi = la$$

then

$$a(\varphi + \psi) = a\varphi + a\psi = ka + la = (k + l)a,$$

$$a(\varphi\psi) = (a\varphi)\psi = (ka)\psi = (kl)a.$$

Because in the ring of integers only the numbers 1 and -1 have inverses, *the group of automorphisms of the infinite cyclic group $\{a\}$ is a cyclic group of order two,* which consists of the *identity* automorphism and the automorphism which carries every element of the group into its additive inverse.

* The ring of endomorphisms of a finite cyclic group of order n is isomorphic to the ring C_n of residues modulo n. The ring of endomorphisms of the additive group of rational numbers is isomorphic to the field of rational numbers. Thus, every non-zero endomorphism of these groups is an automorphism.*

10. In the theory of Abelian groups a very large part is played by the *group of type* p^∞, where p is a prime number: this is the multiplicative group of all those complex numbers which are roots of unity of some degree p^n, $n = 1, 2, \ldots$ As is well known, the group of p^n-th roots of unity, where n is fixed, is cyclic of order p^n with generating element

$$a_n = \cos \frac{2\pi}{p^n} + i \sin \frac{2\pi}{p^n}.$$

The group of type p^∞ will thus be Abelian and infinite, and in fact the union of an increasing sequence of cyclic subgroups $\{a_n\}$, $n = 1, 2, \ldots$ The system of elements

$$a_n, \quad n = 1, 2, \ldots, \tag{6}$$

is a system of generators of this group. If we agree to use the additive instead of the multiplicative notation for the group of type p^∞, then the generating elements (6) will be connected by the equations

$$pa_1 = 0, \quad pa_{n+1} = a_n, \quad n = 1, 2, \ldots \tag{7}$$

Let us determine the ring of endomorphisms of the group of type p^∞. If φ is an endomorphism of this group, then it is completely defined by giving the images of all the generating elements (6). Because the element a_n has order p^n, the order of the element $a_n\varphi$ cannot exceed the number p^n. All such elements, however, lie in the cyclic subgroup $\{a_n\}$, and therefore

$$a_n\varphi = k_n a_n, \quad n = 1, 2, \ldots, \tag{8}$$

where

$$0 \leqslant k_n < p^n. \tag{9}$$

Further, equations (7), which are true for the elements (6), must also be satisfied for their images under the endomorphism φ, and therefore

$$p(a_{n+1}\varphi) = a_n\varphi,$$

whence

$$p(k_{n+1}a_{n+1}) = k_{n+1}a_n = k_na_n.$$

From this it follows that the difference $k_{n+1}-k_n$ must be divisible by the order p^n of the element a_n, or, using a symbol taken from the theory of numbers

$$k_{n+1} \equiv k_n \,(\mathrm{mod}\,p^n). \qquad (10)$$

Thus, to every endomorphism φ of the group of type p^∞ there corresponds a sequence of non-negative integers

$$(k_1, k_2, ..., k_n, ...), \qquad (11)$$

subject to the conditions (9) and (10). To two different endomorphisms there correspond here different sequences of the form (11), because at least one of the generating elements (6) has different images under these endomorphisms.

Conversely, every sequence of the form (11), subject to the conditions (9) and (10) corresponds to some endomorphism φ of the group of type p^∞. In fact, on the basis of equations (8) we can define the mapping φ for all the elements of our group, and it is easy to verify that this mapping will be an endomorphism.

If in the group of type p^∞ we take two endomorphisms, φ and ψ, given respectively by the sequences (11) and

$$(l_1, l_2, ..., l_n, ...), \qquad (12)$$

then

$$a_n(\varphi + \psi) = (k_n + l_n)a_n,$$

$$a_n(\varphi\psi) = (k_nl_n)a_n.$$

From the fact that conditions of the type of condition (10) are valid for the sequences (11) and (12) it follows that

$$k_{n+1} + l_{n+1} \equiv k_n + l_n \,(\mathrm{mod}\,p^n),$$

$$k_{n+1}l_{n+1} \equiv k_nl_n \,(\mathrm{mod}\,p^n);$$

these congruences are not violated if their left-hand sides are replaced by positive residues modulo p^{n+1} (i.e. remainders after division by p^{n+1}), and their right-hand sides by positive residues modulo p^n, so that the conditions (9) are also satisfied.

Thus the ring of endomorphisms of the group of type p^∞ is isomorphic to the ring of sequences of non-negative integers of the form (11), satisfying the conditions (9) and (10), where the addition and multiplication of these sequences are derived componentwise with successive transition in every n-th place to the residue modulo p^n. This commutative ring is called the *ring of p-adic integers*. Its zero is the sequence $(0, 0, ..., 0, ...)$ corresponding to the zero endomorphism of the group of type p^∞, and its identity is the sequence $(1, 1, ..., 1, ...)$, corresponding to the identity automorphism of this group.

11. For the p-adic integers other notations are possible. Let the p-adic integer α be given by the sequence of non-negative integers (11), subject to the conditions (9) and (10). If we set †

$$a_0 = k_1, \qquad a_n = \frac{k_{n+1} - k_n}{p^n}, \qquad n = 1, 2, ..., \qquad (13)$$

then all the $a_n, n = 0, 1, 2, ...$, will be integers, and in fact will be positive residues modulo p, i.e.

$$0 \leqslant a_n < p, \qquad n = 0, 1, 2, ... \qquad (14)$$

Because, by (13),

$$k_n = a_0 + a_1 p + a_2 p^2 + ... + a_{n-1} p^{n-1}, \qquad n = 1, 2, ... \qquad (15)$$

the p-adic integer α can be represented by the infinite series

$$a_0 + a_1 p + a_2 p^2 + ... + a_n p^n + ... ; \qquad (16)$$

here, obviously, different series of the form (16) correspond to different p-adic numbers. Conversely, if there is given an arbitrary series of the form (16), whose coefficients are integers and are subject to the conditions (14), then, by defining the number k_n by means of equations (15), we obtain a sequence of the form (11), satisfying the conditions (9) and (10).

We have established a one–one correspondence between all the p-adic integers and all series of the form (16), whose coefficients are the residues modulo p. By using (15), it is easy to carry over the operations defined for the p-adic numbers to series of the form (16): if the number α is given by the series (16), and the number β by the series

$$b_0 + b_1 p + b_2 p^2 + ... + b_n p^n + ...$$

also satisfying conditions (14), then

$$\alpha + \beta = c_0 + c_1 p + c_2 p^2 + ... + c_n p^n + ...,$$

---

† [1] These numbers a_n are, of course, not related to the a_n used in **10**. (Ed.).

where all the coefficients c_n are residues modulo p, and where
$$c_0 = c_0 + b_0 - pq_0,$$
$$c_n = a_n + b_n + q_{n-1} - pq_n, \quad n = 1, 2, \ldots;$$
on the other hand,
$$\alpha\beta = d_0 + d_1 p + d_2 p^2 + \ldots + d_n p^n + \ldots,$$
where the coefficients d_n will also be residues modulo p, and where
$$d_0 = a_0 b_0 - ps_0,$$
$$d_n = \sum_{k+l=n} a_k b_l + s_{n-1} - ps_n, \quad n = 1, 2, \ldots$$

12. From this description of multiplication it follows at once, because the number p is prime, that *the ring of p-adic numbers does not contain any divisors of zero* and therefore, by II.5.5, there exists a quotient field for it, called the *field of p-adic numbers*. This field can be constructed in the following way.

We consider all possible series of the form
$$a_k p^k + a_{k+1} p^{k+1} + \ldots + a_n p^n + \ldots, \tag{17}$$
where all the coefficients a_n are residues modulo p, and k is greater than, equal to or less than zero; the series (17) may thus contain a finite number of terms with negative powers of the number p. If not all the coefficients of the series (17) are equal to zero, then we will assume that $a_k \neq 0$; on the other hand, series with zero coefficients are all regarded as identical.

By extending in the natural way the definition of operations on series of the form (16) to those on series of the form (17), we find that these latter series form an associative-commutative ring, whose identity is the series of the form (17) in which $a_0 = 1$, and all of whose remaining coefficients are equal to zero. This ring will in fact be a field: if the series (17) is distinct from zero, i.e. $a_k \neq 0$, then its inverse will be the series
$$b_{-k} p^{-k} + b_{-k+1} p^{-k+1} + \ldots + b_n p^n + \ldots,$$
whose coefficients, which are residues modulo p, are found successively from the following equations, which are soluble because the number p is prime:
$$a_k b_{-k} - ps_{-k} = 1,$$
$$a_k b_{-k+1} + a_{k+1} b_{-k} + s_{-k} - ps_{-k+1} = 0,$$
$$\cdots$$
$$a_k b_n + a_{k+1} b_{n-1} + \ldots + a_{n+2k} b_{-k} + s_{n-1} - ps_n = 0,$$

Those series of the form (17) in which $k \geqslant 0$ form a subring in the field which we have constructed, isomorphic to the ring of p-adic integers, and the field is its quotient field: every series of the form (17) after multiplication (in the sense of our definition of this operation) by some positive power of the number p (which is, of course, a p-adic integer) becomes a series of the form (16), i.e. a p-adic integer.

§ 4. Normal and composition series

1. *If in the Ω-group G we are given an ideal A and an Ω-subgroup B, then the Ω-subgroup $\{A, B\}$ generated by them consists of those elements of G which, in at least one way, can be written in the form $a + b$, where $a \in A$, $b \in B$, therefore the notation*

$$\{A, B\} = A + B \tag{1}$$

has a meaning.

It is clear, in fact, that every element of the form $a + b$ belongs to $\{A, B\}$. We will show that these elements themselves form an Ω-subgroup, which obviously contains both A and B. In fact, if $a, a' \in A$, $b, b' \in B$, then $b + a' - b \in A$, because A is a normal subgroup of the additive group. Therefore

$$(a + b) + (a' + b') = [a + (b + a' - b)] + (b + b') = a'' + b'',$$

where $a'' \in A$, $b'' \in B$. Further, $0 = 0 + 0$, but the zero is contained both in A and in B. If an element $a + b$ is given, then its additive inverse will be the element $a' - b$, where $a' = -b - a + b \in A$. Finally, for any n-ary operation $\omega \in \Omega$ and any elements

$$a_1, a_2, ..., a_n \in A \text{ and } b_1, b_2, ..., b_n \in B,$$

by virtue of (4) from III.2.4, we have

$$(a_1 + b_1)(a_2 + b_2) \, ... \, (a_n + b_n)\omega \in b_1 b_2 \, ... \, b_n \omega + A,$$

but

$$b_1 b_2 \, ... \, b_n \omega = b \in B,$$

because B is an Ω-group, and $b + A = A + b$.

2. The following isomorphism theorem is very often useful.

If A and B are Ω-subgroups of the Ω-group G, where A is an ideal in the Ω-subgroup $\{A, B\}$, then the intersection $A \cap B$ will be an ideal in B and the isomorphism

$$\{A, B\}/A \simeq B/(A \cap B) \tag{2}$$

holds.

In fact, equation (1) shows that every coset of the Ω-group $\{A, B\}$ with respect to the ideal A contains at least one element of B. Thus, under the natural homomorphism of $\{A, B\}$ onto $\{A, B\}/A$ the Ω-subgroup B will be mapped homomorphically onto the whole of this Ω-factor-group. The kernel of the given homomorphism (see. III.2.6) is, obviously, the intersection $A \cap B$. It will thus be an ideal in B, and the validity of the isomorphism (2) follows from the theorems in III.1.8 and III.2.5.

3. Now we will prove Zassenhaus' lemma, a generalization of the isomorphism theorem, which is a fundamental tool used below in the proof of Schreier's theorem.

If in the Ω-group G we are given the Ω-subgroups A, A', B and B' where A' and B' are respectively ideals in A and in B, then $A' + (A \cap B')$ and $B' + (B \cap A')$ will be respectively ideals in $A' + (A \cap B)$ and in $B' + (B \cap A)$ and the isomorphism

$$A' + (A \cap B)/A' + (A \cap B') \simeq B' + (B \cap A)/B' + (B \cap A') \qquad (3)$$

holds.

This lemma obviously reduces to the isomorphism theorem when $A \supseteq B$ and $B' = 0$.

To prove the lemma we set

$$C = A \cap B.$$

Because B' is an ideal in B, and $C \subseteq B$, then, by the theorem on isomorphisms,

$$C \cap B' = A \cap B \cap B' = A \cap B'$$

will be an ideal in C. The same is true for the intersection $B \cap A'$, and therefore also for the sum C' of these two ideals (see III.2.4),

$$C' = (A \cap B') + (B \cap A'). \qquad (4)$$

We set

$$D = C/C'.$$

On the other hand, because A' is an ideal in A, then, by III.4.1,

$$\{A', A \cap B\} = A' + (A \cap B) = A' + C.$$

An arbitrary element of this sum has the form $a' + c$, where $a' \in A'$, $c \in C$. We make it correspond to the coset (i.e. element of the group D) $C' + c$. If the element $a' + c$ can be written in another way in this form,

$$a' + c = a'_1 + c_1, \quad a'_1 \in A', \quad c_1 \in C,$$

then
$$-a_1' + a' = c_1 - c \in A' \cap C \subseteq A' \cap B \subseteq C'$$
and therefore
$$c_1 = (-a_1' + a') + c \in C' + c.$$

We obtain a single-valued mapping of the Ω-group $A' + C$ into the Ω-group D, in fact onto the whole of this Ω-group, because every element $c \in C$, belonging, of course, to $A' + C$, in mapped by this into its coset $C' + c$. This mapping is a homomorphism: because A' is an ideal in $A' + C$, then
$$(a_1' + c_1) + (a_2' + c_2) = a_3' + (c_1 + c_2), \quad a_3' \in A',$$
and, by (4) from III.2.4, for any n-ary operation $\omega \in \Omega$
$$(a_1' + c_1)(a_2' + c_2) \dots (a_n' + c_n)\omega = a_0' + c_1 c_2 \dots c_n \omega,$$
where $a_0' \in A'$, and $c_1 c_2 \dots c_n \omega \in C$, because C is an Ω-group.

The kernel of the homomorphism constructed is the sum $A' + (A \cap B')$. In fact, this sum is contained in the kernel, because $A \cap B' \subseteq C'$. On the other hand, if the element $a' + c \in A' + C$ is mapped under the homomorphism considered into C', then $c \in C'$, and therefore, by (4), we can write:
$$c = u + v, \quad \text{where} \quad u \in B \cap A', \quad v \in A \cap B'$$
it is clear that in the notation for the sum of two ideals the summands can be written in any order. Thus,
$$a' + c = (a' + u) + v \in A' + (A \cap B').$$

From this it follows that $A' + (A \cap B')$ will be an ideal in $A' + C = A' + (A \cap B)$ and, moreover, the isomorphism
$$A' + (A \cap B)/A' + (A \cap B') \simeq D$$
holds. From considerations of symmetry we can assert that $B' + (B \cap A')$ will be an ideal in $B' + (B \cap A)$ and
$$B' + (B \cap A)/B' + (B \cap A') \simeq D.$$
The isomorphism (3) is proved by this.

4. A finite system of Ω-subgroups of the Ω-group G contained in one another,
$$G = A_0 \supset A_1 \supset A_2 \supset \dots \supset A_k = 0, \tag{5}$$

begining with G itself and ending with zero, is called a *normal series* of this Ω-group if every Ω-subgroup A_i, $i = 1, 2, ..., k$, is a proper ideal in A_{i-1} (although not necessarily in A_j when $j < i - 1$). The number k is called the *length* of the normal series (5), and the Ω-factor-groups

$$G/A_1, A_1/A_2, ..., A_{k-1}/A_k = A_{k-1}$$

are called the *factors* of this series.

Every Ω-group G has normal series — such as the series† $G \supset 0$, and also, if there is a non-trivial ideal A in G, the series $G \supset A \supset 0$.

A normal series

$$G = B_0 \supset B_1 \supset B_2 \supset ... \supset B_l = 0$$

is called a *refinement* of the series (5) if every Ω-subgroup A_i, $i = 1, 2, ..., k - 1$, coincides with one of the Ω-subgroups B_j; it is clear that $l \geqslant k$.

Finally, two normal series of the Ω-group G are called *isomorphic* if their lengths are equal, and if we can establish between their factors a one–one correspondence such that corresponding factors are isomorphic Ω-groups. Here we do not presuppose that the correspondence keeps the relative arrangement of the factors, i.e. the i-th factor of the first series is not necessarily isomorphic to the i-th factor of the second series.

5. SCHREIER'S THEOREM. *Every two normal series of an arbitrary Ω-group G have isomorphic refinements.*

In fact, let there be given in G the normal series

$$G = A_0 \supset A_1 \supset A_2 \supset ... \supset A_k = 0, \tag{6}$$
$$G = B_0 \supset B_1 \supset B_2 \supset ... \supset B_l = 0. \tag{7}$$

We set

$$A_{ij} = A_i + (A_{i-1} \cap B_j), \quad i = 1, 2, ..., k, \quad j = 0, 1, ... l;$$
$$B_{ji} = B_j + (B_{j-1} \cap A_i), \quad j = 1, 2, ..., l, \quad i = 0, 1, ... k.$$

These notations have a meaning by virtue of III.4.1, because, for instance, A_i is an ideal, and $A_{i-1} \cap B_j$ an Ω-subgroup in A_{i-1}. We note that for $i = 1, 2, ..., k$ and $j = 1, 2, ..., l$ the inclusions

$$A_{i-1} = A_{i0} \supseteq A_{i,j-1} \supseteq A_{ij} \supseteq A_{il} = A_i,$$
$$B_{j-1} = B_{j0} \supseteq B_{j,i-1} \supseteq B_{ji} \supseteq B_{jk} = B_j.$$

hold.

---

† or in case $G = 0$, the series $G = 0$ of length zero (Ed.).

By Zassenhaus' lemma (see III.4.3) A_{ij} and B_{ji} will be respectively ideals in $A_{i,j-1}$ and $B_{j,i-1}$, and the corresponding Ω-factor–groups will be isomorphic:

$$A_{i,j-1}/A_{ij} \simeq B_{j,i-1}/B_{ji}. \tag{8}$$

If we insert all the A_{ij}, $j = 1, 2, \ldots, l-1$, between the A_{i-1} and A_i, $i = 1, 2, \ldots, k$, in the series (6), then, generally speaking, we obtain a *refinement with repetitions* for the series (6), because the equation $A_{i,j-1} = A_{ij}$ may happen to be satisfied. In an analogous way we obtain a refinement with repetitions for the series (7) also. These refinements, because of (8), are isomorphic.

To complete the proof it remains to go over to refinements without repetitions. If $A_{i,j-1} = A_{ij}$, i.e.

$$A_{i,j-1}/A_{ij} = 0,$$

then, by (8), $B_{j,i-1} = B_{ji}$ also. From this it follows that, without violating the isomorphism of the refinements under consideration, we can simultaneously exclude all their repetitions. Thus the theorem is proved.

* An *ascending normal series* of the Ω-group G is a system of Ω-subgroups A_α of it, satisfying the conditions:

1. The indices α form a well ordered set (see I.5.4) with first element 0 and last element μ.

2. $A_0 = 0$, $A_\mu = G$.

3. If $\alpha < \beta$, then $A_\alpha \subset A_\beta$.

4. If the index immediately following α is denoted by $\alpha + 1$, then, for all α, A_α is an ideal in $A_{\alpha+1}$.

5. If the index α is a limit number, then A_α is the set-theoretical union of all the A_β, $\beta < \alpha$.

Any two ascending normal series of an arbitrary Ω-group G have isomorphic refinements, which are also ascending normal series [A. G. Kurosh, *Mat. Sb.* **16**, 59–72 (1945)]. The example of an infinite cyclic group shows that for infinite descending normal series an analogous theorem does not hold.*

6. A normal series of an Ω-group which does not have a refinement distinct from itself is called a *composition series* of this Ω-group. In view of III.2.13 *a normal series of an Ω-group will be a composition series if and only if its factors are simple Ω-groups* (*see* III.2.4).

From Schreier's theorem follow the next two theorems:

THE JORDAN-HÖLDER THEOREM. *If an Ω-group G has composition series, then every two of its composition series are isomorphic.*

If the Ω-group G has composition series, then each of its normal series can be refined to a composition series and therefore has length not exceeding the length of the composition series of G.

To prove this second theorem it is sufficient to apply Schreier's theorem to the given normal series and to one of the composition series of the group under consideration.

In applying the concepts introduced to the case of groups without multi-operators, we note that composition series are possessed both by all finite, and also by some infinite groups. However, neither the infinite cyclic group, nor the group of the type p^∞ (see III.3.10) has a composition series.

7. An *invariant series* of an Ω-group G is a finite system of ideals of the Ω-group G itself, ordered by inclusion, beginning with G and ending with zero. This concept is a special case of the concept of a normal series, and therefore the concepts of the isomorphism of series and refinements of series, introduced in III.4.4, have a meaning for it. An invariant series which has no refinements distinct from itself, which are also invariant series, is called a *principal series*. We have the theorems:

Every two invariant series of an arbitrary Ω-group can be refined to isomorphic invariant series.

If an Ω-group has principal series, then every two of its principal series are isomorphic, and any invariant series can be refined to a principal series.

It is easy to verify that these theorems can be proved by the same methods as the corresponding theorems for normal series. However, they follow immediately from the theorems proved above if we use the following construction. Let there be given an Ω-group G. We extend the system of multi-operators Ω to the system $Ω'$ by adjoining to Ω some, in the general case infinite, system of unary operations. In fact, we adjoin to Ω all the inner automorphisms of the additive group G, and also all the mappings of G into itself defined in the following way: for any n-ary operation $\omega \in \Omega$, any elements $x_1, x_2, \dots, x_n \in G$ and any number i, $1 \leqslant i \leqslant n$, we take the mapping which carries every element $a \in G$ into the element

$$- x_1 x_2 \dots x_n \omega + x_1 \dots x_{i-1}(a + x_i)x_{i+1} \dots x_n \omega.$$

All the additional unary operations carry zero into zero, i.e. satisfy the condition (1) from III.2.1, and therefore G is an Ω'-group. By virtue of the definition of an ideal (see III.2.4) *the Ω'-subgroups in G will be ideals of the Ω-group G and there are no others*, and therefore the normal (composition) series of the Ω'-group G coincide with the invariant (principal) series of the Ω-group G.

§ 5. Abelian, nilpotent and soluble Ω-groups

1. Let us take the Ω-subgroups A and B in the Ω-group G. The *commutator*† $[A, B]$ of these Ω-subgroups is the ideal of the Ω-subgroup $\{A, B\}$ generated in it by the set of all elements of the following two types

$$[a, b] = -a - b + a + b, \quad a \in A, \quad b \in B, \tag{1}$$

—this element is called the *commutator* of the elements a and b— and

$$[a_1, a_2, \ldots, a_n ; \quad b_1, b_2, \ldots, b_n ; \omega] = -a_1 a_2 \ldots a_n \omega -$$
$$b_1 b_2 \ldots b_n \omega + (a_1 + b_1)(a_2 + b_2) \ldots (a_n + b_n) \omega, \tag{2}$$

where ω is an *n*-ary operation from Ω, $a_1, a_2, \ldots, a_n \in A$, $b_1, b_2, \ldots, b_n \in B$.

Thus, in the case of a group G without multi-operators the *commutator* $[A, B]$ of the two subgroups $A, B \subseteq G$ is the normal subgroup generated in the subgroup $\{A, B\}$ by all possible commutators $[a, b]$, where $a \in A$, $b \in B$. If, however, we consider a ring R, then $[a, b]$ is always equal to zero, and the elements (2) take the form

$$[a_1, a_2 ; b_1, b_2] = -a_1 a_2 - b_1 b_2 + (a_1 + b_1)(a_2 + b_2) =$$
$$a_1 b_2 + b_1 a_2 = [a_1, 0 ; 0, b_2] + [0, a_2 ; b_1, 0)].$$

In this case, therefore, the commutator $[A, B]$ of two subrings $A, B \subseteq R$ is the ideal generated in the subring $\{A, B\}$ by all possible products ab and ba, where $a \in A$, $b \in B$.

From the definition of an ideal it follows at once that if in the Ω-group G we take the Ω-subgroup A, and in it some subset M, then the ideal generated by the set M in A is contained in the

---

† or commutator ideal (Ed.).

ideal generated by M in G. From this it follows that *if in the
Ω-group G we are given the Ω-subgroups A', B', A, B, where
$A' \subseteq A$, $B' \subseteq B$, then*

$$[A', B'] \subseteq [A, B].$$

* In a group without multi-operators the commutator
$[A, B]$ coincides with the subgroup generated by all the commutators $[a, b]$, $a \in A$, $b \in B$.*

2. *For any Ω-subgroups A and B of the Ω-group G the equation*

$$[A, B] = [B, A] \tag{3}$$

holds.

In fact, for any $b \in B$, $a \in A$

$$[b, a] = -a + [-a, b] + a \in [A, B], \tag{4}$$

because $[A, B]$ is a normal subgroup under addition in $\{A, B\}$.
On the other hand, for any n-ary operation $\omega \in \Omega$ and any
b_1, b_2, ..., $b_n \in B$, $a_1, a_2, ..., a_n \in A$

$$b_1 b_2 \ldots b_n \omega \in B, \qquad a_1 a_2 \ldots a_n \omega \in A$$

and therefore, in view of (4),

$$[b_1 b_2 \ldots b_n \omega, \quad a_1 a_2 \ldots a_n \omega] \in [A, B].$$

Further

$$b_i + a_i = [-b_i, -a_i] + a_i + b_i, \quad i = 1, 2, ..., n,$$

and because, by (4),

$$[-b_i, -a_i] \in [A, B], \quad i = 1, 2, ..., n,$$

and $[A, B]$ is an ideal in $\{A, B\}$, then, by virtue of (4) from III.2.4,

$$(b_1 + a_1)(b_2 + a_2) \ldots (b_n + a_n) \omega =$$
$$(a_1 + b_1)(a_2 + b_2) \ldots (a_n + b_n) \omega + d,$$

where $d \in [A, B]$. We find that

$$[b_1, b_2, ..., b_n; a_1, a_2, ..., a_n; \omega] = [b_1 b_2 \ldots b_n \omega, a_1 a_2 \ldots a_n \omega] +$$
$$[a_1, a_2, ..., a_n : b_1, b_2, ..., b_n; \omega] + d \in [A, B]. \tag{5}$$

From (4) and (5) there follows the inclusion

$$[B, A] \subseteq [A, B],$$

from which, by considerations of symmetry, there follows the
equation (3).

3. As the definition shows, the commutator $[A, G]$ of any Ω-subgroup A with the Ω-group G itself is an ideal in G. This is true, in particular, for

$$G' = [G, G].$$

This ideal is called the commutator† of the Ω-group G.

For a group G without multi-operators the commutator G' will, therefore, be a normal subgroup, generated by all the commutators $[a, b]$, $a, b \in G$. For a ring R the commutator is an ideal, generated by all the products ab, $a, b \in R$; in the theory of rings this ideal is usually called the *square* of the ring R.

An Ω-subgroup A of the Ω-group is an ideal in G if and only if

$$[A, G] \subseteq A. \tag{6}$$

In fact, if A is an ideal in G, then for all $a \in A$, $x \in G$, A contains the element $-x + a + x$, and therefore also the element $[a, x]$. On the other hand, in view of (4) from III.2.4, for every n-ary operation $\omega \in \Omega$ and all $a_1, a_2, \ldots, a_n \in A$, $x_1, x_2, \ldots x_n \in G$, A contains the element

$$- x_1 x_2 \ldots x_n \omega + (a_1 + x_1)(a_2 + x_2) \ldots (a_n + x_n) \omega,$$

and therefore also the element

$$[a_1, a_2, \ldots, a_n ; x_1, x_2, \ldots, x_n ; \omega].$$

The ideal A therefore also contains the ideal generated by all the elements mentioned, i.e. the ideal $[A, G]$.

Conversely, if (6) is satisfied, then A contains, in particular, all the commutators $[a, x]$, $a \in A$, $x \in G$, whence $-x + a + x \in A$, i.e. condition (1) of III.2.4 is satisfied. Condition (2) is also satisfied; in fact, (2) of III.2.4 follows from

$$[0, \ldots, 0, a, 0, \ldots, 0 ; x_1, x_2, \ldots, x_n ; \omega] \in A,$$

because $0 \ldots 0 a 0 \ldots 0 \omega \in A$.

From this theorem it follows, because of the inclusion

$$[A, G] \subseteq [G, G)] = G',$$

that *every Ω-subgroup A of the Ω-group G containing the commutator G' will be an ideal in G.*

---

† or derived group (Ed.).

128 LECTURES IN GENERAL ALGEBRA

4. An Ω-group G is called *Abelian* if its commutator is equal to zero,

$$[G, G] = 0.$$

This means, in particular, that for all $a, b \in G$

$$[a, b] = 0,$$

from which it follows that

$$a + b = b + a. \tag{7}$$

i.e. *an Abelian Ω-group has an Abelian additive group.* On the other hand, for every n-ary operation $\omega \in \Omega$ and any $a_1, a_2, \ldots, a_n$, $b_1, b_2, \ldots, b_n \in G$ it will be true that

$$[a_1, a_2, \ldots, a_n; b_1, b_2, \ldots, b_n; \omega] = 0,$$

i.e., because of (7),

$$(a_1 + b_1)(a_2 + b_2) \ldots (a_n + b_n)\omega = a_1 a_2 \ldots a_n \omega + b_1 b_2 \ldots b_n \omega. \tag{8}$$

For groups without multi-operators this concept reduces to the concept of an ordinary Abelian group, and for rings to the concept of a ring with zero multiplication, because for rings condition (8) is equivalent to the condition $ab = 0$ for all a and b.

Every Ω-subgroup A of an Abelian Ω-group G is an ideal in G, because $A \supseteq G' = 0$.

Every Ω-subgroup A and every Ω-factor-group G/A of an Abelian Ω-group G is itself Abelian, because if the conditions (7) and (8) are satisfied in G, then they are also satisfied both in A and in G/A.

5. *An Ω-factor-group G/A of an Ω-group G is Abelian if and only if the ideal A contains the commutator G' of the Ω-group G,*

$$A \supseteq G'. \tag{9}$$

Indeed, the fact that the Ω-factor-group G/A is Abelian shows that for all $x, y \in G$

$$[x + A, y + A] = A$$

and for every n-ary operation $\omega \in \Omega$ and any $x_1, x_2, \ldots, x_n, y_1, y_2, \ldots, y_n \in G$

$$[x_1 + A, x_2 + A, \ldots, x_n + A; y_1 + A,$$
$$y_2 + A, \ldots, y_n + A; \omega] = A.$$

This, however, is equivalent to the inclusions

$$[x, y] \in A,$$

$$[x_1, x_2, \ldots, x_n; y_1, y_2, \ldots, y_n; \omega] \in A,$$

i.e. it is equivalent to the inclusion (9).

In particular, *the Ω-factor-group G/G' of the Ω-group G by its commutator is Abelian.*

6. A normal series

$$G = A_0 \supset A_1 \supset A_2 \supset \ldots \supset A_k = 0 \tag{10}$$

of an Ω-group G (see III.4.4) is called a *central series* if

$$[A_i, G] \subseteq A_{i+1}, \quad i = 0, 1, \ldots, k-1. \tag{11}$$

We note that from (11) there follows for all i the inclusion

$$[A_i, G] \subseteq A_i,$$

and therefore, by III.5.3, all the A_i will be ideals in G, i.e. every central series is an invariant series (see III.4.7).

An Ω-group G is called *nilpotent* if it has at least one central series. Amongst the nilpotent Ω-groups there are, in particular, all Abelian Ω-groups G, because for these groups $G \supset 0$ is a central series.

The *lower central chain* of an arbitrary Ω-group G is the descending chain of ideals

$$G = G_0 \supseteq G_1 \supseteq G_2 \supseteq \ldots \supseteq G_i \supseteq \ldots \tag{12}$$

where

$$G_{i+1} = [G_i, G], \quad i = 0, 1, 2, \ldots \tag{13}$$

We note that once it is proved that G_i is an ideal, it follows that the ideal G_{i+1} will be contained in G_i.

An Ω-group G is nilpotent if and only if the lower central chain (12) reaches the zero subgroup after a finite number of steps, i.e. $G_k = 0$ for some k.

In fact, if $G_k = 0$, then the chain (12) reduces, because of (13), to a finite central series. Conversely, let the Ω-group G have a central series (10). Then $G_0 = G = A_0$. If it has already been proved that $G_i \subseteq A_i$, then, by (13) and (11).

$$G_{i+1} = [G_i, G] \subseteq [A_i, G] \subseteq A_{i+1}.$$

From this it follows that

$$G_k \subseteq A_k = 0,$$

i.e. $G_k = 0$.

Every Ω-subgroup A of a nilpotent Ω-group G is itself nilpotent. In fact, let

$$A = A_0 \supseteq A_1 \supseteq A_2 \supseteq \ldots \supseteq A_i \supseteq \ldots$$

be the lower central chain of the Ω-group A. Then

$$A_0 = A \subseteq G = G_0.$$

Suppose that it is already proved that $A_i \subseteq G_i$. Then

$$A_{i+1} = [A_i, A] \subseteq [G_i, G] = G_{i+1}.$$

From $G_k = 0$ it now follows that $A_k = 0$.

Every homomorphic image $H = G\varphi$ of a nilpotent Ω-group G is itself nilpotent.

In fact, let (12) and

$$H = H_0 \supseteq H_1 \supseteq H_2 \supseteq \ldots \supseteq H_i \supseteq \ldots$$

be the lower central chains respectively of the Ω-groups G and H. Then

$$H_0 = H = G\varphi = G_0\varphi.$$

Suppose that it is already proved that

$$H_i \subseteq G_i\varphi. \tag{14}$$

If $a' \in H_i$, $b' \in H$, then, because of (14), there exist $a \in G_i$ and $b \in G$ such that $a\varphi = a'$, $b\varphi = b'$, and therefore, by the definition of a homomorphism,

$$[a, b]\varphi = [a', b']. \tag{15}$$

In an analogous way, for any n-ary operation $\omega \in \Omega$ and any $a_1', a_2', \ldots, a_n' \in H_i$, $b_1', b_2', \ldots, b_n' \in H$ there exist $a_1, a_2, \ldots, a_n \in G_i$ and $b_1, b_2, \ldots, b_n \in G$ such that $a_i\varphi = a_i'$, $b_i\varphi = b_i'$, $i = 1, 2, \ldots, n$, and therefore

$$[a_1, a_2, \ldots, a_n; b_1, b_2, \ldots, b_n; \omega]\varphi =$$
$$[a_1', a_2', \ldots, a_n'; b_1', b_2', \ldots, b_n'; \omega]. \tag{16}$$

Because, by the remark made at the end of III.2.13, the image $G_{i+1}\varphi$ of the ideal G_{i+1} is an ideal in H, then, because of (15) and (16),

$$H_{i+1} = [H_i, H] \subseteq G_{i+1}\varphi.$$

From this and from $G_k = 0$ it follows that $H_k = 0$.

7. A normal series

$$G = A_0 \supset A_1 \supset A_2 \supset \dots \supset A_k = 0 \tag{17}$$

of an Ω-group G is called a *soluble series* if all the factors

$$A_i/A_{i+1}, \quad i = 0, 1, \dots, k-1,$$

of this series are Abelian Ω-groups, i.e., by III.5.5, if

$$[A_i, A_i] \subseteq A_{i+1}, \quad i = 0, 1, \dots, k-1. \tag{18}$$

The Ω-group G is called *soluble* if it has at least one soluble series. *Every nilpotent Ω-group G is soluble.*

In fact, if there is given a central series (10) in G, then, because of (11)

$$[A_i, A_i] \subseteq [A_i, G] \subseteq A_{i+1}, \quad i = 0, 1, \dots, k-1,$$

which is what we were required to prove.

The *chain of commutators* or *derived series* of the Ω-group G is the descending chain of Ω-subgroups

$$G = G^{(0)} \supseteq G' \supseteq G'' \supseteq \dots \supseteq G^{(i)} \supseteq \dots, \tag{19}$$

where

$$G^{(i+1)} = [G^{(i)}, G^{(i)}], \quad i = 0, 1, 2, \dots \tag{20}$$

An Ω-group G is soluble if and only if its derived series (19) reaches zero after a finite number of steps, i.e. $G^{(k)}=0$ for some k.

In fact, if $G^{(k)} = 0$, then the chain (19), in view of (20), reduces to a finite soluble series. Conversely, let the Ω-group G have a soluble series (17). Then $G^{(0)} = G = A_0$. If it has already been proved that $G^{(i)} \subseteq A_i$, then, by (20) and (18),

$$G^{(i+1)} = [G^{(i)}, G^{(i)}] \subseteq [A_i, A_i] \subseteq A_{i+1}.$$

From this it follows that

$$G^{(k)} \subseteq A_k = 0,$$

i.e. $G^{(k)} = 0$.

Every Ω-subgroup A of a soluble Ω-group G is itself soluble. In fact, let

$$A = A^{(0)} \supseteq A' \supseteq A'' \supseteq \ldots \supseteq A^{(i)} \supseteq \ldots$$

be the derived series of the Ω-group A. Then

$$A^{(0)} = A \subseteq G = G^{(0)}.$$

If it has already been proved that $A^{(i)} \subseteq G^{(i)}$, then

$$A^{(i+1)} = [A^{(i)}, A^{(i)}] \subseteq [G^{(i)}, G^{(i)}] = G^{(i+1)}.$$

From $G^{(k)} = 0$ it now follows that $A^{(k)} = 0$.

Every homomorphic image of a soluble Ω-group G is itself soluble.

It is sufficient to prove this assertion for the Ω-factor-group G/A. Because every refinement of a soluble series is itself soluble, then, by Schreier's theorem in III.4.5, for the normal series $G \supset A \supset 0$ there exists in this case a soluble refinement, which, by III.2.12 and III.2.13, determines a soluble series in G/A.

8. Both in the case of groups and in the case of non-associative, in particular Lie, rings solubility is essentially wider than nilpotency. The situation is different in the case of associative rings:

Every soluble associative ring is nilpotent.

We note first that *if we are given an associative ring R and a natural number n, then the ideal generated in R by the set of all possible products of n elements of R coincides with the subgroup generated by this set in the additive group of the ring R.* In fact, the subgroup mentioned consists of zero and all possible sums of a finite number of products of n elements. By multiplying such a sum on the left or on the right by any element of R, we obtain the sum of several products with $n + 1$ elements in each. However, if we replace one pair of neighbouring factors by their product in each of the terms of this sum, we again arrive at a sum of products of n elements.

From this it is easy to derive the following two assertions.

In an associative ring R the i-th term of the derived series $R^{(i)}$ coincides with the ideal generated in R by the set of all products of 2^i elements of R.

For $i = 1$ we know this from III.5.3. Suppose that the assertion has already been proved for i, i.e. $R^{(i)}$ consists of sums of products of 2^i elements. Then, in view of (20), $R^{(i+1)}$ is a subgroup of the additive group of the ring R, generated by all products of pairs of elements of $R^{(i)}$, i.e., by the distributive laws, it is generated by all products of 2^{i+1} elements.

In an associative ring R the i-th term of the lower central chain R_i coincides with the ideal generated in R by the set of all products of $i+1$ elements of R.

For $i = 1$ this is true. Suppose that our assertion has already been proved for i, i.e. R_i consists of sums of products of $i+1$ elements. Then, view of (13) and III.5.1, R_{i+1} is an ideal, generated in R by the products of elements of R_i by any elements of R, on the left or on the right, i.e., by the distributive laws, it is generated by all products of $i+2$ elements.

Thus, for an associative ring R

$$R^{(i)} = R_{2^i - 1}, \qquad i = 0, 1, 2, \dots,$$

and therefore from $R^{(k)} = 0$ it follows that $R_{2^k - 1} = 0$, which is what we were required to prove.

§ 6. Primitive classes of universal algebras

1. We return to the study of arbitrary universal algebras. The concept of algebras of the same type (see III.1.5) is too general to single out reasonable classes of algebraic structures. Thus, by no means every universal algebra with one binary operation (multiplication), one unary operation (taking the inverse element) and one nullary operation (taking the identity) will be a group, although it is of the same type as groups. Groups are singled out amongst all these algebras by the fact that in them, as we well know, the following identical relations hold: for any x, y, z

$$(xy)z = x(yz), \qquad x \cdot 1 = x, \qquad xx^{-1} = 1.$$

We wish to define the concept of an identical relation for the case of universal algebras with any fixed system of operations Ω.

2. Let there be given some non-empty auxiliary set X, whose elements will be called *free elements* and will be denoted by x with indices, and also by y, z and so on. In addition, all the nullary operations in Ω, if such exist, will be given certain symbols, which will be called *the symbols of the nullary operations*.

We will define the concept of a *word*. To begin with, all free elements and all symbols of nullary operations will be regarded as being words. If we already know that the expressions $w_1, w_2, \dots, w_n$

are words, then for any n-ary operation $\omega \in \Omega$, where $n \geqslant 1$, the formal expression

$$w_1 w_2 \ldots w_n \omega \tag{1}$$

will also be regarded as a word.

Thus, every word will be a finite expression in which there occur free elements, symbols of nullary operations and symbols ω for n-ary operations from Ω, $n \geqslant 1$, with any number of repetitions; here the symbol of an n-ary operation ω always "acts" on the n words preceding it.

Thus, suppose Ω contains a ternary operation ω, unary operations ω' and ω'' and a nullary operation with the symbol 0. Then, for instance, the expressions

$$[(x\omega')0 \, y\omega]x(y\omega'')\omega \quad \text{or} \quad (xyz\omega)(x\omega')(y\omega')\omega$$

will be words. It is obvious that these words could be written without any of the brackets:

$$x\omega'0y\omega xy\omega''\omega, \quad xyz\omega x\omega'y\omega'\omega.$$

We will call the words w_1, w_2, ..., w_n *subwords* of the word (1). We remark, further, that the property of being a subword is transitive, so that subwords of the words w_1, w_2, ..., w_n will also be subwords of the word (1), and so on. In particular, all the free elements and symbols of nullary operations which occur in writing down the word (1) will be subwords of (1). We will agree to assume also that every word is a subword of itself.

It is clear that the concept of a word depends essentially on the system of operations Ω. When considering a universal algebra with the system of operations Ω, we will, of course, only use words which have a meaning in Ω.

3. Let us suppose that we are given the words w_1 and w_2, related to the system of operations Ω. We denote by $x_1, x_2, \ldots, x_k$ all the different free elements which occur in at least one of these words, and by $0_1, 0_2, \ldots, 0_l$ all the symbols of nullary operations which occur in at least one of these words. We will say that in the universal algebra G with system of operations Ω the *identical relation*

$$w_1 = w_2, \tag{2}$$

is satisfied if equation (2) holds in G when the free elements x_i, $i = 1, 2, \ldots, k$, are replaced by arbitrary elements $a_i \in G$, which are not necessarily different. Here the symbols 0_j, $j = 1, 2, \ldots, l$, are obviously replaced by elements of G. Taking these elements means a corresponding nullary operation in G, and, in general, the operations of Ω are satisfied by the rules for operations in the algebra G.

If we are given a set of identical relations Λ, then all universal algebras with system of operations Ω, in which all the identical relations from Λ are satisfied, form a *primitive class*† of algebras. We will agree to denote this primitive class by the same letter Λ as is used to define its set of identical relations.

Thus, groups form a primitive class, considered as algebras with one binary, one unary and one nullary operation. Abelian groups form a narrower primitive class—here we impose the additional identical relation $xy = yx$. We obtain a still narrower primitive class if we impose the identical relation $x^2 = 1$.

Rings, associative rings, associative-commutative rings, Lie rings, and Jordan rings will also be primitive classes of universal algebras.

The whole class of universal algebras of a given type with system of operations Ω can also be regarded as a primitive class, with, in fact, the empty set of identical relations. The class of Ω-groups with a given system of operations Ω will also be a primitive class—it is defined by the identical relations included in the definition of a group, and the relations (1) from III.2.1. On the other hand, the set of identical relations may be such that from it there follows the identical relation $x = y$, i.e. the corresponding primitive class consists of one unique‡ algebra, containing only one element.

4. *Every primitive class of universal algebras contains, together with each of its algebras, all its subalgebras and all its homomorphic images.*

It is clear that if the identical relation (2) is satisfied in the algebra G, then it is also satisfied, in particular, for the elements of any subalgebra. On the other hand, let the identical relation (2) be satisfied in G and let there be given a homomorphism φ of the algebra G onto an algebra H of the same type. We denote by w_1'', w_2'' the elements of H which are obtained from the words w_1 and w_2 after we have substituted in place of the free elements

---

† also called *equationally definable class* or *variety* (Ed.).

‡ up to isomorphism (Ed.).

x_i, $i = 1, 2, ..., k$, some elements $b_i \in H$, $i = 1, 2, ..., k$. We choose elements a_i, $i = 1, 2, ..., k$, in the algebra G such that $a_i\varphi = b_i$ for all i, and we denote by w_1', w_2' the elements of G which are obtained from w_1 and w_2 after substituting a_i in place of x_i, $i = 1, 2, ..., k$. From the definition of a homomorphism it follows that

$$w_j'\varphi = w_j'', \quad j = 1, 2,$$

and because $w_1' = w_2'$, then $w_1'' = w_2''$ also, which is what we were required to prove.

5. The concept of a word can also be used for other purposes. We consider the universal algebra G with the system of operations Ω and we take an arbitrary word

$$w = w(x_1, x_2, ..., x_n)$$

in these operations with respect to the free elements $x_1, x_2, ..., x_n$, $n \geqslant 1$. We replace k of these elements, $0 \leqslant k \leqslant n$, for instance the elements $x_{n-k+1}, x_{n-k+2}, ..., x_n$, by some fixed elements b_1, $b_2, ..., b_k \in G$. The expression

$$w(x_1, x_2, ..., x_{n-k}, b_1, b_2, ..., b_k), \tag{3}$$

which is obtained in this way, determines an $(n-k)$-ary operation in the set G in the following way: to the system of elements $a_1, a_2, ..., a_{n-k} \in G$ this operation relates a uniquely defined element

$$w(a_1, a_2, ..., a_{n-k}, b_1, b_2, ..., b_k).$$

All operations which can be obtained in G in this way are called *derived operations* of the algebra G. It is obvious that different expressions of the form (3) may perhaps define the same derived operation in G. A derived operation will be called *principal*, if $k = 0$, i.e. if we make no preliminary replacement of part of the free elements by elements of G. Amongst the principal derived operations of an algebra G there are, in particular, the operations of the system Ω itself.

6. Suppose that there are given two universal algebras on the set G, corresponding to the systems of operations Ω and Ω'. We will say that these two algebras define the same *algebraic system* on G if every operation of Ω' in G is derived from an operation of the system Ω and conversely; the systems of operations Ω and Ω' themselves are called *equivalent* in G.

If the algebras G and H are of the same type with respect to the system of operations Ω and if we go over in G to an equivalent system of operations Ω', then in H such a transition has no meaning in the general case—if the derived operation was obtained in G by replacing part of the free elements in some word by fixed elements of G, then in H this operation may not be uniquely defined. From this it follows that the concept of a homomorphism is only related to a given system of operations Ω and may lose its significance in the transition to an equivalent system of operations Ω'. The same is true for the concept of a subalgebra—it is sufficient to take into account that the elements $b_1, b_2, \ldots, b_k$, which occur in the expression (3), do not necessarily belong to the subalgebra under consideration (with respect to operations from Ω).

The reader can verify without difficulty that the situation will be different if every operation of either of the systems Ω, Ω' is a principal derived operation of the other system. From this it follows that the two ways of considering a group as a universal algebra, which were mentioned in III.1.3, from the point of view of homomorphisms and subgroups are in fact equivalent, which, however, we already knew.

§ 7. Free universal algebras

1. The set of all possible words with respect to a system of operations Ω and a set of free elements X can be regarded as an algebra with system of operations Ω. In fact, if we are given an n-ary operation $\omega \in \Omega$, $n \geqslant 1$, and words $w_1, w_2, \ldots, w_n$ then the word $w_1 w_2 \ldots w_n \, \omega$ will be regarded as the result of applying the operation ω to the given words. The application of any nullary operation of Ω will be understood as taking the symbol of this nullary operation, which belongs, as we know, to the set of words.

We denote this *word-algebra* by $S(\Omega, X)$. It is obvious that in it no non-trivial identical relations are satisfied, i.e. relations of the form

$$w_1 = w_2, \tag{1}$$

where w_1 and w_2 are different words. It is also obvious that the set X is a system of generators for this algebra (see III.1.4). If, however, we are given a subset $X' \subset X$, then it generates a subalgebra in $S(\Omega, X)$, which is a word-algebra $S(\Omega, X')$.

2. Now we will consider an arbitrary system of identical relations Λ. The words v' and v'' will be called *equivalent* with respect to Λ, if it is possible to pass from one to the other by means of a finite number of transformations of the following form: let the relation (1) be contained in the system Λ; we replace the free elements x_i, $i = 1, 2, ..., k$, occurring in it by certain words, after which the left and right-hand sides of the relation (1) become the words $\overline{w}_1$ and $\overline{w}_2$: if $\overline{w}_1$ (or $\overline{w}_2$) is a subword of the word v', then it is replaced by $\overline{w}_2$ in the word v' (or respectively by $\overline{w}_1$).

This relation will obviously be reflexive, transitive and symmetric, i.e. we have introduced an equivalence relation in the algebra $S(\Omega, X)$. *It will even be a congruence* (see III.1.7), because if we are given the word $w_1 w_2 ... w_n \omega$, obtained from the words $w_1, w_2, ..., w_n$ by the application of the operation ω, and then replace the words w_i, $i = 1, 2, ..., n$, by words equivalent to them, it can be realized by applying a finite number of transformations of the type described above to the given word.

The factor algebra of the algebra $S(\Omega, X)$ with respect to the congruence just constructed (see III.1.7) will be denoted by the symbol $S(\Omega, X, \Lambda)$ and will be called the *free algebra* of the primitive class Λ, and the set X its *system of free generators*. Of course, in fact the system of generators for this algebra is not the set X itself, but the set† of corresponding classes of equivalent words; we will denote it, however, by the same letter X. Every algebra isomorphic to the algebra $S(\Omega, X, \Lambda)$ will also be called free, and the set of images of the elements of X under this isomorphism will be called its system of free generators.

From the definition of a free algebra $S(\Omega, X, \Lambda)$ it follows that all the identical relations of Λ are satisfied in it, i.e. *it belongs to the primitive class* Λ.

3. *Let us choose a system of generators M in the universal algebra G of the primitive class Λ. The algebra G will be a free algebra in the primitive class Λ, and M its system of free generators, if and only if the following condition is satisfied: for any algebra H of the class Λ and any single-valued mapping φ of the set M into*

---

† This set is in one-one correspondence with X, provided the algebra has more than one element, i.e. provided the class Λ is not absolutely degenerate (cf. III. 7.5) (Ed.).

*the algebra H there exists a unique homomorphic mapping of G
into H, which coincides with* φ *on the set M.*

First we suppose that $G = S(\Omega, X, \Lambda)$, $M = X$ and that the
mapping φ of the set X into the algebra H has already been given.
The mapping $\overline{\varphi}$ of the whole algebra $S(\Omega, X, \Lambda)$ into the algebra
H we define in the following way: on the set X it coincides with
φ; $\overline{\varphi}$ maps the symbols of the nullary operations into those elements
of H, the taking of which denotes in H the corresponding nullary
operation; finally, if for the words $w_1, w_2, \ldots, w_n$ the images,
under $\overline{\varphi}$ are uniquely defined, and the operation $\omega \in \Omega$ is n-ary
then we set

$$(w_1 w_2 \ldots w_n \omega) \varphi = (w_1 \varphi)(w_2 \overline{\varphi}) \ldots (w_n \overline{\varphi}) \omega ; \qquad (2)$$

it is clear that the image of the word $w_1 w_2 \ldots w_n \omega$ under the
mapping $\overline{\varphi}$ can only be defined by equation (2) if we wish this
mapping to be a homomorphism.

We note that the application of the mapping $\overline{\varphi}$ to a word
equivalent to the word $w_1 w_2 \ldots w_n \omega$ in the sense of III.7.2 gives
an element equal in the algebra H to the right side of equation
(2), because all the identical relations from Λ are satisfied in
H. Thus, the mapping $\overline{\varphi}$ is defined for the elements of the algebra
$S(\Omega, X, \Lambda)$; the fact that it is single-valued and homomorphic
follow from (2).

Now suppose that we are given an algebra G and its system
of free generators M, satisfying the condition of our theorem.
We take as the algebra H the free algebra $S(\Omega, X, \Lambda)$ such that
the sets M and X have the same cardinal number, i.e. there exists
a one–one mapping φ of the set M onto X. By hypothesis, there
exists a homomorphism $\psi: G \rightarrow S(\Omega, X, \Lambda)$, which coincides
with φ on M. On the other hand, from what was said above
it follows that there exists a homomorphism $\chi: S(\Omega, X, \Lambda) \rightarrow G$,
which coincides with φ^{-1} on X.

The product $\chi \psi$ will be an endomorphism of the algebra
$S(\Omega, X, \Lambda)$, the identity on the system of generators X, and the
product $\psi \chi$ will be an endomorphism of the algebra G, the identity on the system of generators M. From the hypothesis of uniqueness, presupposed for G and already proved for $S(\Omega, X, \Lambda)$,
it follows that these endomorphisms will be identity automorphisms of the given algebras. From this it follows that each of
the homomorphisms ψ, χ will in fact be an isomorphism between

the algebras G and $S(\Omega, X, \Lambda)$, which is what we were required to prove.

4. From the theorem which we have proved follows the next result, which explains the true value of the concept of a free algebra:

Every algebra G of a primitive class Λ is the homomorphic image of some free algebra of this class.

In fact, we take any system of generators M in G and we consider a free algebra $S(\Omega, X, \Lambda)$ such that there exists a mapping φ of the set X onto the set M, i.e. the cardinal number of X is greater than or equal to the cardinal number of M. Then, by what we have proved, the mapping φ can be extended to a homomorphism $\varphi \colon S(\Omega, X, \Lambda) \to G$, where this will be a homomorphism onto the whole algebra G, because the image of the algebra $S(\Omega, X, \Lambda)$ under φ contains the whole set M.

5. It is clear that if the sets X and Y have the same cardinal number then the free algebras $S(\Omega, X, \Lambda)$ and $S(\Omega, Y, \Lambda)$ will be isomorphic. On the question of whether it follows, conversely, from the fact that the given free algebras are isomorphic, that the sets of free generators X and Y have the same cardinal number, the answer in the general case will be negative, as is shown by the primitive class mentioned in III.6.3, which consists of one algebra with one element; this class, in which, of course, any identical relations are satisfied, we will agree to call *absolutely degenerate*.

The following theorems of Fujiwara [*Proc. Jap. Acad.* **31**, 135–136 (1955)] are true:

If a primitive class Λ is not absolutely degenerate and if the free algebras $S(\Omega, X, \Lambda)$ and $S(\Omega, Y, \Lambda)$ are isomorphic, where at least one of the sets X, Y is infinite, then these sets have the same cardinal number.

Suppose that this is not true and suppose, for instance, that the cardinal number of the set X is greater than the cardinal number of the set Y†. We may assume that the algebras under consideration are not only isomorphic, but even coincide

$$S(\Omega, X, \Lambda) = S(\Omega, Y, \Lambda) = S. \tag{3}$$

---

† Here we use the assertion, based on the axiom of choice, that any two cardinal numbers can be compared in size.

Every element of Y can thus be written in the form of a word with respect to a finite number of free generators from X. By fixing one such representation for each $y \in Y$ and collecting all the elements of X which are used in these representations for all $y \in Y$, we obtain a subset $X' \subset X$, which is known to have a smaller cardinal number than X; it is finite if the set Y is finite, and has cardinal number not exceeding the cardinal number of Y, if Y is infinite. Hence we can choose an element $x_0 \in X \setminus X'$.

The element x_0 can be written in the form of a word in a finite number of elements of Y. By writing in turn these elements in terms of elements of X', we have that x_0 is equal in the algebra S to some word w_1 of elements of X',

$$x_0 = w_0.$$

This equation means that the words x_0 and w_0 are equivalent in the algebra of words (see III.7.2), i.e. it is obtained by the application of identical relations from Λ. But then, taking into account that the free element x_0 does not occur in the word w_0, with the help of the same identical relations we could obtain in the algebra S the equation $a = w_0$, where a is an arbitrary element of S. Thus, in S all the elements are equal to each other, i.e. from the identical relations of Λ follows the identical relation $x = y$, and therefore the primitive class Λ turns out to be absolutely degenerate, contrary to the hypothesis. Thus the theorem is proved.

6. *Let the system of identical relations Λ be such that it can be extended to a system Λ^* such that the primitive class Λ^* is not absolutely degenerate, but finite sets of free generators generate finite free algebras in it. Then in the class Λ isomorphic free algebras have systems of free generators with the same cardinal number.*

In fact, suppose that we are given in the class Λ the isomorphic free algebras with systems of free generators X and Y. As above, we can assume that these algebras coincide, i.e. equations (3) hold. Moreover, by virtue of the preceding theorem both the sets X, Y can be taken to be finite.

We suppose that X contains more elements than Y. We impose the identical relations from the system $\Lambda^* \setminus \Lambda$ on the algebra S, i.e. we go over to the factor algebra S^* with respect to the corresponding congruence. This will obviously be a free algebra in the primitive class Λ^*, and by the hypotheses of the theorem it will be finite, because it has as its system of free generators the finite sets X and Y.

Suppose that the subset $X' \subset X$ contains as many elements as Y. Then the subalgebra $\{X'\}$ of the algebra S^* which is a free algebra $S(\Omega, X', \Lambda^*)$ must in fact consist of as many elements as S^*, i.e. it coincides with the whole of the algebra S^*. From this it follows that every element $x_0 \in X \setminus X'$ can be written in the form of a word in elements from X', which, however, as in the proof of the preceding theorem, reduces to a contradiction.

7. The class of groupoids is a primitive class with respect to one binary operation and the empty set of identical relations; as usual, we will call this operation multiplication and write it in the form ab. A *free groupoid* with the set X of free generators coincides with the groupoid of words. A *word* in this case will be any finite ordered system of elements of X,

$$x_1 x_2 \ldots x_n, \quad n \geqslant 1,$$

with any repetitions, where in this system there is given a *distribution of brackets*: each of the symbols $x_i, i = 1, 2, \ldots, n$, is regarded as being taken in brackets, and then the brackets are arranged so that each time only two brackets are "multiplied together". The *product* of two words means that the given words are taken in brackets and written one after the other.

Of course, when writing words in groupoids, we can write, for instance,

$$((x_1 x_2) x_1)(x_3 x_2),$$

and not

$$((((x_1)(x_2))(x_1))((x_3)(x_2))).$$

8. The class of semigroups is a primitive class with the identical relation of associativity. In this case a *word* with respect to the set X of free generators can be written in the form

$$x_1 x_2 \ldots x_n, \quad n \geqslant 1, \tag{4}$$

without any brackets. The *product* of two words (4) now means that the given words are written one after the other without brackets.

The assertion that we have constructed a *free semigroup* with set X of free generators is justified only after we have shown that different words of the form (4) will be distinct elements in this semigroup. However, the multiplication of words defined in the preceding paragraph obviously turns the set of all words of the form (4) into a semigroup with set of generators X. This semigroup is the homomorphic image of a free semigroup with the set X of free generators, and because in it different words of the form (4) are distinct elements, then this is also true for the free semigroup. By the same token the given homomorphism is, of course, an isomorphism.

The use of powers of elements enables us to write words in semigroups more concisely: instead of the word $x_1x_1x_1x_2x_1x_2x_2$ we can write $x_1^3 x_2 x_1 x_2^2$.

9. Now we consider the primitive class of all groups with the operations of multiplication, taking the inverse element and taking the identity. The identical relations enable us to write every *word* with respect to the set X of free generators either in the form 1—this word, which contains no free element, is called *empty*,—or else in the form

$$w = x_1^{\varepsilon_1}x_2^{\varepsilon_2} \ldots x_n^{\varepsilon_n}, \qquad n \geqslant 1, \qquad (5)$$

where the x_i, $i = 1, 2, \ldots, n$, are elements of X, not necessarily different, $\varepsilon_i = \pm 1$, $i = 1, 2, \ldots, n$, where if $x_i = x_{i+1}$, then $\varepsilon_i = \varepsilon_{i+1}$ also; in other words, there cannot stand in series in (5) the element $x \in X$ and its inverse element x^{-1}. We call the number n the length of the word (5).

Different words of the form (5) *are distinct elements of the free group with set X of free generators and are not equal to the empty word of this group.*

To prove this we construct a group whose elements are the empty word and all possible words of the form (5). We define the multiplication of words in the way corresponding to that in which it would be carried out in a free group. In fact, the empty word must play the part of the identity. If, however, we are given two words of the form (5),

$$w_1 = x_1^{\varepsilon_1}x_2^{\varepsilon_2} \ldots x_n^{\varepsilon_n}, \quad w_2 = y_1^{\eta_1}y_2^{\eta_2} \ldots y_m^{\eta_m},$$

where, obviously, $y_1 \in X$, $i = 1, 2, \ldots, m$, then we write these words one after the other,

$$x_1^{\varepsilon_1}x_2^{\varepsilon_2} \ldots x_n^{\varepsilon_n}y_1^{\eta_1}y_2^{\eta_2} \ldots y_m^{\eta_m}.$$

If here $x_n = y_1$ and $\varepsilon_n = -\eta_1$, then we *cancel* them. After this the elements $x_{n-1}^{\varepsilon_{n-1}}$ and $y_2^{\eta_2}$ become neighbours, and it may again be necessary to cancel. We continue thus up to a position k such that either $x_{n-k} \neq y_{k+1}$ or $x_{n-k} = y_{k+1}$, but $\varepsilon_{n-k} = \eta_{k+1}$ also. Then we set

$$w_1 w_2 = x_1^{\varepsilon_1} x_2^{\varepsilon_2} \dots x_{n-k}^{\varepsilon_{n-k}} y_{k+1}^{\eta_{k+1}} y_{k+2}^{\eta_{k+2}} \dots y_m^{\eta_m}. \tag{6}$$

It is clear that on the right in (6) there stands a word of the form (5), if $n \neq m$ or $n = m$ but $k < n$, in the opposite case the empty word will stand on the right. Hence, we have that the *inverse* of the word (5) will be the word

$$w^{-1} = x_n^{-\varepsilon_n} \dots x_2^{-\varepsilon_2} x_1^{-\varepsilon_1}.$$

The multiplication of words which we have introduced is associative.

We will prove the equation

$$w_1(w_2 w_3) = (w_1 w_2) w_3 \tag{7}$$

by induction on the length of the word w_2, where all the words w_1, w_2, w_3 can be regarded as distinct from the empty word.

First let $w_2 = y^\eta$, where $y \in X$, $\eta = \pm 1$. If the last symbol of the word w_1 and the first symbol of the word w_3 are such that at least one of them is distinct from $y^{-\eta}$, then in at least one of the products $w_1 w_2$, $w_2 w_3$ we need not cancel and therefore equation (7) holds. If, however,

$$w_1 = x_1^{\varepsilon_1} \dots x_{n-1}^{\varepsilon_{n-1}} y^{-\eta}, \qquad w_3 = y^{-\eta} z_2^{\delta_2} \dots z_s^{\delta_s},$$

then

$$x_1^{\varepsilon_1} \dots x_{n-1}^{\varepsilon_{n-1}} y^{-\eta} z_2^{\delta_2} \dots z_s^{\delta_s}$$

will be a word of the form (5), equal both on its left and right-hand sides to equation (7).

Now let $w_2 = w_2' \cdot y_m^{\eta_m}$, where the word w_2' has the form

$$w_2' = y_1^{\eta_1} \dots y_{m-1}^{\eta_{m-1}}.$$

Assuming that equation (7) has been proved for the case when the length of the word w_2 is less than m, we obtain

$$w_1(w_2 w_3) = w_1[(w_2' \cdot y_m^{\eta_m}) w_3] = w_1[w_2'(y_m^{\eta_m} w_3)] =$$
$$(w_1 w_2')(y_m^{\eta_m} w_3) = [(w_1 w_2') y_m^{\eta_m}] w_3 =$$
$$[w_1(w_2' y_m^{\eta_m})] w_3 = (w_1 w_2) w_3.$$

which is what we were required to prove.

We have constructed a group from the words of the form (5) and the empty word, where the set X serves as its system of generators. This group is the homomorphic image of a free group with the set X of free generators. Therefore the given words are also distinct in the free group, which is what we were required to prove. *Hence, the group we have constructed is itself a free group with system of free generators X.*

Words of the form (5) can, obviously, be written more concisely, by using, as in the case of semigroups, the powers of elements, in this case negative powers also.

A free group with one free generator x will obviously be the infinite cyclic group $\{x\}$. If, however, the set of free generators X contains more than one element, then the free group generated by them is non-commutative, because the words xy and yx, $x, y \in X$, will be distinct.

In III.8.12 we will describe the subgroups of a free group.

10. In the primitive class of all Abelian groups written additively, *words* with respect to the set X of free generators will be sums of a finite number of distinct elements of X, taken with integral coefficients, distinct from zero, and also the empty word 0. We define the *addition* of such words as the addition of coefficients for identical elements $x \in X$; if here x does not occur in one of the words, then we take its coefficient to be equal to zero. It can be verified immediately that we obtain an Abelian group which will also be a free Abelian group with the set X of free generators.

11. We will now consider the primitive class of all rings. By reasoning in the same way as in the case of semigroups or groups, we find that the additive group of a *free ring* with set X of free generators is a free Abelian group (see III.7.10) with respect to the set of free generators $\overline{X}$, which in turn is a free multiplicative groupoid with set X of free generators (see III.7.7). Multiplication in a free ring reduces, by the distributive laws, to the multiplication of elements of $\overline{X}$, which is carried out by the rule of multiplication of words in a free groupoid (see III.7.7).

All that has been said remains true for a *free associative ring* with set X of free generators. In this case, however, the set $\overline{X}$ will be a free semigroup with set X of free generators (see III.7.8), and the multiplication of elements from $\overline{X}$ is carried out by the rule for the multiplication of words in a free semigroup.

Finally, a *free associative-commutative ring* with set X of free generators is simply the ring of polynomials in the elements of X with integral coefficients.

We note that far from every primitive class of universal algebras can be obtained by such a single-valued ("canonical") representation of the elements of free algebras of this class, such as were obtained in the cases considered above.†

12. *Free Abelian groups* (*and also free groups, free rings, free associative or associative-commutative rings*) *are isomorphic if and only if their systems of free generators have the same cardinal number.*

In fact, by imposing the identical relation $2x = 0$ on an Abelian group, we obtain the primitive class of those Abelian groups, all of whose non-zero elements have order 2. We take a finite system of free generators X, consisting of the elements $x_1, x_2, \ldots, x_n$. Then a word in the case under consideration will be an expression of the form

$$k_1x_1 + k_2x_2 + \ldots + k_nx_n,$$

where all the k_i, $i = 1, 2, \ldots, n$, are equal to one or to zero. The addition of words reduces to the addition of coefficients for equal elements x_1, carried out modulo 2, i.e. $1+1 = 0$. We find that in the primitive class considered free groups generated by finite systems of free generators are themselves finite.

We arrive at the same primitive class by imposing on the class of groups the identical relations $xy = yx$ and $x^2 = 1$ (it is easy to see, however, that the first of these follows from the second). Essentially the same primitive class is obtained if we impose on the classes of rings mentioned in the formulation of the theorem the identical relations

$$xy = 0, \quad 2x = 0.$$

To prove the theorem it now remains to refer to Fujiwara's second theorem (III.7.6).

13. We consider an arbitrary primitive class of Ω-groups. Every Ω-group G of this class is, by III.7.4, the homomorphic

---

† i.e. in most cases no canonical form for the elements of a free algebra (of a given primitive class) is known (Ed.).

image of some free Ω-group S of this same class, i.e., by III.2.6 and III.1.8, it is isomorphic to the Ω-factor-group of the free Ω-group S with respect to some ideal A. Let the elements s_i, where i varies through the set of indices I, generate the ideal A in S. The corresponding elements in G are equal to zero. The system of equations

$$s_i = 0, \quad i \in I, \tag{8}$$

where s_i is assumed to be written in terms of free generators of the free Ω-group S, completely defines the ideal A in the free Ω-group S, i.e. it defines the Ω-factor-group S/A, and therefore to within isomorphism it defines the desired Ω-group G. The system of equations (8) is called a *system of defining relations* for the Ω-group G.

Thus, every Ω-group, in particular every group and every ring, can be given by a system of defining relations in some system of generators. This method of specification, of course, is by no means unique.

Example. The symmetric group of the degree 3, S_3 (see II.1.8) can be given in the class of groups by two generators a, b and the defining relations

$$a^3 = 1, \quad b^2 = 1, \quad abab = 1. \tag{9}$$

In fact, the permutations

$$a = \begin{pmatrix} 123 \\ 231 \end{pmatrix}, \quad b = \begin{pmatrix} 123 \\ 213 \end{pmatrix}$$

generate the whole group S_3 and satisfy the relations (9). On the other hand, from (9) follows the equation $ba = a^2b$, and therefore every element of the group given by the defining relations (9) can be written in the form $a^k b^l$, where $k = 0, 1, 2, l = 0, 1$, i.e. this group consists of not more than six elements; the order of the group S_3 is, however, equal to six.

§ 8. Free products of groups

1. The characteristic property of free algebras of a given primitive class Λ, which we mentioned in III.7.3, prompts the following definition. If A_i, $i \in I$, is a family of algebras of the class Λ, then we call the algebra G of the class Λ the *free union* of this family if $A_i \subset G$, $i \in I$, and if for any algebra H of the class Λ and any collection of homomorphisms φ_i of the algebras A_i into the algebra H, $i \in I$, there exists a unique homomorphism φ of the algebra G into the algebra H, which coincides with φ_i on the subalgebra A_i, $i \in I$.

If both the algebra G and the algebra G' are free unions of the algebras A_i, $i \in I$, then there exists an isomorphism between G and G', which is an extension of the identity automorphisms of the subalgebras A_i, $i \in I$.

In fact, the given identity automorphisms can be regarded as homomorphisms φ_i of the subalgebras A_i of the algebra G, $i \in I$, into the algebra G', and also as homomorphisms ψ_i of the subalgebras A_i of the algebra G', $i \in I$, into the algebra G. Hence, they induce homomorphisms $\varphi: G \to G'$ and $\psi: G' \to G$. The product $\varphi\psi$ is a unique homomorphism of G into itself, which is defined by the isomorphic embedding of all the A_i in G as subalgebras, i.e. it will be an identity automorphism of the algebra G. Analogously, $\psi\varphi$ is an identity automorphism of the algebra G', and therefore φ and ψ will be isomorphisms inverse to one another.

The free union G of the algebras A_i, $i \in I$, coincides with the subalgebra generated in G by all the A_i, $i \in I$.

In fact, suppose that the subalgebras A_i, $i \in I$, generate a subalgebra G_0 in G (see III.1.4). If we are given the algebra H of the class Λ and the homomorphisms $\varphi_i: A_i \to H$, $i \in I$, then the homomorphism $\varphi: G \to H$ defined by these homomorphisms induces the homomorphism $\varphi_0: G_0 \to H$, which coincides with φ_i on the subalgebra A_i, $i \in I$. This will be the unique homomorphism of G_0 into H with the given property. In fact, one can verify without difficulty that the subalgebra G_0 consists of those and only those elements of the algebra G, which can be expressed in at least one way in terms of elements of the subalgebras A_i, $i \in I$, with the help of operations of the algebra G, applied a finite number of times. The homomorphisms φ_i, $i \in I$, can thus generate only one homomorphism of the algebra G_0.

Thus, the algebra G_0 is itself a free union of the algebras A_i, $i \in I$. Then there exists, as we have proved, an isomorphism φ of the algebra G_0 onto the algebra G, which is an extension of the identity automorphisms of the algebras A_i, $i \in I$. But, by virtue of what we said in the preceding paragraph, these identity automorphisms can only generate the identity automorphism of the algebra G_0, and therefore $G_0 = G$.

2. The group G is called the *free product* of its subgroups A_i, $i \in I$, if these subgroups together generate the whole group G and if every element $g \in G$ distinct from 1 has a unique expansion in a product of the form

$$g = a_1 a_2 \dots a_n, \qquad n \geqslant 1, \tag{1}$$

where $a_k \in A_{i_k}$ and $a_k \neq 1$, $k = 1, 2, \dots, n$, and where elements of the same subgroup A_i cannot be adjacent, i.e.

$$i_k \neq i_{k+1}, \qquad k = 1, 2, \dots, n-1.$$

The product with these properties, standing on the right in (1), will be called the *irreducible expression* for the element g. We call the number n the *length* of this element and we denote it by $\lambda(g)$. We will call the indices i_1 and i_n respectively the *first index* and the *last index* of the element g. In addition we set $\lambda(1) = 0$.

To express a free product we will use the symbol

$$G = \prod_{i \in I}{}^* A_i$$

or, if the number of free factors is finite,

$$G = A_1{}^* A_2{}^* \dots {}^* A_n.$$

Comparison with III.7.9 shows that *a free group is the free product of infinite cyclic groups*.

If the group G is the free product of the subgroups A_i, $i \in I$, then G will be the free union of the groups A_i in the primitive class of groups.

In fact, if for a collection of homomorphisms φ_i of the subgroups A_i into some group H, $i \in I$, there exists a homomorphism φ of the group G into H such that $\varphi = \varphi_i$ on the subgroup A_i, $i \in I$, then, by (1), for all $g \in G$

$$g\varphi = a_1\varphi_{i_1} \cdot a_2\varphi_{i_2} \dots a_n\varphi_{i_n}, \tag{2}$$

i.e. φ is defined uniquely. It is easy to verify, on the other hand, that if (2) is regarded as being the definition of the mapping φ of the group G into the group H, then φ will be a homomorphism.

This theorem admits a converse, which follows immediately from the results of the present and preceding sections, in view of the theorem proved in the next section.

3. We will prove that *for any family of groups A_i, $i \in I$, there exists a free product of this family of groups*, i.e., more precisely, a free product of groups isomorphic to the given groups.

We will call a formal expression

$$a_1 a_2 \ldots a_n, \quad n \geqslant 1, \tag{3}$$

a *word*, where $a_k \in A_{i_k}$, $a_k \neq 1$, $k = 1, 2, \ldots, n$ and $i_k \neq i_{k+1}$, $k = 1, 2, \ldots, n-1$.

We will also introduce the *empty word* (the case $n = 0$). The set of all words we will denote by M, and the symmetric group on this set (see II.1.8) by S.

Every element $a \in A_i$ defines a mapping $\bar{a}$ of the set M into itself in the following way: the empty word goes into the word a of length 1, from which it follows that when $a \neq b$, $a, b \in A_i$, it will be true that $\bar{a} \neq \bar{b}$; on the other hand, for a word of the form (3) we set

$$(a_1 a_2 \ldots a_n)\bar{a} = \begin{cases} a_1 a_2 \ldots a_n a, & \text{if } i_n \neq i; \\ a_1 a_2 \ldots (a_n a), & \text{if } i_n = i \text{ and } a_n a \neq 1; \\ a_1 a_2 \ldots a_{n-1}, & \text{if } i_n = i \text{ and } a_n a = 1. \end{cases}$$

From this it follows, in particular, that the identity of the group A_i corresponds to the identity mapping of the set M onto itself.

It is easy to verify that

$$\overline{ab} = \bar{a}\bar{b}, \quad a, b \in A_i,$$

where the product on the right is understood in the sense of the multiplication of mappings, and therefore the mapping $\overline{a^{-1}}$ is the inverse of the mapping $\bar{a}$. Thus, every mapping $\bar{a}$ will be a permutation in the set M and, hence, the mappings $\bar{a}$, taken for all $a \in A_i$, form a subgroup $\overline{A_i}$ in the group S, isomorphic to the group A_i.

We denote by G the subgroup of the group S generated by all the subgroup $\overline{A_i}$, $i \in I$. The group G will be the free product of the subgroups $\overline{A_i}$, $i \in I$: every element of G distinct from the identity can be written in the form of a product

$$\bar{a}_1 \bar{a}_2 \ldots \bar{a}_n, \tag{4}$$

where $a_1 a_2 \ldots a_n$ is a word, and where this representation is unique, because the permutation (4) carries the empty word precisely into the word $a_1 a_2 \ldots a_n$.

4. We will prove the following theorem on the subgroups of a free product of groups [A. G. Kurosh, *Math. Ann.* **109** 647–660 (1934)]:

If

$$G = \prod_{i \in I}{}^* A_i, \tag{5}$$

then every subgroup U of the group G is the free product of subgroups conjugate in G (see II.7.4) to subgroups of the free factors A_i and some free subgroup.

In order to give a more explicit form of this theorem, we introduce the following concept. The elements x, $y \in G$ are called *equivalent with respect to the double module* (A_i, U) if

$$y = a_i x u, \qquad a_i \in A_i, \qquad u \in U.$$

Because A_i and U are subgroups, we obtain a partition of the group G into non-intersecting classes of the form $A_i x U$, which we will call the *decomposition* (A_i, U); each class $A_i x U$ is called a *double coset*.

We note that if D is a double coset of the decomposition (A_i, U), then D, together with each of its elements x, also contains the whole left coset xU, i.e. it consists of several left cosets with respect to U.

The expanded form of the theorem on subgroups is as follows:

If (5) *holds and $U \subset G$, then in all the double cosets D of each of the decompositions (A_i, U), $i \in I$, we can so choose the individual representative*

$$s = s(i, D),$$

that

$$U = \prod_{i \in I, D \in (A_i, U)}^* (U \cap s^{-1} A_i s) * F, \tag{6}$$

where F is a free subgroup. It is possible to choose the representatives here in such a way that for all $i \in I$ the identity will be the representative of its own class $A_i U$, i.e. all the intersections $U \cap A_i$, $i \in I$, distinct from E, are contained as the free factors in the decomposition (6).

5. The proof of this theorem, given below, is due to MacLane [*Mathematika* **5** 13–19 (1958)].

LEMMA 1. *There exist choices, depending on $i \in I$, of systems of representatives $r_i(C)$ in all the left cosets C with respect to the subgroup U, such that the following requirements are satisfied*:

(1) $r_i(U) = 1$;

(2) *if $a_i \in A_i$, then $r_i(a_i C) = a_i' r_i(C)$, where $a_i' \in A_i$;*

(3) *if $r_i(C) = a_i s$, where $a_i \in A_i$ (here a_i may be equal to the identity), and $s \neq 1$ and the first index j of the element s is distinct from i, then*

$$r_i(sU) = r_j(sU) = s.$$

We will make a choice of representative $r_i(C)$ by induction with respect to the minimal length $\lambda(A_i C)$ of the elements of the double coset $A_i C$ of the decomposition with respect to (A_i, U), of which C is a part. Further we will assume that the following requirement is also satisfied

(4) $\lambda(r_i(C)) \leqslant 1 + \lambda(A_i C)$.

If $\lambda(A_i C) = 0$, i.e. $A_i C = A_i \cdot 1 \cdot U = A_i U$, then elements of A_i are contained in C and as $r_i(C)$ we choose any of these elements, taking $r_i(U) = 1$. The requirements (1), (2) and (4) can be verified without difficulty, and in the case under consideration requirement (3) is vacuous.

Now let the double coset D of the decomposition (A_i, U) be such that $\lambda(D) = n \geqslant 1$. If $g \in D$ and $\lambda(g) = n$, then $D = A_i g U$, and the first index j of the element g is distinct from i, because otherwise there would occur in the class D an element whose length was less than n. Because $\lambda(A_j g U) < n$, then, by the inductive hypothesis, the representative $r_j(gU) = s$ is already chosen, and, by (4), $\lambda(s) \leqslant n$. Because $D = A_i s U$, then $n = \lambda(D) \leqslant \lambda(s)$ and, hence, $\lambda(s) = n$, and therefore the first index k of the element s is distinct from i, where, by the inductive hypothesis (condition (3)), $r_k(sU) = s$.

Now we choose representatives $r_i(C)$ for all C which occur in D. In fact, if $C = sU$, then we set $r_i(C) = s$; for every other $C \subseteq D$ we choose as $r_i(C)$ one of the elements $a_i s$, $a_i \in A_i$, contained in C. It is clear that the requirements (2), (3) and (4) are satisfied, and requirement (1) asserts nothing about the case $n \geqslant 1$.

The lemma has thus been proved. At the same time we have found that in each double coset $D \in (A_i, U)$, amongst the representatives $r_i(C)$ for all the left cosets C occurring in D there is precisely one representative s which is either equal to 1, or else its first index is distinct from i. In fact, this representative is chosen as $s(i, D)$. Once again we note that for every coset C occurring in D, the representative $r_i(C)$ differs from $s(i, D)$ by a left factor belonging to A_i.

6. LEMMA 2. *The subgroup U is generated by all the elements $r_i^{-1}(C) r_j(C)$, where $i, j \in I$, and C varies through the left cosets with respect to U, and by all the intersections $U \cap (s^{-1} A_i s)$, where $s = s(i, D)$, $D \in (A_i, U)$, $i \in I$.*

We note first that the representatives $r_i(C)$ and $r_j(C)$ both belong to C, i.e. they differ from one another by a right factor from U, and therefore $r_i^{-1}(C) r_j(C) \in U$.

Now we take an arbitrary element $g \in G$, an arbitrary representation of it (not necessarily irreducible) of the form

$$g = a_1 a_2 \dots a_n, \ a_k \in A_{i_k}, \quad k = 1, 2, \dots, n, \tag{7}$$

and any left coset C with respect to U. Then it is easy, by working from the lower indices to the higher, to verify that the following equation is valid, which has on its right-hand side the product of the elements in the square brackets:

$$r_{i_1}^{-1}(gG) \cdot g \cdot r_{i_n}(C) = r_{i_1}^{-1}(gC) \cdot a_1 a_2 \dots a_n \cdot r_{i_n}(C) =$$
$$[r_{i_1}^{-1}(gC) \cdot a_1 \cdot r_{i_1}(a_2 \dots a_n C)] \times$$
$$\cdot \quad \cdot \quad \cdot \quad \cdot \quad \cdot \quad \cdot \quad \cdot \quad \cdot \quad \cdot \quad \cdot$$
$$\times [r_{i_{n-2}}^{-1}(a_{n-1} a_n C) \cdot r_{i_{n-1}}(a_{n-1} a_n C)] \times$$
$$[r_{i_{n-1}}^{-1}(a_{n-1} a_n C) \cdot a_{n-1} \cdot r_{i_{n-1}}(a_n C)] \times$$
$$[r_{i_{n-1}}^{-1}(a_n C) \cdot r_{i_n}(a_n C)] \cdot [r_{i_n}^{-1}(a_n C) \cdot a_n \cdot r_{i_n}(C)].$$

In each row the first factor has the form

$$r_i^{-1}(C') r_j(C').$$

We consider any of the other factors

$$x = r_{i_k}^{-1}(a_k a_{k+1} \dots a_n C) \cdot a_k \cdot r_{i_k}(a_{k+1} \dots a_n C),$$
$$k = 1, 2, \dots, n,$$

and we show that it is contained in the intersection $U \cap s^{-1} A_{ik} s$, where $s = s(i_k, D)$, $D \in (A_{i_k}, U)$ and $C' \subseteq D$, where

$$C' = a_{k+1} \dots a_n C.$$

In fact, because

$$r_{i_k}(a_k C') = a_{i_k} s, \qquad r_{i_k}(C') = a'_{i_k} s,$$

where $a_{i_k},\ a'_{i_k} \in A_{i_k}$, then

$$x = s^{-1}(a_{i_k}^{-1} a_k a'_{i_k}) s \in s^{-1} A_{i_k} s.$$

On the other hand, if $C = cU$, then

$$r_{i_k}(a_k a_{k+1} \ldots a_n C) = a_k a_{k+1} \ldots a_n cu_1,\ u_1 \in U,$$

$$r_{i_k}(a_{k+1} \ldots a_n C) = a_{k+1} \ldots a_n cu_2, u_2 \in U,$$

and therefore $x = u_1^{-1} u_2 \in U$.

Now we note that if $C = U$ and $g \in U$, then

$$r_{i_1}(gC) = r_{i_n}(C) = 1,$$

and therefore the fundamental equation obtained above reduces to an expression for g, which proves our lemma.

7. Now let us introduce the symbols $[C, i, j]$ for any $i, j \in I$ and any left cosets C with respect to U. We denote by F the group which has the set of all these symbols as its system of generators and is given in these generators by the system of defining relations (see III.7.13), consisting of all equations of the following types:

(a) $[C, i, j][C, j, k] = [C, i, k]$,
(b) $[U, i, j] = 1$,
(c) $[sU, i, j] = 1$, if $s = s(i, D)$, and j is the first index of the element s.

LEMMA 3. *The group F is a free group.*

In fact, from (a) and (b) follows the equation

$$[C, i, j] = [C, i, k] \cdot [C, j, k]^{-1},$$

and therefore in the system of generators we need only take symbols $[C, i, k]$ with fixed second index k. The defining relations in these generators are the equations of the following types:

(a') $[C, k, k] = 1$,
(b') $[U, i, k] = 1$,
(c') $[sU, i, k] = [sU, j, k]$, where $s = s(i, D)$ and j is the first index of the element s.

Finally, by rejecting all the generators equal to 1, and leaving only one representative in each class of equal generators, we obtain a system of generators for F which are not connected by any non-trivial relations, i.e. a system of free generators.

8. With every subgroup $U \cap s^{-1}A_i s$, where $s = s(i, D)$, $D \in (A_i, U)$, $i \in I$, we associate the group $B_{i,d}$ isomorphic to it, and we fix a definite isomorphism $\sigma_{i,d}: B_{i,d} \to (U \cap s^{-1}A_i s)$. On the other hand, with every element $[C, i, j]$ of the group F we associate the element $r_i^{-1}(C)r_j(C)$ of the subgroup U. Because, if we interchange these elements, the equations (a), (b) and (c) are not violated (see (1) and (3) of Lemma 1), then these define a homomorphism σ_F of the group F into the group U.

Now, as in III.8.3, we take the group

$$B = \prod_{i \in I, \, D \in (A_i, U)}^{*} B_{i, D} * F. \tag{8}$$

The collection of all the homomorphisms $\sigma_{i, D}$ and σ_F induces, by III.8.2, a uniquely defined homomorphism σ of the group B into the group U, which is in fact, by Lemma 2, onto U.

9. Now we consider the fundamental formula of III.8.6, which gives an expression for the element $r_{i_1}^{-1}(gC) \cdot g \cdot r_{i_n}(C)$. If we replace every factor on the right-hand side of this formula which has the form $r_i^{-1}(C)r_j(C)$ by the corresponding element $[C, i, j]$ from F, and every factor from the subgroup of the form $U \cap s^{-1} A_i s$ by the element of $B_{i, D}$ which corresponds to it under the isomorphism $\sigma_{i, D}$, then we obtain a well defined element of the group B, which we denote by $m(g, C)$.

LEMMA 4. *The element $m(g, C)$ does not depend on the choice of representation* (7) *for the element g and has the following properties*:

$$m(gh, C) = m(g, hC) \cdot [hC, i, j] \cdot m(h, C), \tag{9}$$

where i is the last index of the element g, and j is the first index of the element h;

$$m(1, C) = 1, \tag{10}$$

$$m(g^{-1}, C) = m^{-1}(g, g^{-1} C). \tag{11}$$

All these assertions follow without difficulty from the definition of the element $m(g, C)$. One need only take into account that the element g has a unique irreducible representation with repect to the free decomposition (5) and that from one representation of the form (7) for the element g one can go over to any other such representation by a finite number of the following transformations and the transformations inverse to them: if $i_k = i_{k+1}$ and $a_k a_{k+1} = a' \in A_{i_k}$, then in (7) the segment $a_k a_{k+1}$ is replaced by the element a' when $a' \neq 1$ and is rejected when $a' = 1$.

The equation (9) when $C = U$ and g, $h \in U$ shows, in view of (6) from III.8.7, that *the mapping* τ, *which relates to every element* $g \in U$ *the element* $m(g, U) \in B$, *will be a homomorphism of* U *into* B.

LEMMA 5. *The product* $\tau\sigma$ *is the identity mapping of the group* U *onto itself.*

In fact, from the definition of the homomorphism σ and of the element $m(g, C)$ it follows that

$$m(g, C)\sigma = r_{i_1}^{-1}(gC) \cdot g \cdot r_{i_n}(C), \tag{12}$$

and therefore for $g \in U$, in view of (1) from Lemma 1,

$$g(\tau\sigma) = m(g \cdot U)\sigma = g.$$

10. LEMMA 6. *If* $r = r_i(C)$, *then* $m(r, U) = 1$.

We carry out the proof by induction with respect to $\lambda(r)$; for $r = 1$ the assertion of the lemma follows from (10). Let $r = ag$, where $a \in A_i$, $\lambda(g) = \lambda(r) - 1$ and therefore either $g = 1$ or else the first index k of the element g is distinct from j. If $j \neq i$, then by (3) from Lemma 1, $r_j(C) = r$, and therefore, again by (3) from Lemma 1, it will be true that $r_j(gU) = g$. Hence, by the inductive hypothesis,

$$m(g, U) = 1. \tag{13}$$

Let $g \neq 1$. Then, by (9),

$$m(r, U) = m(ag, U) = m(a, gU) \cdot [gU, j, k] \cdot m(g, U).$$

However, it follows from $j \neq k$ (see the last paragraph in III.8.5) that $g = s(j, D)$, where $D = A_j gU$, and therefore, by (c) from III.8.7,

$$[gU, j, k] = 1.$$

Hence it also follows from (13) that

$$m(r, U) = m(a, gU).$$

This equation is obviously also valid when $g = 1$. Because, finally, $a \in A_j$, then, by the definition of the element $m(g, C)$,

$$m(r, U) = m(a, gU) = [r_j^{-1}(rU) \cdot a \cdot r_j(gU)]\sigma_{j,D}^{-1} =$$
$$(r^{-1}ag)\sigma_{j,D}^{-1} = 1.$$

11. LEMMA 7. *The product $\sigma\tau$ is the identity mapping of the group B onto itself.*

It is sufficient, in view of (8), to find the images under $\sigma\tau$ for the elements of the form $[C, i, j]$ and for the elements of the subgroups $B_{i,D}$.

If $b = [C, i, j]$, then

$$b(\sigma\tau) = (b\sigma_F)\tau = [r_i^{-1}(C) r_j(C)]\tau.$$

We set $r_i(C) = r$, $r_j(C) = r_0$ and we denote first indices of these elements respectively by k and k_0. Then, since $r^{-1} r_0 \in U$ and because of (9),

$$b(\sigma\tau) = (r^{-1}r_0)\tau = m(r^{-1}r_0, U) =$$
$$m(r^{-1}, r_0 U)[r_0 U, k, k_0] m(r_0, U).$$

But, by Lemma 6 and (11),

$$m(r_0, U) = 1,$$
$$m(r^{-1}, r_0 U) = m^{-1}(r, r^{-1}r_0 U) = m^{-1}(r, U) = 1$$

and therefore, because $r_0 U = C$,

$$b(\sigma\tau) = [C, k, k_0].$$

If $k = i$, $k_0 = j$, then $b(\sigma\tau) = b$. If $k_0 \neq j$, then, because $r_0 = r_j(C)$, $r_0 = s(j, D)$ for the corresponding D. Therefore, by (c) from III.8.7, $[r_0 U, j, k_0] = 1$, and then, by (a) from III.8.7,

$$b(\sigma\tau) = [C, k, k_0] = [C, k, j][C, j, k_0] = [C, k, j].$$

If, finally, $k \neq i$ also, then similar reasoning enables us to replace k by i, i.e. again $b(\sigma\tau) = b$.

Now let $b \in B_{i,D}$. Then

$$b\sigma = b\sigma_{i,D} = s^{-1}as, \qquad (14)$$

where $a \in A_i$, $s = s(i, D)$. At the same time $b\sigma \in U$, and therefore

$$asU = sU. \qquad (15)$$

Hence, because of (9), if we denote by j the first index of the elements $s, j \neq i$,

$$b(\sigma\tau) = (s^{-1}as)\tau = m(s^{-1}as, U) =$$

$$m(s^{-1}, asU) \cdot [asU, j, i] \cdot m(a, sU) \cdot [sU, i, j] \cdot m(s, U).$$

But, by Lemma 6 and (11)

$$m(s, U) = 1,$$

$$m(s^{-1}, asU) = m^{-1}(s, s^{-1}asU) = m^{-1}(s, U) = 1.$$

On the other hand, by (c), (a) and (a') from III.8.7 and (15),

$$[sU, i, j] = 1,$$

$$[asU, j, i] = [sU, j, i] = [sU, j, i]^{-1} = 1.$$

We obtain, because of (14) and (15), that

$$b(\sigma\tau) = m(a, sU) = [r_i^{-1}(asU) \cdot a \cdot r_i(sU)]\sigma_{i,D}^{-1} = (s^{-1}as)\sigma_{i,D}^{-1} = b,$$

which is what we were required to prove.

12. From Lemmas 5 and 7 it follows that each of the mappings σ and τ is an isomorphism between U and B. Because of (8), these, the definition of σ and Lemma 3 prove the basic assertion of the subgroup theorem. Its second assertion is proved by the choice of the representative $s(i, D)$ in III.8.5.

Because every subgroup, conjugate in some group to a subgroup of an infinite cyclic group, is itself an infinite cyclic group, and the free product of free groups will itself be a free group, then from the theorem we have proved follows

THE NIELSEN-SCHREIER THEOREM. *Every subgroup of a free group distinct from the identity subgroup is itself free.*

13. We note the following obvious property of free products: *If*

$$G = \prod_{i \in J}^{*} A_i \tag{16}$$

and

$$A_i = \prod_{j \in J_i}^{*} A_{ij}, \quad i \in I,$$

then

$$G = \prod_{i \in I, j \in J_i}^{*} A_{ij}. \tag{17}$$

The free decomposition (17) is called a *refinement* of the decomposition (16).

Two free decompositions of the group G,

$$G = \prod_{i \in I,}^* A_i * F_1 = \prod_{j \in J}^* B_j \,\bar{*}\, F_2,$$

are called *isomorphic*, if F_1 and F_2 are isomorphic free groups, and if we can establish between the free factors A_i and B_j a one–one correspondence such that corresponding factors are conjugate in the group G.

The following theorem is true [A. G. Kurosh, *Math. Ann.* **109**, 647–660 (1934); Baer and Levi, *Comp. Math.* **3**, 391–398 (1936)]:

Any two free decompositions of an arbitrary group have isomorphic refinements.

In fact, if

$$G = \prod_{i \in I}^* A_i = \prod_{j \in J}^* B_j, \tag{18}$$

then, by applying the subgroup theorem, we obtain

$$B_j = \prod_{i \in I, D \in (A_i, B_j)}^* (B_j \cap s^{-1}A_i s) * F_j, \quad s = s(i, D), \quad j \in J;$$

$$A_i = \prod_{j \in J, D' \in (B_j, A_i)}^* (A_i \cap t^{-1}B_j t) * F_i', \quad t = s(j, D'), \quad i \in I.$$

These determine *refinements* of the free decompositions (18), and we wish to prove that they are isomorphic.

We fix a pair of indices $i \in I$, $j \in J$ and we note that if $D \in (A_i, B_j)$, then the totality D^{-1} of elements inverse to all the elements of D will be a double coset of the expansion (B_j, A_i), and in this way we establish a one–one correspondence between the classes of the two given expansions. We will prove that the subgroups $B_j \cap s^{-1}A_i s$ and $A_i \cap t^{-1}B_j\, t$ are conjugate in G, where $s = s(i, D)$, $t = s(i, D^{-1})$. Because

$$D^{-1} = B_j t A_i = (A_i s B_j)^{-1} = B_j s^{-1} A_i,$$

then

$$t = b_j s^{-1} a_i, \quad b_j \in B_j, \quad a_i \in A_i.$$

Therefore

$$A_i \cap t^{-1}B_j\, t = A_i \cap a_i^{-1} s b_j^{-1} B_j b_j s^{-1} a_i =$$
$$A_i \cap a_i^{-1} s B_j s^{-1} a_i = a_i^{-1} s (s^{-1}A_i s \cap B_j) s^{-1} a_i.$$

To complete the proof it remains to note that the normal subgroup generated in a group by some system of subgroups is not altered if each of its subgroups is replaced by a subgroup conjugate to it, and then to make use of the following property of a free product:

If $G = A*B$ and A generates a normal subgroup $\overline{A}$ in G, then B is isomorphic to the factor group $G/\overline{A}$.

In fact, the normal subgroup $\overline{A}$ consists of those elements of G, and only those elements, for which the product of the elements of B which occur in their irreducible representations (preserving their relative order) is equal to 1. From this it follows that every coset of G with respect to $\overline{A}$ contains precisely one element of B.

CHAPTER FOUR

LATTICES

§ 1. Lattices, complete lattices

1. The parallelism between the theory of groups and the theory of rings causes us to introduce into algebra, together with the concept of an Ω-group, several other concepts also. One of these, the concept of a lattice, is prompted by the fact that both the set of all subgroups or all normal subgroups of a group, and the set of all subrings or all ideals (two-sided, left or right) of a ring are partially ordered by set-theoretical inclusion, and this partial ordering has certain additional properties.

A partially ordered set S is called a *lattice*† if it satisfies the following two conditions:

I_1. For every pair of elements a, $b \in S$ there exists an element $c = a \cap b$ in S, the *intersection* of the elements a and b, such that

$$c \leqslant a, \quad c \leqslant b,$$

where if some element c' also has the property $c' \leqslant a$, $c' \leqslant b$, then $c' \leqslant c$.

I_2. For every pair of elements a, $b \in S$ there exists an element $d = a \cup b$, in S the *union* of the elements a and b, such that

$$d \geqslant a, \quad d \geqslant b,$$

where if some element d' also has the property $d' \geqslant a$, $d' \geqslant b$, then $d' \geqslant d$.

It is clear that both the intersection $a \cap b$ and the union $a \cup b$ of the elements a and b are defined uniquely. It is also clear that a partially ordered set inverse isomorphic to a lattice

---

† also called a *structure*; in fact Kurosh (and other Russian writers) use this term, but it seemed preferable to replace it by the more usual term 'lattice' (Ed.).

161

(see I.4.6) will itself be a lattice, where the concepts of intersection and union are dual to each other (see I.5.5).

We see that we can speak of the *lattice of subgroups* and the *lattice of normal subgroups* of some group G, and also of the *lattice of subrings, the lattice of ideals, the lattice of left* (*right*) *ideals* of some ring R. In all these cases the intersection of the subgroups (or subrings) A and B is their set-theoretical intersection $A \cap B$, and the part of the union is played by the subgroup (subring) $\{A, B\}$ generated by these subgroups (subrings). In general, we can speak of the *lattice of subalgebras* of a given universal algebra, and also of the *lattice of Ω-subgroups* and of the *lattice of ideals* of a given Ω-group.

We will mention some other examples of lattices. Thus, all the subsets of a set M form a lattice with respect to set-theoretical inclusion, where the intersection and union have the set-theoretical meaning; this *lattice of subsets* $\tilde{M}$ will be used in what follows.

Every linearly ordered set L is a lattice, where if a, $b \in L$ and $a \leqslant b$, then
$$a \cap b = a, \quad a \cup b = b.$$

The set of all natural numbers will be a lattice, if as the relation of order we take the relation of divisibility. The part of the intersection is played here by the greatest common divisor, and the union will be the least common multiple.

2. Lattices can be regarded as special cases of universal algebras. In fact, the concept of a lattice can be defined without the use of partial ordering, merely by means of the properties of the binary operations of intersection and union:

The set S with two binary operations $a \cap b$ and $a \cup b$ will be a lattice if and only if these operations satisfy the following identical relations:

II_1. $a \cap a = a$, $a \cup a = a$;
II_2. $a \cap b = b \cap a$, $a \cup b = b \cup a$;
II_3. $(a \cap b) \cap c = a \cap (b \cap c)$, $(a \cup b) \cup c = a \cup (b \cup c)$;
II_4. $a \cap (a \cup b) = a$, $a \cup (a \cap b) = a$.

We suppose first that we are given a lattice S, i.e. that the operations $a \cap b$ and $a \cup b$ are defined by the conditions I_1 and I_2. Then it is obvious that the properties II_1 and II_2 are satisfied. We will verify the property II_3, for instance for intersection.

Because, by I_1,

$$(a \cap b) \cap c \leqslant a \cap b \leqslant a,$$
$$(a \cap b) \cap c \leqslant a \cap b \leqslant b,$$
$$(a \cap b) \cap c \leqslant c,$$

then, again by I_1,

$$(a \cap b) \cap c \leqslant b \cap c,$$

$$(a \cap b) \cap c \leqslant a \cap (b \cap c).$$

Analogously,

$$a \cap (b \cap c) \leqslant (a \cap b) \cap c,$$

and therefore II_3 holds.

In addition, it is clear, by I_1, that

$$a \cap (a \cup b) \leqslant a;$$

however, $a \leqslant a$ and, by I_2, $a \leqslant a \cup b$, and therefore, by I_1,

$$a \leqslant a \cap (a \cup b).$$

From this it follows that II_4 is true.

Now suppose that we are given a set S with two binary operations which have the properties II_1–II_4. If a, $b \in S$, then the equations

$$a \cap b = a, \quad a \cup b = b \tag{1}$$

are either both satisfied or neither is satisfied.

In fact, if $a \cap b = a$, then, by II_4 and II_2,

$$a \cup b = (a \cap b) \cup b = b;$$

if, however, $a \cup b = b$, then, by II_4,

$$a \cap b = a \cap (a \cup b) = a.$$

If the equations (1) hold for the elements a and b, then we set $a \leqslant b$. This introduces a partial ordering into the set S. In fact, $a \leqslant a$ because of II_1. Further, if $a \leqslant b$ and $b \leqslant c$, i.e. $a \cap b = a$, $b \cap c = b$, then, by virtue of II_3,

$$a \cap c = (a \cap b) \cap c = a \cap (b \cap c) = a \cap b = a,$$

i.e. $a \leqslant c$. Finally, if $a \leqslant b$ and $b \leqslant a$, i.e. $a \cap b = a$, $b \cap a = b$, then, by II_2, $a = b$.

We will show that condition I_1 is satisfied. From $(a \cap b) \cap a = a \cap (a \cap b) = (a \cap a) \cap b = a \cap b$ it follows that $a \cap b \leqslant a$.

Analogously, $a \cap b \leqslant b$. If, however, we take an arbitrary element c' in S, satisfying the conditions $c' \leqslant a$, $c' \leqslant b$, i.e. $c' \cap a = c'$, $c' \cap b = c'$, then

$$c' \cap (a \cap b) = (c' \cap a) \cap b = c' \cap b = c',$$

whence $c' \leqslant a \cap b$. The element $a \cap b$ is thus the intersection of the elements a and b in the sense of condition I_1. Analogously, we can prove that the element $a \cup b$ will be the union of the elements a and b in the sense of condition I_2.

3. The second definition which we have obtained of the concept of a lattice shows that *lattices form a primitive class of universal algebras with two binary operations* (see III.6.3). This definition must be regarded as the fundamental one, as follows from the definitions introduced below of sublattices and the isomorphic embedding of lattices.

In fact, a subset T of the lattice S is called a *sublattice* of this lattice if it is a subalgebra of the lattice S, regarded as a universal algebra in the sense of the definition in IV.1.2. In other words, T contains, together with all its elements a and b, their intersection $a \cap b$ and their union $a \cup b$, understood in the sense of the operations in the lattice S, i.e. T itself is a lattice with respect to the operations defined in S.

It is necessary to take into account that a subset T of a lattice S may be a lattice with respect to the partial ordering which is induced in T by the partial ordering given in S, and yet not be a sublattice in the sense of the definition given above. Thus, although in the lattice of subgroups of the group G the ordering is set-theoretical, yet this lattice need not be a sublattice in the lattice of all subsets of the set G, because the unions in these two lattices have different meanings. Analogously the lattice of subrings of the ring R will not be a sublattice of the lattice of subgroups of the additive group of this ring.

The lattice of normal subgroups of the group G is a sublattice of the lattice of all subgroups of this group, as was proved in II.7.5. In general, from what was said in III.2.4 it follows that *the lattice of ideals of the Ω-group G will be a sublattice both in the lattice of all Ω-subgroups of this Ω-group, and in the lattice of subgroups of its additive group*.

4. A one–one mapping φ of the lattice S into the lattice S' is called an *isomorphic mapping* or an *isomorphic embedding* of S into S' if for any $a, b \in S$

$$(a \cap b)\varphi = a\varphi \cap b\varphi, \qquad (a \cup b)\varphi = a\varphi \cup b\varphi.$$

In other words, this will be an isomorphism of lattices, regarded as universal algebras (see III.1.5).

An isomorphic embedding φ of the lattice S in the lattice S' is an isomorphic embedding of S in S' in the sense of the isomorphism of partially ordered sets (see I.4.4). In fact, let $a, b \in S$. If $a \leqslant b$, i.e. $a \cap b = a$, then

$$(a \cap b)\varphi = a\varphi \cap b\varphi = a\varphi,$$

whence $a\varphi \leqslant b\varphi$. By carrying out this reasoning in the reverse order and using the fact that the mapping φ is one–one, we find that from $a\varphi \leqslant b\varphi$ it follows that $a \leqslant b$.

The examples given above show that the converse does not hold: if we are given the partially ordered sets S and S' and if φ is an isomorphic mapping of S into S', then in the case when S and S' are lattices, φ need not be an isomorphic mapping of the lattice S into the lattice S'. The position will, however, be different, if we are considering isomorphic mappings of S *onto* S':

If we are given the lattices S and S', then every isomorphic mapping of S onto S', understood in the sense of the partial ordering, will be an isomorphic mapping of the lattice S onto the lattice S'.

In fact, if $a, b \in S$, then from $a \cap b \leqslant a$ it follows that $(a \cap b)\varphi \leqslant a\varphi$; analogously, $(a \cap b)\varphi \leqslant b\varphi$. If, however, the element $c' \in S'$ is such that $c' \leqslant a\varphi$ and $c' \leqslant b\varphi$, and if c is the element of S for which $c\varphi = c'$, then $c \leqslant a$ and $c \leqslant b$, i.e. $c \leqslant a \cap b$, whence $c\varphi \leqslant (a \cap b)\varphi$. This proves that

$$(a \cap b)\varphi = a\varphi \cap b\varphi.$$

We carry out the proof for the union in the same way.

We note that we can also apply to lattices the concept of a homomorphism and in general everything which relates to arbitrary primitive classes of universal algebras; in particular, in connection with III.7.2, there is a meaning for the concept of a free lattice on a given set X of free generators.

5. As follows from I.2.1, the binary relations on the set M form a lattice which coincides with the lattice of all subsets of the set $M \times M$. The equivalence relations on the set M also form a lattice, as was proved in I.3.3. This *lattice of equivalence relations* is not, however, a sublattice of the lattice of binary relations.

* Every lattice can be isomorphically embedded in the lattice of equivalence relations, defined in some set [Whitman, *Bull. Amer. Math. Soc.* **52**, 507–522 (1946)].

The lattice of equivalence relations, defined in an arbitrary given set, can be isomorphically embedded in the lattice of subgroups of some group [Birkhoff, *Proc. Camb. phil. Soc.* **31**, 433–454 (1935)].

Thus every lattice can be isomorphically embedded in the lattice of subgroups of some group.*

6. Many of the lattices mentioned above—the lattice of subsets of a set M, the lattice of subgroups of a group G, the lattice of the subrings of a ring R (and, in general, the lattice of Ω-subgroups of an Ω-group G), the lattice of equivalence relations in a set M—have the property that the intersection and union are defined not only for two and therefore, by associativity, for any finite number of elements, but also for any infinite subsets. In other words, these lattices are complete lattices in the sense of the following definition:

A partially ordered set S is called a *complete lattice* if for any non-empty subset $A \subseteq S$ there exist elements c and d in S with the following properties:

I_1'. For all $a \in A$ the inequality $c \leqslant a$ is satisfied, and if some element c' also satisfies the condition $c' \leqslant a$ for all $a \in A$, then $c' \leqslant c$.

I_2'. For all $a \in A$ the inequality $d \geqslant a$ is satisfied, and if some element d' also satisfies the condition $d' \geqslant a$ for all $a \in A$, then $d' \geqslant d$.

The uniquely defined elements c and d are called respectively the *intersection* and *union* of the elements of the subset A. They will be written in the following way:

$$c = \bigcap_{a \in A} a, \quad d = \bigcup_{a \in A} a$$

or, if the elements of A are denoted by a_α, where the index α varies over some set M,

$$c = \bigcap_{\alpha \in M} a_\alpha, \quad d = \bigcup_{\alpha \in M} a_\alpha.$$

It is clear that a complete lattice is also simply a lattice.

7. The intersection of all the elements of a complete lattice S is called the *zero* of this lattice and will be denoted by the symbol 0. This element is uniquely defined by any of the following three conditions: for all $a \in S$

$$1) \ 0 \leqslant a; \quad 2) \ 0 \cap a = 0; \quad 3) \ 0 \cup a = a.$$

The union of all the elements of a complete lattice is called the *identity element* of this lattice and will be denoted by the symbol 1. This element is uniquely defined by any of the following three conditions: for all $a \in S$

$$1') \ 1 \geqslant a; \quad 2') \ 1 \cup a = 1; \quad 3') \ 1 \cap a = a.$$

A zero and an identity element (or one of them) may obviously also be possessed by lattices which are not complete.

The part of the zero and of the identity element in the lattice of subgroups of a group G are played, respectively, by the identity subgroup and the group G itself, in the lattice of subrings of the ring R by the zero-subring and the ring R itself, in the lattice of subsets of a set M by the empty subset and the set M itself. In the lattice of natural numbers, ordered by divisibility, and also in the chain of natural numbers with their natural ordering, the zero is the number 1, but the identity element does not exist.

8. *A partially ordered set S will be a complete lattice if and only if it has an identity element and if there exist in it the intersections of any non-empty subsets.*

For the proof we only need show that if the identity element and all the intersections exist in S, then the unions also exist. Let A be a non-empty subset of S. In S there exist elements b such that $b \geqslant a$ for all $a \in A$; in every case 1 is such an element. Let B be the non-empty set of all these elements b, and d their intersection,

$$d = \bigcap_{b \in B} b.$$

We will prove that d is the union of the elements of the subset A. In fact, if $a \in A$ then $a \leqslant b$ for all $b \in B$, and therefore $a \leqslant d$. On the other hand, if the element $s \in S$ is such that $s \geqslant a$ for all $a \in A$, then $s \in B$, and therefore $d \leqslant s$. Thus

$$d = \bigcup_{a \in A} a.$$

Because the property that a partially ordered set bis a complete lattice (like the property of being a lattice) is preserved under inverse isomorphism (see I.4.6), in the theorem just proved we could require the existence of the zero and the unions of all non-empty subsets.

* We will call the mapping φ of the partially ordered set M into the partially ordered set N *monotonic* if, for a, $b \in M$, from $a \leqslant b$ it always follows that $a\varphi \leqslant b\varphi$. A lattice S will be a complete lattice if, and only if, for any monotonic mapping φ of the lattice S into itself there exist fixed elements, i.e. elements a such that $a\varphi = a$ [Tarski, *Pacif. J. Math.* **5**, 285–309 (1955); Davis, *Pacif. J. Math.* **5**, 311–319 (1955)].*

9. In I.4.5 we proved that every partially ordered set M can be isomorphically embedded in the complete lattice $\overline{M}$ of all its subsets. Now we wish to prove the following theorem:

Every lattice can be isomorphically embedded (*in the sense of the isomorphism of lattices, see* IV.1.4) *in a complete lattice.*

This theorem follows, however, from this next assertion, which is a stronger form of the theorem in I.4.5:

Every partially ordered set M can be isomorphically embedded in some complete lattice S, and in such a way that for every subset $A \subseteq M$, for which there exist an intersection and a union in M, they are preserved under this embedding φ, i.e.

$$\left(\bigcap_{a \in A} a \right) \varphi = \bigcap_{a \in A} a\varphi, \quad \left(\bigcup_{a \in A} a \right) \varphi = \bigcup_{a \in A} a\varphi. \qquad (2)$$

It is clear that the inclusion of M in $\overline{M}$, constructed in I.4.5, does not satisfy the requirements which we have imposed. We proceed in the following way. We will assume, first of all, that the set M has a zero 0, because otherwise it could be adjoined to M. We will call a non-empty subset $X \subseteq M$ an *ideal* in M if: (1) X contains together with each of its elements x also all elements $y \in M$ such that $y \leqslant x$; (2) for every $X' \subseteq X$ for which there exists a union in M, this union is contained in X.

The set S of all ideals of the set M is partially ordered by set-theoretical inclusion. Because S has an identity element—M will obviously be an ideal in itself—and because the set-theoretical intersection of any set of ideals contains zero and satisfies all the requirements which occur in the definition of an ideal, then the set S will be, by IV.1.8, a complete lattice.

For any element $a \in M$ the set (a) of all elements $b \in M$ such that $b \leqslant a$ will be an ideal; this is the *principal ideal* generated by the element a. By associating with every $a \in M$ the principal ideal (a) generated by it, we obtain, as in I.4.5, an isomorphic embedding φ of the partially ordered set M in the complete lattice S.

Now we suppose that for the subset $A \subseteq M$ in M there exists an intersection

$$c = \bigcap_{a \in A} a.$$

Then $c \leqslant a$ and therefore $(c) \subseteq (a)$ for all $a \in A$. If, however, the set-theoretical intersection of all the principal ideals (a), $a \in A$, contains the element x, then $x \leqslant a$ for all $a \in A$ and therefore $x \leqslant c$. Thus,

$$(c) = \bigcap_{a \in A} (a),$$

which proves the first of the equations (2).

Finally, suppose that for the subset $A \subseteq M$ there exists in M the union

$$d = \bigcup_{a \in A} a.$$

Then $(d) \supseteq (a)$ for all $a \in A$. If, however, some ideal X contains all the elements $a \in A$, then, by the definition of an ideal, it also contains their union d, and therefore $(d) \subseteq X$. Thus,

$$(d) = \bigcup_{a \in A} (a).$$

This also proves the second of the equations (2), i.e. it completes the proof of the theorem.

The reader can verify without difficulty that the construction used in this proof, when applied to the ordered set of rational numbers gives essentially the usual completion of the system of rational numbers by Dedekind sections.

10. *This partially ordered set S will be a complete lattice if and only if S has a zero and if every ideal in S is principal.*

In fact, if S is a complete lattice, then for any ideal X there exists a union a of all its elements, where, by virtue of the definition of an ideal, $a \in X$, and therefore $X = (a)$. Conversely, suppose that in the partially ordered set S there exists a zero and every ideal is principal. In particular, S itself will be a principal ideal, and therefore there exists an identity element in S. If, however, A is a non-empty subset of S, then the totality X of all elements $x \in S$ such that $x \leqslant a$ for all $a \in A$ contains 0 and is an ideal. This ideal must be principal, $X = (b)$, and the element b will be the intersection of the elements of the subset A. In view of IV.1.8, S is a complete lattice.

Thus, the application to a complete lattice of the construction used in the preceding paragraph cannot give anything new.

§ 2. Modular lattices

1. Of the axioms $II_1 — II_4$ which define a lattice (see IV.1.2), only axiom II_4 connects intersection and union. This connection is very weak. Some lattices, for instance the lattice of all subsets of a set, satisfy in addition the distributive condition

$$a \cap (b \cup c) = (a \cap b) \cup (a \cap c) \qquad (1)$$

(see I.1.1). Lattices which satisfy this condition for any a, b and c are called *distributive* and will be studied in § 6 of the present chapter. However, the lattice of normal subgroups of a group and more generally the lattice of all subgroups, as a rule, are not distributive.

The desire to single out as far as possible the narrow class of lattices to which belong the lattices of normal subgroups of arbitrary groups (although not necessarily the lattice of all subgroups) leads us to the following definition:

A lattice S is called *modular* (or a *Dedekind lattice*) if for any a, b, $c \in S$ satisfying the condition $a \geqslant b$ the equation

$$a \cap (b \cup c) = b \cup (a \cap c) \qquad (2)$$

is satisfied.

Every distributive lattice is modular, because from $a \geqslant b$ it follows that $a \cap b = b$ and therefore with the condition $a \geqslant b$, (2) follows from (1).

Every sublattice T of a modular lattice S (see IV.1.3) *is itself modular*, because equation (2) must be satisfied, in particular, for the elements a, b, $c \in T$ which satisfy the condition $a \geqslant b$.

The property of being modular is obviously preserved under the isomorphism of lattices. On the other hand, *a lattice inverse isomorphic to a modular lattice is itself modular*, because, if we replace the symbol $\geqslant$ in the definition of a modular lattice by the symbol $\leqslant$ and interchange the symbols $\cap$ and $\cup$, we arrive at the same definition simply with the letters a and b interchanged.

2. *The lattice of all normal subgroups of an arbitrary group is modular.*

In fact, suppose that in the group G there are given the normal subgroups A, B, and C, where $A \supseteq B$. Taking into account (1) of III.4.1, we need to prove that

$$A \cap BC = B(A \cap C). \tag{3}$$

Because $B \subseteq A$ and $B \subseteq BC$, B is contained in the left-hand side of equation (3). $A \cap C$ is also contained in it, because $C \subseteq BC$. From this follows the inclusion

$$A \cap BC \supseteq B(A \cap C). \tag{4}$$

On the other hand, any element contained in the normal subgroup $A \cap BC$ is an element $a \in A$, which at the same time can be written in the form

$$a = bc, \tag{5}$$

where $b \in B$, $c \in C$. Hence $c = b^{-1} a \in A$, because $B \subseteq A$, i.e.

$$c \in (A \cap C).$$

Therefore, because of (5), every element of the left-hand side of equation (3) is contained in its right-hand side, which, together with the inclusion (4), proves this equation.

The ideals of an arbitrary Ω-group form, by what was said in III.2.4, a sublattice of the lattice of normal subgroups of the additive group of this Ω-group, i.e. they form a modular lattice. From this it follows that *the lattice of all ideals of an arbitrary ring will be modular.*

We note that the lattice of all subgroups of a non-commutative group, as a rule, is not modular.

3. There exist many different definitions of a modular lattice, equivalent to that given above. We will mention some of them.

A lattice S will be modular if, and only if, for any a, b, $c \in S$

$$a \cap [(a \cap b) \cup c] = (a \cap b) \cup (a \cap c). \tag{6}$$

In fact, if the lattice S is modular, then, because $a \geqslant a \cap b$, (6) follows from (2). Conversely, if the condition (6) is satisfied in the lattice S, then for $a \geqslant b$ (2) follows from (6), because in this case $a \cap b = b$.

We see thus that *the modular lattices form a primitive class of universal algebras.*

4. *The lattice S is modular if, and only if, from the fact that the elements a, b, c ∈ S satisfy the conditions*

$$a \leqslant b, \quad a \cap c = b \cap c, \quad a \cup c = b \cup c, \qquad (7)$$

it follows that a = b.

In fact, if the lattice S is modular and the elements a, b, c satisfy the conditions (7), then

$$a = a \cup (a \cap c) = a \cup (b \cap c) = b \cap (a \cup c) = b \cap (b \cup c) = b.$$

Now suppose that the premises of the converse assertion are satisfied and suppose that we are given the elements a, b, c in S, where $a \geqslant b$. It is easy to verify (see the derivation of the inequality (4)) that, whatever the lattice S may be, from $a \geqslant b$ it follows that

$$a \cap (b \cup c) \geqslant b \cup (a \cap c). \qquad (8)$$

At the same time

$$[a \cap (b \cup c)] \cap c = a \cap [(b \cup c) \cap c] = a \cap c, \qquad (9)$$

and because when $a \geqslant b$

$$a \geqslant b \cup (a \cap c),$$

then

$$a \cap c \geqslant [b \cup (a \cap c)] \cap c \geqslant (a \cap c) \cap c = a \cap c,$$

i.e.

$$[b \cup (a \cap c)] \cap c = a \cap c. \qquad (10)$$

From (9) and (10) it follows that when $a \geqslant b$

$$[a \cap (b \cup c)] \cap c = [b \cup (a \cap c)] \cap c. \qquad (11)$$

By going from equation (11) to the dual equation, i.e. by interchanging the symbols $\cap$ and $\cup$, and also by changing the places of the letters a and b, we obtain

$$[a \cap (b \cup c)] \cup c = [b \cup (a \cap c)] \cup c, \qquad (12)$$

where the inequality $a \geqslant b$ is kept, because the symbol $\geqslant$ has also had to be replaced by $\leqslant$. We see that (8), (11) and (12) have the form of the conditions (7), and therefore, by our hypotheses, when $a \geqslant b$, equation (2) holds, which was what we were required to prove.

5. It would be possible to carry over to the theory of modular lattices the properties of invariant and principal series of Ω-groups, which we know from III.4.7. We will not do this completely, but will limit ourselves to the results which are necessary for what follows.

Suppose that we are given a modular lattice S which has a zero and an identity element. An ordered finite system of elements,

$$0 = a_0 < a_1 < a_2 < ... < a_{k-1} < a_k = 1, \qquad (13)$$

is called *a normal series* of this lattice †; the number k is called the *length* of this series. The normal series

$$0 = b_0 < b_1 < b_2 < ... < b_{l-1} < b_l = 1, \qquad (14)$$

is called a *refinement* of the series (13) if every element a_i, $i = 0, 1, ..., k$, is equal to one of the elements b_j, $0 \leqslant j \leqslant l$.

6. *Every two normal series of a modular lattice S have refinements of the same length.*

Suppose, in fact, that we are given in S the arbitrary normal series (13) and (14). To some extent repeating what we did in III.4.5, we set

$$a_{ij} = a_i \cup (a_{i+1} \cap b_j), \quad i = 0, 1, ..., k-1, \ j = 0, 1, ..., l;$$
$$b_{ji} = b_j \cup (b_{j+1} \cap a_i), \quad j = 0, 1, ..., l-1, \ i = 0, 1, ..., k.$$

Because

$$a_{i0} = a_i, \ a_{il} = a_{i+1}$$

and

$$a_{ij} \leqslant a_{i,j+1}, \quad j = 0, 1, ..., l-1,$$

then the elements a_{ij} form a normal series possibly with repetitions, which is a refinement of the series (13). Analogously, the elements b_{ji} form a refinement of the series (14). These two new series have exactly the same length kl, and therefore it remains to show that they have an equal number of repetitions.

In fact, let

$$a_{ij} = a_{i,j+1}. \qquad (15)$$

---

† This is the accepted terminology used here, although it would be more systematic to speak of invariant series.

By using successively the definition of the element $a_{i,j+1}$, equation
(15), the inequality $a_{ij} \leqslant a_{i+1}$, the definition of the element a_{ij}
and, finally, definition (2) of a modular lattice together with
the inequality $a_{i+1} \cap b_j \leqslant b_{j+1}$, we obtain:

$$a_{i+1} \cap b_{j+1} = a_{i,j+1} \cap (a_{i+1} \cap b_{j+1}) = a_{ij} \cap (a_{i+1} \cap b_{j+1}) =$$

$$a_{ij} \cap b_{j+1} = [a_i \cup (a_{i+1} \cap b_j)] \cap b_{j+1} =$$

$$(a_i \cap b_{j+1}) \cup (a_{i+1} \cap b_j).$$

This result together with the definition of the elements b_{ji} and $b_{j,i+1}$
and the obvious inequality $a_{i+1} \cap b_j \leqslant b_j$ reduces to the equations

$$b_{ji} = b_j \cup (b_{j+1} \cap a_i) = b_j \cup (b_{j+1} \cap a_i) \cup (a_{i+1} \cap b_j) =$$

$$b_j \cup (a_{i+1} \cap b_{j+1}) = b_{j,i+1}.$$

We have proved that the repetitions in the refinements of the
normal series (13) and (14) which we have constructed are in
one–one correspondence, i.e. they can be removed simultaneously.
The theorem has thus been proved.

7. We will say that a *principal series* of a modular lattice is
a normal series which cannot be refined without repetitions.
As in III.4.6, from the theorem proved above follow these results:

*If a modular lattice has principal series, then all its principal
series have the same length.*

*If a modular lattice has principal series, then each of its normal
series can be refined to a principal series.*

From this it follows that *every sublattice T of a modular
lattice S, which has principal series, will itself have principal series.*
In fact, if the principal series of the lattice S have length k, then
the lengths of chains in the sublattice T cannot exceed k. If

$$c_0 < c_1 < \dots < c_l, \tag{16}$$

is one of the chains of maximal length contained in T, then c_0
and c_l will be respectively the zero and the identity element of
the lattice T, and (16) will be one of the principal series of this
lattice.

8. The results obtained enable us to give yet another definition of a modular lattice:

*A lattice S is modular if, and only if, in each of its sublattices
which has principal series all the principal series have the same
length.*

In fact, if the lattice S is modular then it is sufficient to refer to IV.2.1 and IV.2.7. If, however, the lattice S is not modular, then from IV.2.4 there follows the existence in S of elements a, b, c such that conditions (7) are satisfied, but $a \neq b$. It is easy to verify that under these conditions the elements $a, b, c, a \cap c$ and $a \cup c$ form a sublattice of the lattice S, and the last two elements are respectively the zero and the identity element of this sublattice. The sublattice constructed has, however, two principal series of different lengths, namely the series

$$a \cap c < a < b < a \cup c,$$

$$a \cap c < c < a \cup c.$$

9. *A modular lattice S has principal series if and only if it satisfies the ascending and descending chain conditions* (see I.5.1 and I.5.5).

In fact, if the modular lattice has principal series of length k, then the length of its normal series cannot exceed k. However, every finite chain of the lattice S, after the addition, if necessary, of the zero and the identity element, reduces to a normal series of this lattice. This proves that there can be no infinite chains in S.

Conversely, suppose that in S the ascending and descending chain conditions are satisfied, and therefore also the conditions equivalent to them (see I.5.1). In view of the minimal condition there exist minimal elements in S, and because the intersection of two minimal elements must coincide with each of them, then in fact there exists only one such element in S; it will be the zero of our lattice. Similarly, there also exists an identity element in S.

If $a \in S$ and $a \neq 1$, then in the non-empty set of elements x such that $x > a$ there exists minimal elements, i.e., as one says, elements which *cover* the element a. By using the axiom of choice, for every a, $a \neq 1$, we can select one of the elements covering it; we denote it by a'. The chain

$$0 = a_0 < a_1 < a_2 < \ldots < a_n < \ldots, \qquad (17)$$

where

$$a_n = a'_{n-1}, \qquad n = 1, 2, \ldots,$$

by hypothesis must break off. Hence, there exists an n such that $a_n = 1$, i.e. the chain (17) will be a principal series of the lattice S.

10. If we take the elements a and b in the arbitrary lattice S, where $a \geqslant b$, then the totality of elements x such that $a \geqslant x \geqslant b$ will be a sublattice in S, which has b as its zero and a as its identity element. We denote this sublattice by a/b.

If we take the arbitrary elements a and b in the modular lattice S, then the sublattices $(a \cup b)/a$ and $b/(a \cap b)$ are isomorphic. In fact, if $x \in b/(a \cap b)$, i.e.

$$a \cap b \leqslant x \leqslant b,$$

then we set

$$x\varphi = x \cup a.$$

It is clear that $a \leqslant x\varphi \leqslant a \cup b$, i.e. $x\varphi \in (a \cup b)/a$.

If there were to exist an element y, $a \cap b \leqslant y \leqslant b$, distinct from x, such that $y\varphi = x\varphi$, then the element $z = x \cup y$ would be known to be distinct from at least one of the elements x, y, for instance from the first, i.e. $z > x$. However,

$$a \cap b \leqslant z \leqslant b,$$

and therefore, because $a \cup a = a$,

$$z \cup a = x \cup y \cup a = (x \cup a) \cup (y \cup a) = x\varphi \cup y\varphi = x\varphi = x \cup a,$$

$$z \cap a = a \cap b = x \cap a,$$

which contradicts the fact that the lattice S is modular, because of IV.2.4.

On the other hand, if $x' \in (a \cup b)/a$, i.e.

$$a \leqslant x' \leqslant a \cup b,$$

then, since the lattice is modular,

$$x' = (a \cup b) \cap x' = a \cup (b \cap x'),$$

and because

$$a \cap b \leqslant b \cap x' \leqslant b,$$

then

$$x' = (b \cap x')\varphi.$$

The mapping φ is a one–one mapping of the sublattice $b/(a \cap b)$ onto the whole sublattice $(a \cup b)/a$. We will prove that this mapping is an isomorphism. If $x, y \in b/(a \cap b)$, then from $x \leqslant y$ it follows that $x \cup a \leqslant y \cup a$, i.e. $x\varphi \leqslant y\varphi$. On the other hand, if $x\varphi \leqslant y\varphi$, i.e. $x \cup a \leqslant y \cup a$, then

$$(x \cup y) \cup a = (x \cup a) \cup (y \cup a) = y \cup a,$$

i.e. $(x \cup y)\varphi = y\varphi$, whence, because the mapping φ is one–one, $x \cup y = y$, i.e. $x \leqslant y$. Now it only remains to apply the last result of IV.1.4.

11. Suppose that the modular lattice S has principal series. Then for any $a \in S$ the sublattice $a/0$ will also have principal series; we denote the length of these series by $l(a)$.

For any elements a and b of the modular lattice S which has principal series, the equation

$$l(a \cup b) = l(a) + l(b) - l(a \cap b) \tag{18}$$

holds.

In fact, we proved above that the sublattices $(a \cup b)/a$ and $b/(a \cap b)$ are isomorphic. Their principal series thus have the same length. However, for the first sublattice this length is equal to the number $l(a \cup b) - l(a)$, and for the second to the number $l(b) - l(a \cap b)$.

§ 3. Direct unions. The Schmidt-Ore theorem

1. In the theory of groups one construction is very useful; it is called the direct product of groups or, in the case of the additive notation for the group operation, their direct sum. In the theory of rings an analogous part is played by the two-sided direct sum of rings. The study of these concepts leads to completely parallel theories, which are in fact special examples of one theory, related to modular lattices. In fact we will make our study in this more general field, and in the following section we will supplement it with remarks relating especially to groups, rings or Ω-groups.

2. Suppose that we are given a modular lattice S, which has a zero. An element $a \in S$ is called the *direct union* of the elements $b_1, b_2, \ldots, b_k \in S$ and will be written in the form

$$a = b_1 \times b_2 \times \ldots \times b_k, \tag{1}$$

f a is the union of these elements

$$a = b_1 \cup b_2 \cup \ldots \cup b_k, \tag{2}$$

and if for $i = 1, 2, \ldots, k$

$$(b_1 \cup \ldots \cup b_{i-1} \cup b_{i+1} \cup \ldots \cup b_k) \cap b_i = 0. \tag{3}$$

If the lattice S is complete (see IV.1.6), then we can also define an infinite direct union: the element a will be the *direct union* of the elements b_i, where i varies through some index set I, if

$$a = \bigcup_{i \in I} b_i \qquad (4)$$

and if for all $i \in I$

$$b_i \cap \overline{b}_i = 0, \qquad (5)$$

where

$$\overline{b}_i = \bigcup_{j \in I, j \neq i} b_j.$$

3. We begin with the study of the fundamental properties of direct unions in a modular lattice S with zero. We will limit ourselves here to the case of finite direct unions. The fact that the lattice S is modular, which played no part in the actual definition in IV.3.2, will now be used fundamentally in many places.

In the definition in IV.3.2, *condition* (3) *can be replaced by the following condition, which is equivalent to it*:

$$(b_1 \cup \ldots \cup b_{i-1}) \cap b_i = 0, \quad i = 2, 3, \ldots, k. \qquad (6)$$

It is clear that (6) follows from (3). To prove that (3) follows from (6), we will prove by induction on l that the intersection of each of the l elements $b_1, b_2, \ldots, b_l$, $2 \leqslant l \leqslant k$, with the union of the remaining $l-1$ elements of this system is equal to zero. In fact, for $l = 2$ this assertion follows from (6) when $i = 2$. Suppose that our assertion is true for $l-1$. From (6) follows the equation

$$(b_1 \cup \ldots \cup b_{l-1}) \cap b_l = 0. \qquad (7)$$

If, however, $j < l$, then the application of the inequality

$$b_j \leqslant b_1 \cup \ldots \cup b_{l-1},$$

of the fact that the lattice S is modular of equation (7) and of the inductive hypothesis gives

$$(b_1 \cup \ldots \cup b_{j-1} \cup b_{j+1} \cup \ldots \cup b_l) \cap b_j =$$
$$[(b_1 \cup \ldots \cup b_{j-1} \cup b_{j+1} \cup \ldots \cup b_{l-1}) \cup b_l] \cap$$
$$(b_1 \cup \ldots \cup b_{l-1}) \cap b_j =$$
$$(b_1 \cup \ldots \cup b_{j-1} \cup b_{j+1} \cup \ldots \cup b_{l-1}) \cap b_j = 0.$$

Our assertion is thus proved for all l, and so also for the number $l = k$, which reduces to the condition (3).

4. By using condition (6), the reader can immediately prove the following properties of a direct union:

If $a = b_1 \times b_2 \times \ldots \times b_k$ and $b_1 \cup b_2 \cup \ldots \cup b_l = c$, $l < k$, then $a = c \times b_{l+1} \times \ldots \times b_k$.

If $a = b_1 \times b_2 \times \ldots \times b_k$ and $b_1 = c_1 \times c_2 \times \ldots \times c_l$, then $a = c_1 \times c_2 \times \ldots \times c_l \times b_2 \times \ldots \times b_k$.

Taking into account that in the definition in IV.3.2 the numbering of the elements $b_1, b_2, \ldots, b_k$ is of no importance, and by applying the second of the assertions just mentioned several times, we arrive at this result:

If

$$a = b_1 \times b_2 \times \ldots \times b_k \qquad (8)$$

and if the elements b_i, all of them or some of them, can themselves be decomposed as direct unions,

$$b_i = c_{i1} \times c_{i2} \times \ldots \times c_{il_i}, \qquad 1 \leqslant l_i, \qquad i = 1, 2, \ldots, \ldots, k,$$

then the element a will be the direct union of all the elements c_{ij}, $1 \leqslant j \leqslant l_i$, $i = 1, 2, \ldots, k$. This new direct decomposition of the element a is called a *refinement* of the direct decomposition (8).

On the other hand, from the definition of a direct union, it follows immediately that *if we take the elements* $b_1, b_2, \ldots, b_l$, $l < k$ *in the* direct decomposition (8), *and we set* $b_1 \cup b_2 \cup \ldots \cup b_l = c$, *then*

$$c = b_1 \times b_2 \times \ldots \times b_l.$$

From this and from the first assertion in this subsection follows the next result:

If we are given the direct decomposition (8) of the element a and if the system of elements $b_1, b_2, \ldots, b_k$ is partitioned into non-intersecting subsystems, then, by replacing each of these subsystems by the union of the elements contained in it, we obtain a new direct decomposition of the element a, for which the decomposition (8) is a refinement.

5. Suppose that we are given the direct decomposition (8) of the element a. If the elements b_i', $0 \leqslant b_i' < b_i$, $i = 1, 2, \ldots, k$, are chosen, and if

$$a' = b_1' \cup b_2' \cup \ldots \cup b_k',$$

then

$$a' = b_1' \times b_2' \times \ldots \times b_k'. \qquad (9)$$

If $b_i' < b_i$ for at least one i, then $a' < a$.

In fact, for $i = 1, 2, \ldots, k$

$$(b_1' \cup \ldots \cup b_{i-1}' \cup b_{i+1}' \cup \ldots \cup b_k') \cap b_i' \leqslant$$
$$(b_1 \cup \ldots \cup b_{i-1} \cup b_{i+1} \cup \ldots \cup b_k) \cap b_i = 0,$$

which proves the assertion (9). On the other hand, if $a' = a$, then, by using the fact that the lattice S is modular, we obtain for $i = 1, 2, \ldots, k$:

$$b_i = b_i \cap a = b_i \cap a' = b_i \cap (b_1' \cup b_2' \cup \ldots \cup b_k') =$$
$$b_i' \cup [b_i \cap (b_i' \cup \ldots \cup b_{i-1}' \cup b_{i+1}' \cup \ldots \cup b_k')] = b_i',$$

because

$$b_i \cap (b_1' \cup \ldots \cup b_{i-1}' \cup b_{i+1}' \cup \ldots \cup b_k') \leqslant$$
$$b_i \cap (b_1 \cup \ldots \cup b_{i-1} \cup b_{i+1} \cup \ldots \cup b_k) = 0.$$

6. *If* $a = b \times c$ *and the element* a' *satisfies the conditions* $b \leqslant a' \leqslant a$, *then*

$$a' = b \times (a' \cap c).$$

In fact, because the lattice is modular

$$a' = a' \cap a = a' \cap (b \cup c) = b \cup (a' \cap c).$$

On the other hand,

$$b \cap (a' \cap c) \leqslant b \cap c = 0.$$

7. We note that if a modular lattice S has principal series and if $a = b \times c$, then, by (18) from IV.2.11,

$$l(a) = l(b) + l(c). \tag{10}$$

In general, if $a = b_1 \times b_2 \times \ldots \times b_k$, then

$$l(a) = l(b_1) + l(b_2) + \ldots + l(b_k). \tag{11}$$

8. In the cases where the concept of a direct union is used, an important part is usually played by the problem of the isomorphism of different direct decompositions of a given group (or a given ring). This problem has been the subject of much research for the most part within the framework of the theory of modular lattices. We will limit ourselves to one special, but important result, which is the basis of all these investigations.

We will introduce one additional concept. Suppose that we are given the modular lattice S, which has a zero 0 and an identity element 1, and that we are given the direct decomposition

$$1 = a_1 \times a_2 \times \ldots \times a_k. \qquad (12)$$

We suppose, as usual, that

$$\overline{a}_i = a_1 \cup \ldots \cup a_{i-1} \cup a_{i+1} \cup \ldots \cup a_k, \; i = 1, 2, \ldots, k, \qquad (13)$$

whence, by IV.3.4,

$$1 = a_i \times \overline{a}_i, \quad i = 1, 2, \ldots, k. \qquad (14)$$

If $b \in S$, then we say that the *component* of this element in the factor a_1 of the direct decomposition (12) is the element

$$b^i = a_i \cap (b \cup \overline{a}_i). \qquad (15)$$

9. *The element b is contained in the union of all its components with respect to the given direct decomposition* (12),

$$b \leqslant b^1 \cup b^2 \cup \ldots \cup b^k.$$

In fact, by using (15), and also by applying several times the definition of a modular lattice, we obtain:

$$b^1 \cup b^2 \cup \ldots \cup b^k = [a_1 \cap (b \cup \overline{a}_1)] \cup [a_2 \cap (b \cup \overline{a}_2)] \cup \ldots$$

$$\ldots \cup [a_k \cap (b \cup \overline{a}_k)] =$$

$$\{a_1 \cup [a_2 \cap (b \cup \overline{a}_2)] \cup \ldots \cup [a_k \cap (b \cup \overline{a}_k)]\} \cap (b \cup \overline{a}_1) =$$

$$\{a_1 \cup a_2 \cup [a_3 \cap (b \cup \overline{a}_3)] \cup \ldots \cup [a_k \cap (b \cup \overline{a}_k)]\} \cap (b \cup \overline{a}_1) \cap (b \cup \overline{a}_2) =$$

$$\cdot \;\; =$$

$$(a_1 \cup a_2 \cup \ldots \cup a_k) \cap (b \cup \overline{a}_1) \cap (b \cup \overline{a}_2) \cap \ldots \cap (b \cup \overline{a}_k) =$$

$$(b \cup \overline{a}_1) \cap (b \cup \overline{a}_2) \cap \ldots \cap (b \cup \overline{a}_k) \geqslant b.$$

We note that in this proof we used such inequalities as, for instance,

$$a_i \cap (b \cup \overline{a}_i) \leqslant a_i \leqslant b \cup \overline{a}_1, \; i \neq 1.$$

10. We call the elements a and b of our lattice S *directly similar* if there exists an element c in S such that

$$1 = a \times c = b \times c.$$

Two direct decompositions of the identity element of the lattice S are called *directly similar* if they consist of the same number of factors and if we can establish a one–one correspondence between these direct factors such that the corresponding factors are directly similar in S.

Finally, we call a non-zero element a of the lattice S indecomposable if it cannot be decomposed as the direct union of two elements distinct from zero.

11. If we are given the direct decomposition

$$1 = a_1 \times a_2 \times \ldots \times a_k$$

of the identity element of the lattice S, then, by setting

$$c_l = a_1 \times a_2 \times \ldots \times a_l, \quad l \leqslant k,$$

we obtain a normal series of length k in S:

$$0 = c_0 < c_1 < c_2 < \ldots < c_k = 1.$$

From this it follows, by IV.2.7, that *if a modular lattice S has principal series and if the length of these series is equal to n then every direct decomposition of the identity element consists of not more than n factors and thus can be refined* (see IV.3.4) *to a direct decomposition with indecomposable factors.*

12. Our purpose is to prove the following theorem [O. Schmidt, Math. Z. **29**, 34–41 (1928); Ore, *Ann. of Math.* **37**, 265–292 (1936)]:

In the modular lattice S, which has principal series, any two decompositions of the identity element into the direct union of indecomposable elements are directly similar.

This theorem follows, however, from the next theorem:

If in the modular lattice S, which has principal series, we are given any two decompositions of the identity element into the direct union of indecomposable elements,

$$1 = a_1 \times a_2 \times \ldots \times a_k, \tag{16}$$

$$1 = b_1 \times b_2 \times \ldots \times b_l, \tag{17}$$

then every factor of each of these decompositions can be replaced by some factor of the other decompositions.

Here, by the possibility of *replacing* the element a_1 in the decomposition (16) by some factor b_j from the decomposition

(17) we must understand the existence of a direct decomposition

$$1 = b_j \times a_2 \times \ldots \times a_k,$$

i.e., by (14),

$$1 = b_j \times \bar{a}_1. \tag{18}$$

The first of the theorems mentioned, in fact, follows from the second. In fact, *if the element b_j from (17) replaces the element a_1 in (16), then,* as equations (14) (for $i = 1$) and (18) show, *the elements a_1 and b_j will be directly similar in S.* Suppose that the direct decomposition

$$1 = b_{j_1} \times \ldots \times b_{j_m} \times a_{m+1} \times \ldots \times a_k, \tag{19}$$

has already been constructed, where $1 \leqslant m \leqslant k$, where $b_{j_1}, \ldots, b_{j_m}$ are different factors of the decomposition (17) and the elements a_i and b_{j_i}, $i = 1, 2, \ldots, m$, are directly similar in S. We apply the second theorem to the direct decompositions (19) and (17). The element a_{m+1} must be replaced in (19) by some factor $b_{j_{m+1}}$ from (17), and therefore a_{m+1} and $b_{j_{m+1}}$ are directly similar. Here the index j_{m+1} differs from all the indices $j_1, \ldots, j_m$, because from

$$1 = b_{j_1} \times \ldots \times b_{j_m} \times b_{j_{m+1}} \times a_{m+2} \times \ldots \times a_k$$

it follows that

$$b_{j_i} \cap b_{j_{m+1}} = 0, \quad i = 1, 2, \ldots, m.$$

By continuing further in the same way, we finally arrive at the direct decomposition

$$1 = b_{j_1} \times b_{j_2} \times \ldots \times b_{j_k},$$

whence $k \leqslant l$. By comparing this with the direct decomposition (17), we obtain that in fact $k = l$ and that the direct decompositions (16) and (17) are directly similar.

13. We will carry out the proof of the second theorem by induction with respect to the length of the principal series of the lattices considered, because only the lattice consisting of two elements, the zero and the identity, has principal series of length 1, and for this lattice the theorem is obviously true.

Suppose that it is desired to replace the element a_1 from the direct decomposition (16). We denote by a_1^i the component (see IV.3.8) of the element a_1 in the direct factor b_i of the decomposition (17). We suppose first that for at least one i the element a_1^i is distinct from b_i. Then, by setting

$$g = a_1^1 \cup a_1^2 \cup \ldots \cup a_1^l,$$

by IV.3.5, we obtain

$$g = a_1^1 \times a_1^2 \times \ldots \times a_1^l. \tag{20}$$

where $g < 1$. Because, by IV.3.9, $a_1 \leqslant g$, then, by IV.3.6,

$$g = a_1 \times d, \tag{21}$$

where

$$d = g \cap (a_2 \times \ldots \times a_k). \tag{22}$$

By the inductive hypothesis the theorem is proved already for the lattice $g/0$. Therefore, by *refining* the decompositions (21) and (20) to direct decompositions with indecomposable factors—we denote these decompositions by (21') and (20') —we will be able to replace the indecomposable element a_1 in (21') by some indecomposable factor c_1 from (20'), i.e.

$$g = c_1 \times d. \tag{23}$$

To be specific, let $c_1 \leqslant a_1^1$.

From (23), (22) and the inequality $c_1 \leqslant g$ it follows that

$$0 = c_1 \cap d = c_1 \cap g \cap (a_2 \times \ldots \times a_k) = c_1 \cap (a_2 \times \ldots \times a_k),$$

i.e. the union

$$h = c_1 \cup (a_2 \times \ldots \times a_k)$$

will be direct:

$$h = c_1 \times a_2 \times \ldots \times a_k.$$

From the fact that the elements a_1 and c_1 are directly similar in g, it follows, by (10) from IV.3.7, that $l(a_1) = l(c_1)$, and therefore, by (11) from IV.3.7, $l(h) = l(1)$, whence $h = 1$. Thus,

$$1 = c_1 \times a_2 \times \ldots \times a_k.$$

However $c_1 \leqslant a_1^1 \leqslant b_1$, and because the element b_1 is indecomposable, then, by IV.3.6,

$$c_1 = a_1^1 = b_1 \tag{24}$$

and therefore

$$1 = b_1 \times a_2 \times \ldots \times a_k.$$

We find that the element a_1 is replaced in the direct decomposition (16) by the element b_1; the elements a_1 and b_1 will thus be directly similar. We note, moreover, that, by (24), the component of the element a_1 in the factor b_1 of the direct decomposition (17) coincides with b_1.

We will show that in the case under consideration the element b_1 in its turn is replaced in the direct decomposition (17) by the element a_1. In fact, because, by (24), $a_1' = b_1$, i.e., by (15)

$$b_1 \cap (a_1 \cup \overline{b_1}) = b_1,$$

then

$$b_1 \leqslant a_1 \cup \overline{b_1},$$

and therefore

$$a_1 \cup \overline{b_1} = 1.$$

On the other hand, from the fact that the elements a_1 and b_1 are directly similar it follows that $l(a_1) = l(b_1)$, and therefore, by (18) from IV.2.11 and (10) from IV.3.7,

$$l(1) = l(b_1) + l(\overline{b_1}) = l(a_1) + l(\overline{b_1}),$$

whence

$$a_1 \cap \overline{b_1} = 0.$$

This proves the existence of the direct decomposition

$$1 = a_1 \times \overline{b_1} = a_1 \times b_2 \times \ldots \times b_l.$$

14. Now we suppose that the components of the element a_1 in all the factors b_i of the decomposition (17) coincide with the elements b_i and at the same time the component in the factor a_1 of the decomposition (16) for at least one b_i, for instance for b_1, coincides with a_1. In this case, as we know from the considerations of the preceding paragraph,

$$a_1 \cup \overline{b_1} = 1, \qquad b_1 \cup \overline{a_1} = 1. \tag{25}$$

From (16), (17) and (25) it follows, by (18) of IV.2.11 and (10) of IV.3.7, that

$$l(1) = l(a_1) + l(\overline{a_1}) = l(b_1) + l(\overline{b_1}),$$

$$l(1) \leqslant l(a_1) + l(\overline{b_1}), \qquad l(1) \leqslant l(b_1) + l(\overline{a_1}).$$

By comparing these equations and inequalities, we obtain

$$l(a_1) = l(b_1), \qquad l(\overline{a_1}) = l(\overline{b_1})$$

and hence

$$a_1 \cap \overline{b}_1 = b_1 \cap \overline{a}_1 = 0,$$

i.e.

$$1 = a_1 \times b_2 \times \ldots \times b_l = b_1 \times a_2 \times \ldots \times a_k.$$

15. It remains to consider the case when the components of the element a_1 in all the factors b_i of the decomposition (17) coincide with the b_i themselves, but the components of all the b_i, $i = 1, 2, \ldots, l$, in the factor a_1 of the decomposition (16) are distinct from a_1. In this case all the direct factors of the decomposition (17) satisfy the same conditions as the element a_1 in the first case considered above. The factors b_i, $i = 1, 2, \ldots l$, can thus be replaced successively in the decomposition (17) by the factors of the decomposition (16). As we know from IV.3.12, in this successive replacement there are some b_i which is replaced by a_1. But then, as was shown in IV.3.13, the component of the element b_i in the direct factor a_1 of the decomposition (16) must coincide with a_1, contrary to our hypothesis.

This contradiction shows that the last case considered is impossible. The theorem has thus been proved.

§ 4. Direct decompositions of Ω-groups

1. As we know, the lattice of normal subgroups of an arbitrary group, the lattice of ideals of an arbitrary ring and, in general, the lattice of ideals of an arbitrary Ω-group are both modular and complete. By applying the definitions of IV.3.2 to these lattices, and to the case when as a we take the group itself, the ring itself or, in general, the Ω-group itself (i.e. the identity elements of the lattices mentioned) we obtain a definite decomposition of the group into a *direct product of its normal subgroups* and a decomposition of the ring or the Ω-group into a *direct sum of its ideals*.

2. These set-theoretical definitions can be rephrased in the language of the operations given in the group, ring or Ω-group. We will do this at once for Ω-groups.

Suppose that we are given in the Ω-group G the Ω-subgroups B_i, $i \in I$. We denote by $\overline{B}_i$ the Ω-subgroup generated in G by all the B_j, where $j \in I$, $j \neq i$. The Ω-group G is *the direct sum of its Ω-*

subgroups B_i, $i \in I$, if the following conditions (α) and (β) are satisfied:

(α) The commutator (see III.5.1) of the Ω-subgroups $\overline{B}_i$ and $\overline{B}_i$ is equal to zero for all $i \in I$,

$$[B_i, \overline{B}_i] = 0, \quad i \in I. \tag{1}$$

We note at once that from the condition (α) follows the equation

$$[B_i, B_j] = 0 \quad \text{when} \quad i \neq j. \tag{2}$$

Therefore, in particular, all the commutators $[b_i, b_j]$ are equal to zero, where $b_i \in B_i$, $b_j \in B_j$, i.e. when $i \neq j$, any elements taken respectively from the subgroups B_i and B_j commute with each other.

(β) Every non-zero element $a \in G$ can be written uniquely (to within the order of summands) as a sum of a finite number of non-zero elements, taken from distinct Ω-subgroups B_i, i.e.

$$a = b_1 + b_2 + \ldots + b_k, \tag{3}$$

where $b_l \in B_{i_l}$, $l = 1, 2, \ldots, k$, and $i_l \neq i_m$ when $l \neq m$.

3. We will prove *the equivalence of these two definitions.* Let the Ω-group G be the direct union of its ideals B_i, $i \in I$, in the sense of IV.3.2. Then, by III.2.4, $\overline{B}_i$, $i \in I$, will also be an ideal. Therefore, by III.5.3,

$$[B_i, \overline{B}_i] \subseteq [B_i, G] \subseteq B_i,$$

$$[B_i, \overline{B}_i] \subseteq [G, \overline{B}_i] \subseteq \overline{B}_i,$$

and because $B_i \cap \overline{B}_i = 0$ by (5) of IV.3.2, condition (α) is proved.

On the other hand, equation (4) of IV.3.2 (where as a we take G itself) and the last theorem of III.2.4 show, because by (α) elements taken from different subgroups B_i commute, that for any element $a \in G$ there exists an expression of the form (3). Let there be two such expressions, namely (3) and

$$a = b_1' + b_2' + \ldots + b_k',$$

without loss of generality—it is sufficient to adjoin to both expressions, if necessary, several summands equal to zero—we can assume that there are the same number of summands in both and that b_i', $i = 1, 2, ..., k$, is contained in the same Ω-subgroup B_{i_l} as b_l. If here, for instance, $b_1 \neq b_1'$, i.e. $-b_1' + b_1 \neq 0$, then

$$-b_1' + b_1 = b_2' + ... + b_k' - (b_2 + ... + b_k) \in B_{i_1} \cap \overline{B}_{i_1},$$

which contradicts equation (5) of IV.3.2.

Now let the Ω-group G be the direct sum of its Ω-subgroups B_i, $i \in I$, in the sense of the definition in IV.4.2. We will prove that every Ω-subgroup B_i is an ideal in G.

If $x \in B_i$ and $a \in G$, then there exists an expression of the form (3) for a, and because elements from different B_j' s, $j \in I$, commute, then

$$-a + x + a = -b_i + x + b_i \in B_i;$$

this proves that B_i is a normal subgroup of the additive group.

On the other hand, from equation (1) it follows that, because of (2) of III.5.1, for any n-ary operation $\omega \in \Omega$ and any elements b_1, b_2, ..., $b_n \in B_i$ and $\overline{b}_1, \overline{b}_2, ..., \overline{b}_n \in \overline{B}_i$

$$(b_1 + \overline{b}_1)(b_2 + \overline{b}_2) ... (b_n + \overline{b}_n)\omega = b_1 b_2 ... b_n \omega + \overline{b}_1 \overline{b}_2 ... \overline{b}_n \omega. \quad (4)$$

Now suppose that we are given an n-ary operation $\omega \in \Omega$, the elements $a_1, a_2, ..., a_n \in G$, the element $b \in B_i$ and the number k, $1 \leqslant k \leqslant n$. By ($\beta$) there exists an expression

$$a_j = b_j + \overline{b}_j, \quad b_j \in B_i, \quad \overline{b}_j \in \overline{B}_i, \quad j = 1, 2, ..., n. \quad (5)$$

Using (4), (5) and the fact that elements from the subgroups B_i and $\overline{B}_i$ commute, we obtain

$$-a_1 ... a_n \omega + a_1 ... a_{k-1}(b + a_k)a_{k+1} ... a_n \omega =$$
$$-(b_1 + \overline{b}_1) ... (b_n + \overline{b}_n)\omega + (b_1 + \overline{b}_1) ...$$
$$... (b_{k-1} + \overline{b}_{k-1})(b + b_k + \overline{b}_k)(b_{k+1} + \overline{b}_{k+1})$$
$$... (b_n + \overline{b}_n)\omega = -\overline{b}_1 ... \overline{b}_n \omega - b_1 ... b_n \omega$$
$$+ b_1 ... b_{k-1}(b + b_k)b_{k+1} ... b_n \omega + \overline{b}_1 ... \overline{b}_n \omega \in B_i.$$

This proves that all the B_i, $i \in I$, are ideals in G. From condition (β) it follows, further, that the ideals B_i together generate the whole Ω-group G. Finally, if the intersection $B_i \cap \overline{B}_i$ were to contain a non-zero element a, then we would have two different expressions of the form (3) for it, which would contradict (β): in one of them the element a is taken from the subgroup B_i, and zero from the other subgroups; in the other the element

a is represented in the form of the sum of elements taken from several subgroups B_j, where $j \neq i$. This completes the proof.

4. *For groups condition* α *of the definition in* IV.4.2 *can be replaced by the condition*:

(α') any elements taken one from each of two subgroups B_i and B_j, where $i \neq j$, commute with each other.

For rings condition (α) *can be replaced by the condition*:

(α'') the product of any elements taken one from each of any two subrings B_i and B_j, where $i \neq j$, is equal to zero.

From what was said in III.5.1 and the inclusion

$$[B_i, B_j] \subseteq [B_i, \overline{B}_i], \quad i \neq j,$$

it follows that (α') and (α'') are respectively consequences of (α). On the other hand, in the case of groups, from (α') it follows that elements from B_i and $\overline{B}_i$ commute, i.e., again by III.5.1, (α) follows. However, in the case of rings, from (β) it follows that every element of $\overline{B}_l$ has an expression of the form (3) with summands taken from several of the subgroups B_j, $j \neq i$. Therefore, by the distributive laws, it follows from (α'') that if $x \in B_1$, $y \in \overline{B}_j$, then

$$xy = yx = 0,$$

and this, by III.5.1, implies (α).

5. Suppose that the normal subgroups A and B of the group are directly similar in the sense of IV.3.10, i.e. there exists a normal subgroup C such that the direct decompositions

$$G = A \times C = B \times C \tag{6}$$

exist. *Then A and B are isomorphic to the factor-group G/C, i.e. they are isomorphic to each other.* In this isomorphism the elements $a \in A$ and $b \in B$ are related in such a way that

$$a = bc, \quad c \in C,$$

where *the element c belongs to the centre of the group G* (see III.3.2); for this reason the given isomorphism between A and B is called *central*.

In fact, by the second of the decompositions (6) the element c commutes with every element of B. On the other hand, for any $c' \in C$ there follows from the first of the decompositions (6) the equation

$$ac' = c'a,$$

i.e.

$$(bc)c' = c'(bc),$$

whence, by what was said above, it follows that

$$cc' = c'c.$$

The element c thus commutes with the elements both of B and of C, and therefore also with all the elements of the group G.

Analogously, if we are given the directly similar ideals A and B of the ring R, i.e. the decompositions in direct sums

$$R = A + C = B + C \qquad (7)$$

exist, then *A and B are isomorphic to the factor ring R/C, and therefore are isomorphic to each other.* In this isomorphism the elements $a \in A$ and $b \in B$ are related to each other thus

$$a = b + c, \quad c \in C, \qquad (8)$$

where *the element c belongs to the annihilator of the ring R*; for this reason the given isomorphism between A and B may be called *annihilatory.* We note that the *annihilator* of the ring R is the totality of elements $a \in R$ such that

$$ax = xa = 0$$

for all $x \in R$.

We will prove that the element c of (8) has this property. From the second of the decompositions (7) it follows that for all $b' \in B$, $c' \in C$

$$b'c' = c'b' = 0. \qquad (9)$$

in particular

$$b'c = cb' = 0. \qquad (10)$$

On the other hand, from the first of the decompositions (7) it follows that for any $c' \in C$

$$ac' = c'a = 0,$$

i.e., by (8),

$$(b + c)c' = c'(b + c) = 0,$$

whence, by (9),

$$cc' = c'c = 0. \qquad (11)$$

From (10) and (11) it follows, by the second of the decompositions that c belongs to the annihilator of the ring R.

From the proof it follows that directly similar direct decompositions in groups and rings (see IV.3.10) will be respectively *centrally isomorphic* and *annihilatorily isomorphic*. The converse, obviously, cannot be asserted.

6. From the Schmidt-Ore theorem (see IV.3.12) there now follow these theorems:

If the group G has principal series, then any two of its direct decompositions with irreducible factors are centrally isomorphic.

If the ring R has principal series, then any two of its direct decompositions with irreducible summands are annihilatorily isomorphic.

* If all the homomorphic images of a group (ring) G, lying in its centre (in its annihilator), satisfy the minimal condition for subgroups (subrings), then any two direct decompositions of G, where the number of direct factors (summands) may be infinite, have centrally (annihilatorily) isomorphic *refinements*. The conditions of this theorem are satisfied, in particular, in the case when the centre (annihilator) of G or of the factor group of G with respect to the commutator (factor ring with respect to the square) satisfy the minimal condition [A. G. Kurosh, *Izv. AN SSSR*, ser. matem. **10**, 47–72 (1946)].*

§ 5. Complete direct sums of universal algebras

1. Suppose that we are given a family of universal algebras G_i with the same system of operations Ω and belonging to the same primitive class Λ (see III.6.3); the index i varies through some set I, finite or infinite. We consider the set G whose elements are all systems $a = (a_i)$ of elements taken one from each of the algebras G_i, i.e. $a_i \in G_i$, $i \in I$. The element a_i will be called the *i-th component* (or the component in the algebra G_i) of the element a.

The set G can be reduced to a universal algebra with system of operations Ω by assuming that the operations of Ω are satisfied in G by components: if we are given the n-ary operation $\omega \in \Omega$ and the n elements of G,

$$a^{(k)} = (a_i^{(k)}), \quad k = 1, 2, \ldots, n,$$

then

$$a'a'' \ldots a^{(n)}\omega = (a_i'a_i'' \ldots a_i^{(n)}\omega).$$

This definition of operations shows that all the identical relations of Λ will be satisfied in the algebra G.

The algebra G is called the *complete direct sum* of the algebras G_i, $i \in I$, and will be written in the form

$$G = \sum_{i \in I}^{\sim} G_i. \tag{1}$$

We can speak, in particular, of the group which is the complete direct sum (or complete direct product) of a given family of groups, and so on.

2. A subalgebra A of the algebra G, represented in the form (1), is called a *subdirect sum* of the algebras G_i, $i \in I$, if for every $i \in I$ the i-th components of all the elements of A exhaust the whole algebra G_i. It is clear that amongst such subalgebras there is the algebra G itself, but, generally speaking, there also exist proper subalgebras with this property in G.

If the subalgebra A is a subdirect sum of the algebras G_i, $i \in I$, then for every $i \in I$ we obtain a homomorphic mapping φ_i of the algebra A onto the algebra G_i, which relates to every element

$$a = (a_i) \in A$$

its i-th component a_i. As we know from III.1.8, the homomorphism φ_i defines a congruence π_i on the algebra A, where the algebras G_i and A/π_i are isomorphic.

The intersection of the congruences π_i, $i \in I$ (see I.3.3), is the zero congruence, i.e. it is the partition of the algebra A into separate elements.

In fact, if we are given two distinct elements in A, then for at least one i they have distinct i-th components, and therefore belong to distinct classes of the congruence π_i.

3. The converse theorem is true:

If in the universal algebra A we are given a system of congruences π_i, $i \in I$, with zero intersection, then the algebra A is isomorphic to the subdirect sum of the factor algebras A/π_i, $i \in I$.

To prove this we denote by G the complete direct sum of the algebras A/π_i, $i \in I$,

$$G = \sum_{i \in I}^{\sim} A/\pi_i.$$

We map the algebra A into the algebra G, by relating to every element $a \in A$ the element of G whose i-th componnt for every

$i \in I$ is the class of the congruence π_i containing the element a. This mapping will be a homomorphism, because in the algebra G the operations are carried out by components, and in the algebra A/π_i, $i \in I$, the application of the operations to the classes of the congruence π_i is defined by the application of the operations to the elements of A, chosen one from each of these classes.

The homomorphism obtained will in fact be an isomorphism, because from the condition that the intersection of the congruences π_i must be zero it follows that for any two different elements of A we can find at least one $i \in I$ such that these elements lie in different classes of the congruence π_i, and therefore their images in G have different i-th components. Finally, the subalgebra of the algebra G onto which the algebra A is mapped isomorphically will be a subdirect sum of the algebras A/π_i, $i \in I$, because for all $i \in I$ any class of the congruence π_i, i.e. any element of the algebra A/π_i, is the i-th component of the images of all its elements in G.

In the case of Ω-groups the congruences are given by ideals, as we know from III.2.5, and it is easy to see that the intersection of the congruences is defined by the intersection of the corresponding ideals. Thus, *the representation of any Ω-group (in particular, of a group, or of a ring) in the form of a subdirect sum corresponds in a one–one fashion to the system of its ideals (normal subgroups) with zero intersection.*

4. A universal algebra A is called *subdirectly irreducible* if any system of non-zero congruences in A has non-zero intersection. From what was said in IV.5.2 and IV.5.3 it follows that this will be the case if, and only if, for any representation of the algebra A in the form of a subdirect sum of several algebras G_i, $i \in I$, for at least one i the homomorphism φ_i, which maps every element of A into its i-th component, will be an isomorphism between A and G_i.

The following theorem is true [Birkhoff, *Bull. Amer. Math. Soc.* **50**, 764–768 (1944)]:

Every universal algebra A can be decomposed as the subdirect sum of subdirectly irreducible algebras, belonging to the same primitive class as the algebra A.

For the proof we consider any pair of distinct elements x, $y \in A$ and we denote by $M(x, y)$ the set of all congruences on the algebra A *separating* these elements, i.e. such that x and

y belong to different classes for each of these congruences. The set $M(x, y)$ is not empty, because the zero congruence is contained in it. We will show that this set, which is partially ordered by I.2.1, has maximal elements.

For this, by the Kuratowski-Zorn theorem (see I.6.3), it is sufficient to show that every chain of the set $M(x, y)$ has an upper bound. Let the congruences $\pi_i \in M(x, y)$, where i varies through an ordered set I, form a chain, i.e. $\pi_i \leqslant \pi_j$ when $i < j$. Then the binary relation π^*, defined by the condition that $b\pi^*c$ will obviously be an equivalence relation if, and only if, there exists an $i \in I$ such that $b\pi_i c$. It will also be a congruence: if we take the elements $b_1, b_2, \ldots, b_n$ and $c_1, c_2, \ldots, c_n$ in A, where $b_j\pi^*c_j, j = 1, 2, \ldots, n$, then there exist $i_1, i_2, \ldots, i_n \in I$ such that $b_j\pi_j c_j, j = 1, 2, \ldots, n$. If i_0 is the greatest of the indices $i_1, i_2, \ldots, i_n$, then $b_j\pi_{i_0}c_j, j = 1, 2, \ldots, n$. Let ω be any n-ary operation given in the algebra A. Because π_{i_0} is a congruence, then

$$(b_1b_2 \ldots b_n\omega)\pi_{i_0}(c_1c_2 \ldots c_n\omega),$$

and therefore also

$$(b_1b_2 \ldots b_n\omega)\pi^*(c_1c_2 \ldots c_n\omega),$$

i.e. π^* is in fact a congruence. This congruence separates the elements x and y, because they were separated by each of the congruences π_i, $i \in I$, and is obviously the upper bound for the given chain of congruences.

Now for every pair of distinct elements x, $y \in A$ we fix one of the maximal congruences separating them; we denote it by $\pi(x, y)$. The intersection of these congruences is zero, because any pair of distinct elements of A is separated by at least one of these congruences. Therefore, by the theorem in IV.5.3, the algebra A is the subdirect sum of all the factor-algebras $A/\pi(x, y)$.

It remains to show that every factor algebra $A/\pi(x, y)$ is subdirectly irreducible. For this we note that between all the congruences of this factor algebra and all the congruences of the algebra A which contain the congruence $\pi(x, y)$ there exists a unique one-one correspondence, which preserves the relation of inclusion. However, the intersection of all the congruences of the algebra A, strictly greater than $\pi(x, y)$, is itself strictly greater than these congruences, because all the given congruences do not separate the elements x and y, while $\pi(x, y)$ does separate them. From this it follows that the intersection of all the non-zero congurences of the algebra $A/\pi(x, y)$ will itself be non-zero. The theorem has thus been proved.

5. Now we consider the complete direct sum of the Ω-groups G_i, $i \in I$,

$$G = \sum_{i \in I}^{\sim} G_i.$$

From what was said in IV.5.1 it follows that G will itself be an Ω-group of the same primitive class as that to which all the G_i belong, $i \in I$. Its zero will be the element, each of whose components is equal, respectively, to the zero of the corresponding Ω-group G_i.

The subset G' of the Ω-group G, consisting of all those elements $a = (a_i)$ which have only a finite number of components a_i, $i \in I$, distinct from zero, will be an Ω-subgroup in G, because the componentwise application to the elements of G' of addition or subtraction, and also of the operations from Ω, does not take us outside G'.

The Ω-group G' is called the *direct sum* of the Ω-groups G_i, $i \in I$. The basis for this is the following theorem:

The Ω-group G' is the direct sum (in the sense of the definitions in IV.3.2 and IV.4.2) of its ideals G'_i, $i \in I$, which are respectively isomorphic to the Ω-groups G_i.

For the proof we denote by G'_i the subset of those elements of G', all of whose components, except, perhaps, the i-th, are equal to zero. Because the operations are applied componentwise, this G'_i will be an Ω-subgroup in G' and in fact an ideal, which is obviously isomorphic to the Ω-group G_i.

We note, further, that every element of G' has only a finite number of non-zero components and therefore can be represented in the form of a sum of a finite number of elements, each of which has only one non-zero component. From this it follows that G' is the sum (see III.2.4) of all the ideals G'_i, $i \in I$. On the other hand, the sum $\overline{G}'_i$ of all the ideals G'_j where $j \in I$ and $j \neq i$, consists of only those elements of G' whose i-th component is equal to zero. It is clear, finally, that

$$G'_i \cap \overline{G}'_i = 0,$$

i.e. all the requirements contained in the definition in IV.3.2 are satisfied.

6. Hence for the concept of a direct sum of Ω-groups we have three equivalent definitions: the lattice-theoretical definition of IV.3.2, the "internal" definition of IV.4.2 and the "external" definition of IV.5.5, which appears as a construction, enabling us to speak of the direct sum of any Ω-groups given in advance. We note that the concept of a complete direct sum of an infinite number of direct summands is not lattice-theoretical.

§ 6. Distributive lattices

1. In IV.2.1 the lattice S was called distributive if the equation

$$a \cap (b \cup c) = (a \cap b) \cup (a \cap c). \qquad (1)$$

was satisfied identically in S. We will show that *the identity* (1) *is equivalent to the identity*

$$a \cup (b \cap c) = (a \cup b) \cap (a \cup c) \qquad (2)$$

which is its dual.

In fact, by applying (1) and the definition of a lattice in IV.1.2, we obtain:

$$a \cup (b \cap c) = [a \cup (a \cap c)] \cup (b \cap c) = a \cup [(a \cap c) \cup (b \cap c)] =$$
$$a \cup [(a \cup b) \cap c] = [(a \cup b) \cap a] \cup [(a \cup b) \cap c] = (a \cup b) \cap (a \cup c).$$

Dual reasoning enables us to deduce (1) from (2).

If the lattice S is distributive, then for any elements a, b, c in S it follows from

$$a \cap c = b \cap c, \quad a \cup c = b \cup c$$

that $a = b$. In fact,

$$a = a \cup (a \cap c) = a \cup (b \cap c) = (a \cup b) \cap (a \cup c) =$$
$$(a \cup b) \cap (b \cup c) = b \cup (a \cap c) = b \cup (b \cap c) = b.$$

* The property of distributive lattices just proved can be taken as their definition.*

2. As we know from I.1.1, the lattice of all subsets of any set is distributive. This is also true for any sublattice of such lattices, i.e., as we shall say, for any *lattice of sets*. It turns out that these essentially exhaust all the distributive lattices.

Every distributive lattice is isomorphic to some lattice of sets.

3. Distributive lattices form a primitive class of universal algebras, and therefore the theorem of IV.5.4 is applicable to them: every distributive lattice is a subdirect sum of subdirectly irreducible distributive lattices.

An example of a subdirectly irreducible lattice is the lattice T consisting of two elements—zero and the identity. The fact that this lattice is distributive is obvious. If the lattice T were subdirectly reducible, then it would be a sublattice of a complete direct sum of lattices T_i, $i \in I$, and there would exist homomorphisms $\varphi_i \colon T \to T_i$, $i \in I$, which are not isomorphisms. But in this case every lattice T_i, $i \in I$, would consist of one element, and then the direct sum of these lattices would also have one element and could not contain T.

Every subdirectly irreducible distributive lattice consisting of more than one element is isomorphic to the lattice T.

In fact, suppose that we are given the distributive lattice S. If it consists of two elements, then it is obviously isomorphic to the lattice T. If, however, not less than three elements are contained in S, then we can find an element a, distinct both from zero, and from the identity, if S has a zero and an identity. We denote by U the sublattice of all elements x of S which satisfy the condition $x \leqslant a$, and by V the sublattice of those $x \in S$ such that $x \geqslant a$. By hypothesis, depending on the choice of the element a, each of the lattices U, V does not consist only of the element a alone.

We denote by $U + V$ the complete direct sum of the lattices U and V in the sense of IV.5.1: its elements are the pairs (u, v), $u \in U$, $v \in V$, on which the operations are carried out by components. We relate to every $x \in S$ the pair $(x \cap a, x \cup a) \in U + V$. This mapping of S into $U + V$ is one–one, because for $x, y \in S$ it follows from

$$x \cap a = y \cap a, \quad x \cup a = y \cup a$$

as was proved in IV.6.1, that $x = y$.

This mapping is in fact an isomorphism, because

$$((x \cup y) \cap a, (x \cup y) \cup a) = ((x \cap a) \cup (y \cap a), (x \cup a) \cup (y \cup a)) =$$
$$(x \cap a, x \cup a) \cup (y \cap a, y \cup a);$$
$$((x \cap y) \cap a, (x \cap y) \cup a) = ((x \cap a) \cap (y \cap a), (x \cup a) \cap (y \cup a)) =$$
$$(x \cap a, x \cup a) \cap (y \cap a, y \cup a).$$

We can thus regard S as a sublattice of the lattice $U + V$. Because the pair (x, a) corresponds to the element $x \in U$, and the pair (a, x) to the element $x \in V$, we obtain that the homomorphisms mapping every element of S respectively into its first or second component will map S onto the whole of U or respectively the whole of V and will not be isomorphisms. The lattice S is thus subdirectly reducible.

4. Now we will prove the fundamental theorem of IV.6.2. If we are given distributive lattice S, then, by what was said above, it is the subdirect sum of the lattices T_i, $i \in I$, where every T_i consists of two elements—a zero 0_i and an identity 1_i (direct summands of one element can, of course, be excluded from our considerations). We denote by M the set of all the identities 1_i, $i \in I$, and we relate to every element $a \in S$ the subset A of the set M consisting of all those elements 1_i which are the i-th components in the expression for a as an element of the complete direct sum of the lattices T_i, $i \in I$. It is clear that if $a \neq b$, then the sets corresponding to them will be distinct. On the other hand, from the componentwise application of the operations in the complete direct sum of the lattices T_i, $i \in I$, and the properties of the identity and the zero, it now follows that to the element $a \cup b$ corresponds the set-theoretical union $A \cup B$ of the sets A and B, and to the element $a \cap b$ the set-theoretical intersection $A \cap B$ of these sets. Thus the theorem has been proved.

We note that *if the distributive lattice S has a zero and an identity, then in the representation by sets obtained above the empty subset of the set M corresponds to the zero, and the set M itself to the identity. We note also that if the lattice S is finite, then,* as the proof of the theorem in IV.5.4 shows, it will be a subdirect sum of a finite number of subdirectly irreducible lattices, and therefore *it will be isomorphic to some lattice of subsets of a finite set.*

5. A distributive lattice S with a zero and an identity is called a *Boolean lattice* (or *Boolean algebra*), if every element $a \in S$ has a *complement* $\overline{a}$, where $\overline{a} \in S$ and

$$a \cap \overline{a} = 0, \quad a \cup \overline{a} = 1.$$

Every element $a \in S$ has a unique complement, as follows from the proof in IV.6.1.

The lattice of all subsets of any set is a Boolean lattice, because for every subset A there exists the set-theoretical complement

$\overline{A}$. A lattice of sets (see IV.6.2), which contains together with every subset its set-theoretical complement, will be called a *Boolean lattice of sets*.

Every Boolean lattice S is isomorphic to some Boolean lattice of sets.

This theorem has already been proved in essence in the preceding section. In fact, if the subset $A \subseteq M$ corresponds to the element $a \in S$, then the set-theoretical complement $\overline{A}$ of set A in M corresponds to the complement $\overline{a}$: the expressions for the elements a and $\overline{a}$ in the complete direct sum of the lattices T_i, $i \in I$, are such that if the i-th component in one of them is 1_i, then in the other it will be 0_i and conversely.

6. *Every finite Boolean lattice S is isomorphic to the lattice of all subsets of some finite set.*

In fact, the results obtained above enable us to regard S as a Boolean lattice of subsets of a finite set M. We denote by N the set of all those subsets of M which are minimal elements of the lattice S distinct from zero.

Every subset A which is an element of the lattice S coincides with the union A_0 of all the subsets contained in it, which occur in N. In fact, in the opposite case the intersection $A \cap \overline{A_0}$ would be a non-empty element of S (because $\overline{A_0} \in S$), i.e. it would contain at least one subset occurring in N, which contradicts the definition of the set A_0.

Now it is easy to see that, by relating to every $A \in S$ the set of all elements of N contained in it, we obtain a one–one correspondence and in fact an isomorphic mapping of the lattice S onto the lattice of all subsets of the set N.

7. An associative ring R with identity is called a *Boolean ring* if all its elements are idempotent, i.e.

$$a^2 = a, \quad a \in R. \tag{3}$$

Every Boolean ring is commutative and satisfies the identity

$$2a = 0. \tag{4}$$

In fact, for any $a, b \in R$ it follows from (3) that

$$a + b = (a + b)^2 = a^2 + ab + ba + b^2 = a + ab + ba + b,$$

whence

$$ab + ba = 0. \tag{5}$$

By setting $b = a$ in (5) and using (3), we obtain (4), i.e. $a = -a$, and then (5) can be rewritten in the form

$$ab - ba = 0.$$

* Every Boolean lattice can be made into a Boolean ring, if we set

$$a + b = (a \cap \overline{b}) \cup (\overline{a} \cap b), \quad ab = a \cap b$$

Conversely, every Boolean ring can be made into a Boolean lattice, if we set

$$a \cup b = a + b - ab, \quad a \cap b = ab.$$

In this way we establish a one–one correspondence between Boolean lattices and Boolean rings [M. H. Stone, *Trans. Amer. math. Soc.* **40**, 37–111 (1936)].*

CHAPTER FIVE

OPERATOR GROUPS AND RINGS. MODULES. LINEAR ALGEBRAS

§ 1. Operator groups and rings

1. As is well known, a real vector space is an Abelian group with respect to addition, in which there is also defined a multiplication of vectors by real numbers, connected with the addition of vectors by well-known axioms. Multiplication by real numbers also has a meaning in the ring of real functions of a real variable, and in the ring of real square matrices of a given order. These and many other examples have led to the introduction of algebraic structures with operators.

If we are given a groupoid (in particular, a semigroup or group) G, then we can choose an arbitrary system of endomorphisms Σ in G (see III.3.4) and consider only those subgroupoids which are mapped into themselves under all the endomorphisms of Σ. Generalizing this idea, we denote by Σ some set consisting of the elements α, β, ..., and we will say that G is a Σ-operator groupoid, and that the set Σ is its *domain of operators*, if with every element $\alpha \in \Sigma$ we can associate some endomorphism of the groupoid G. Distinct elements of Σ may here be associated with the same endomorphism. The operator α may be regarded as the symbol of the endomorphism corresponding to it, so that for any a, $b \in G$ and any $\alpha \in \Sigma$

$$(ab)\alpha = a\alpha \cdot b\alpha. \tag{1}$$

If G is a Σ-operator group with identity e, then from (1) it follows that

$$e\alpha = e, \quad \alpha \in \Sigma.$$

Thus, *an operator group is a special case of a multi-operator group* (see III.2.1): all the multi-operators are unary and the condition (1) is satisfied for each of them.

· 201

2. A subgroupoid A of a Σ-operator groupoid G is said to be Σ-*admissible* if under all endomorphisms corresponding to operators from Σ it is mapped into itself, i.e. for all $\alpha \in \Sigma$

$$A\alpha \subseteq A.$$

Any operator $\alpha \in \Sigma$ thus generates some endomorphism in every Σ-admissible subgroupoid A, which enables us to regard this subgroupoid as an operator groupoid with the same domain of operators Σ.

The intersection of any system of Σ-admissible subgroupoids, if it is not empty, will itself, of course, be Σ-admissible. On the other hand, by using (1) and II.3.8, we can easily show that the subgroupoid generated by a system of Σ-admissible subgroupoids will itself be Σ-admissible.

Operator groupoids G and G' with the same domain of operators Σ are said to be Σ-*operator isomorphic* if there exists an isomorphic mapping φ of the groupoid G onto the groupoid G', called a Σ-*operator isomorphism*, such that for any $a \in G$ and $\alpha \in \Sigma$

$$(a\alpha)\varphi = (a\varphi)\alpha. \tag{2}$$

By means of equation (2) we can also define Σ-*operator homomorphisms*. We can speak, in particular, of Σ-*operator endomorphisms* and *automorphisms* of a Σ-operator groupoid G.

From (2) it follows that *an endomorphism φ of a Σ-operator groupoid G will be a Σ-operator if, and only if, it commutes (in the semigroup of endomorphisms, see* III.3.4) *with all endomorphisms corresponding to operators from Σ.*

We note that if the set Σ is empty or consists only of the identity automorphism of the groupoid G, then the study of G as a Σ-operator groupoid is equivalent to studying it as a groupoid without operators.

3. Suppose that we are given a semigroup Σ and a Σ-operator groupoid G. We will say that G is a *groupoid with semigroup of operators* Σ, if for any $a \in G$ and any $\alpha, \beta \in \Sigma$

$$a(\alpha\beta) = (a\alpha)\beta. \tag{3}$$

We note that condition (3) is known to be satisfied if for Σ we take a subsemigroup of the semigroup of all endomorphisms of the groupoid G.

An arbitrary set Σ can be embedded in a semigroup Γ in such a way that every Σ-operator groupoid will be a groupoid with semigroup of operators Γ. Here Σ-admissible subgroupoids will also be Γ-admissible and Σ-operator isomorphic groupoids will also be Γ-operator isomorphic.

As the set Γ we can take the set of all *words* of the form

$$\alpha_1\alpha_2 \dots \alpha_n, \tag{4}$$

i.e. the set of finite ordered systems of elements of Σ, where $n \geqslant 1$, and the elements $\alpha_1, \alpha_2, \dots, \alpha_n$ are not necessarily distinct. By defining the multiplication of words by means of the equation

$$(\alpha_1\alpha_2 \dots \alpha_n)(\beta_1\beta_2 \dots \beta_s) = \alpha_1\alpha_2 \dots \alpha_n\beta_1\beta_2 \dots \beta_s, \tag{5}$$

we make Γ into a semigroup. By setting up a correspondence between the word (4) and the endomorphism of the Σ-operator groupoid G which is the product of the endomorphisms corresponding to the operators $\alpha_1, \alpha_2, \dots, \alpha_n$, we make the groupoid G into a Γ-operator groupoid, where the requirement (3) will be satisfied, because of (5). All the remaining assertions of the theorem will also, of course, be true.

4. Let G be an Abelian group written additively, and R an associative ring. The group G is called *an Abelian group with ring of operators R* or an *R-module*, if G is an R-operator group, i.e. for any a, $b \in G$ and $\alpha \in R$ equation (1) holds, now written in the form

$$(a + b)\alpha = a\alpha + b\alpha, \tag{6}$$

and if, moreover, for any $a \in G$ and α, $\beta \in R$ the equations

$$a(\alpha + \beta) = a\alpha + a\beta, \tag{7}$$

$$a(\alpha\beta) = (a\alpha)\beta, \tag{8}$$

are satisfied.

The naturality of this concept follows from the fact that *every Abelian group will be a module with respect to any subring of its ring of endomorphisms*, because in this case, by III.3.8, the conditions (6)–(8) are satisfied.

This example prompts the following additional requirement: if the ring R has an identity ε, then we will consider the R-modules such that ε is the *identity operator*; in other words, to the operator ε corresponds the identity automorphism of the group G,

$$a\varepsilon = a, \qquad a \in G. \tag{9}$$

An R-module with the property (9) is called a *unital R-module*.

* If R is an associative ring with identity, then the study of arbitrary R-modules is reduced completely to the study of unital R-modules and R-modules in which operators from R act trivially, i.e. for any a from the module and α from R

$$a\alpha = 0.$$

An arbitrary set Σ can be embedded in an associative ring R with identity in such a way that every Σ-operator Abelian group will be a unital R-module, Σ-admissible subgroups will be R-admissible, i.e. will be *submodules* of the R-module, and Σ-operator isomorphic Abelian groups will be isomorphic R-modules.*

5. Let us consider some examples.

For an arbitrary group G the group of its inner automorphism (see III.3.2) is a group of operators, because, as we know, the conditions (1) and (3) are satisfied. The admissible subgroups with respect to this domain of operators will be the normal subgroups of the group G and only these.

For a group G the group of all its automorphisms will also be a group of operators, and the semigroup of all its endomorphisms will be a semigroup of operators (see III.3.4). Subgroups, admissible with respect to these domains of operators, are called respectively *characteristic* and *completely characteristic.*†

A real n-dimensional vector space is a unital module over the field of real numbers. The linear subspaces are submodules of this module, and the linear transformations are operator endomorphisms (see V.1.2).

6. If in an arbitrary ring R we take an element a, then the mapping $x \to xa$, $x \in R$, will be an endomorphism of the additive group of the ring R, which follows from the distributive law; this endomorphism is called a *right multiplication*. The additive group of the ring R can thus be regarded as an operator group with the set R itself as the domain of operators; the admissible subgroups here will be the right ideals of the ring R (see

---

† or *fully invariant* (Ed.).

II.7.10) and only these. Analogously, we define *left multiplication* i.e. R is once again a domain of operators for its additive group, where in this case the admissible subgroups will be the left ideals. Finally, by joining these two domains of operators, we obtain for the additive group of the ring R a domain of operators for which the admissible subgroups will only be the (two-sided) ideals.

If the ring R is associative, then, considered as a set of right multiplications, it will in fact be a ring of operators for its additive group in the sense of V.1.4, because conditions (7), (8) and, in the case of a ring with identity, (9) are known to be satisfied. If, however, we consider R as a set of left multiplications, then equation (8) will not be satisfied. In this case, as the equation

$$(bc)a = b(ca),$$

valid in R shows, the ring of operators for the additive group of the ring R can be regarded as a ring anti-isomorphic to the ring R. We remark that the rings R and R' are called *anti-isomorphic* if there exists an isomorphism φ between the additive groups of these rings such that for all $a, b \in R$

$$(ab)\varphi = b\varphi \cdot a\varphi.$$

7. To define the concept of operators for rings one can, of course, use the endomorphisms of a ring, by analogy with the case of groups. Examples, for instance multiplication by a number in the ring of functions and in the ring of matrices, suggest other methods—the consideration of those endomorphisms φ of the additive group of the ring R which commute (in the sense of the multiplication of endomorphisms) with right and left multiplications (see V.1.6), i.e. they satisfy the condition (for all $a, b \in R$)

$$(ab)\varphi = (a\varphi)b = a(b\varphi). \tag{10}$$

In fact this is the method we choose. Thus, if Σ is a set with elements $\alpha, \beta, \ldots$, then the ring R is called a Σ-*operator* ring if its additive group is a Σ-operator group and if, moreover, for any $a, b \in R$ and any $\alpha \in \Sigma$

$$(ab)\alpha = (a\alpha)b = a(b\alpha). \tag{11}$$

The concepts of a Σ-*admissible subring, a* Σ-*admissible ideal,* Σ-*operator isomorphism and* Σ-*operator homomorphism* are defined by analogy with these definitions in the case of groups.

If the Σ-operator ring R has an identity, then the endomorphisms corresponding to the operators from Σ are themselves multiplications (simultaneously right and left) by elements of the ring R, commuting with all elements of R, and therefore all ideals and all one-sided ideals of the ring R will be Σ-admissible.

In fact, for all $a \in R$ and $\alpha \in \Sigma$

$$a\alpha = (a \cdot 1)\alpha = a \cdot (1\alpha),$$

$$a\alpha = (1 \cdot a)\alpha = (1\alpha) \cdot a,$$

whence

$$a \cdot (1\alpha) = (1\alpha) \cdot a, \quad a \in R.$$

We note, without developing this further, that the definition of a Σ-operator ring can be carried over without difficulty to the case of any multi-operator group.

8. *The endomorphisms of the additive group of the ring R which satisfy the condition* (10) *form a subring in the ring of all endomorphisms of this group.* In fact, if the endomorphisms φ and ψ have the property (10), then, for instance,

$$(ab)(\varphi \pm \psi) = (ab)\varphi \pm (ab)\psi = (a\varphi)b \pm (a\psi)b =$$

$$(a\varphi \pm a\psi)b = [a(\varphi \pm \psi)]b,$$

$$(ab)(\varphi\psi) = [(ab)\varphi]\psi = [(a\varphi)b]\psi = [(a\varphi)\psi]b = [a(\varphi\psi)]b.$$

This ensures the validity of the following concept. If Σ is some associative ring, then the ring R is called *an operator ring with ring of operators* Σ, if it is a Σ-operator ring and if, in addition to this, the ring Σ is a ring of operators for the additive group of the ring R in the sense of V.1.4.

We note that if n is an integer, then the mapping $a \to na$, defined for all elements a of the ring R, will be an endomorphism of the additive group of this ring, and the conditions (7), (8), (9) and (11) will also be satisfied. Thus, *every ring R can be regarded as an operator ring with the ring of integers as its ring of operators.* All subrings of the ring R will be admissible here, and all isomorphisms will be operator isomorphisms.

9. Suppose that the endomorphisms φ and ψ of the additive group of the ring R satisfy condition (10). If $\varphi\psi \neq \psi\varphi$, then there exists an element $a \in R$ such that

$$a\varphi\psi \neq a\psi\varphi.$$

Then for any $x \in R$ we obtain, by using (10):

$$(a\varphi\psi)x = (a\varphi \cdot x)\,\psi = a\varphi \cdot x\psi = (a \cdot x\psi)\varphi =$$
$$[(ax)\,\psi]\varphi = (a\psi \cdot x)\varphi = (a\psi\varphi)x.$$

From this it follows that the element

$$b = a\varphi\psi - a\psi\varphi$$

distinct from zero, satisfies the equation

$$bx = 0$$

for all $x \in R$, i.e. it is a *left annihilator* for the ring R. In the same way we verify that b will also be a *right annihilator* for R, therefore in general it will be an *annihilator*, i.e. (see IV.4.5)

$$bx = xb = 0$$

for all $x \in R$.

Of course, rings with annihilators exist—such as every zero ring (see II.2.2) consisting only of annihilators. Nevertheless, we are justified when studying rings with a ring of operators Σ, in assuming that this ring Σ is not merely associative, but also commutative.

10. Σ-operator groups (Σ-operator rings) for given Σ form a primitive class of multi-operator groups. We add only a few remarks to what was said in Chapter Three, in particular on the homomorphisms of multi-operator groups.

The ideals of Σ-operator groups (rings), considered as multi-operator groups, coincide with their Σ-admissible normal subgroups (Σ-admissible ideals).

In fact, if G is a Σ-operator group, then for its normal subgroup A the inclusion $a\alpha \in A$ for all $a \in A$, $\alpha \in \Sigma$ holds if, and only if, for all $a \in A$, $x \in G$, $\alpha \in \Sigma$

$$(x\alpha)^{-1}(a\alpha)(x\alpha) = (x\alpha)^{-1}(ax)\alpha \in A.$$

However, the last inclusion is simply different a form, rewritten for the present case, of the inclusion (2) from III.2.4.

On the other hand, if A is a subgroup of the additive group of a Σ-operator ring R, then for all $a \in A$, $x \in R$, $\alpha \in \Sigma$ the inclusion $a\alpha \in A$ and

$$-xa + a\alpha + x\alpha = -x\alpha + (a + x)\alpha \in A$$

are equivalent; the last inclusion is again, however, the inclusion (2) from III.2.4. We know, in addition, that for a ring, considered as a multi-operator group, the concept of an ideal coincides with the concept of a (two-sided) ideal.

11. *The operator endomorphisms of a Σ-operator Abelian group G form a subring in the ring of all endomorphisms of this group* (see III.3.8). This follows without difficulty from the definition of addition and multiplication of endomorphisms, if we use the characterization of operator endomorphisms mentioned in V.1.2. The subring obtained is called the *ring of operator endomorphisms* of the Σ-operator Abelian group G.

Thus, the ring of operator endomorphisms for n-dimensional real vector space (see V.1.5) is the ring of linear transformations, isomorphic, as is known from any course in higher algebra, to the ring of real square matrices of order n.

12. *Let G be a group (ring) with arbitrary domain of operators Σ, and H an admissible normal subgroup (an admissible ideal) of G. Then the factor group (factor ring) G/H can be made into an operator group (ring) with domain of operators Σ, in such a way that the natural homomorphism of G onto G/H will be a Σ-operator homomorphism.*

In fact, if G is a group, then for any $a \in G$, $h \in H$ and $\alpha \in \Sigma$

$$(ah)\alpha = a\alpha \cdot h\alpha = a\alpha \cdot h',$$

where $h' \in H$ because H is admissible. This enables us to define the effect of the operator α on the element aH of the factor group G/H by means of the equation

$$(aH)\alpha = a\alpha \cdot H. \tag{12}$$

The validity of condition (1) of V.1.1 can be verified without difficulty:

$$(aH \cdot bH)\alpha = (abH)\alpha = (ab)\alpha \cdot H = (a\alpha \cdot b\alpha)H =$$
$$(a\alpha \cdot H)(b\alpha \cdot H) = (aH)\alpha.(bH)\alpha$$

The group G/H is a Σ-operator group; the last assertion of the theorem follows immediately from (12).

If, however, G is a ring, then equation (12), which defines the effect of the operators in G/H, can be rewritten in the form

$$(a + H)\alpha = a\alpha + H.$$

We verify condition (11) of V.1.7:

$$[(a + H)(b + H)]\alpha = (ab + H)\alpha = (ab)\alpha + H = a\alpha \cdot b + H =$$
$$(a\alpha + H)(b + H) = (a + H)\alpha \cdot (b + H),$$

In the same way we can also verify the second half of condition (11). Thus theorem has been proved.

The reader can verify without difficulty that *if G is a group with semigroup of operators* Σ, *or an Abelian group with ring of operators* Σ, *or else a ring with ring of operators* Σ, *then the same assertion can be made for G/H, where H is a* Σ-*admissible normal subgroup or ideal.*

§ 2. Free modules. Abelian groups

1. All the modules considered below are unital modules over an associative ring R with identity; the identities (6)–(9) of V.1.4 are thus satisfied. All these modules with respect to the operations of an Abelian group and operators from R, form a primitive class of universal algebras (III.6.3), and therefore we can speak of *free R-modules* (III.7.2). We will call a system of free generators of a free R-module its *basis*.

By applying the definition of an Abelian group and the identities (6)–(9) mentioned above, we now find that every element of a free R-module S with basis X can be written as a finite sum

$$x_1\alpha_1 + x_2\alpha_2 + \ldots + x_n\alpha_n, \qquad (1)$$

where $x_1, x_2, \ldots, x_n$ are distinct elements of X, $\alpha_1, \alpha_2, \ldots, \alpha_n \in R$ and are distinct from zero, $n \geqslant 0$. We will show that *this expression is unique*, after which we will speak of it as *the expression* for the element under consideration in the basis X.

For the proof we associate with every $x \in X$ the R-module R_x, isomorphic to the ring R, considered as a right module over itself (see V.1.6) and we take, corresponding to IV.5.5, the direct sum S' of all these modules R_x, $x \in X$. If we denote by x the element of the module R_x which corresponds to the identity of the ring R, then, by IV.4.2, every element of the module S' can be expressed uniquely in the form (1). The assertion which we wish to prove now follows from the fact that, by III.7.3, there exists a homomorphism of S into S', which maps every element $x \in X$ into the element x of the corresponding module R_x.

At the same time we have proved that *every free R-module is the direct sum of some set of R-modules isomorphic to R itself as a right R-module, and conversely.*

2. A right ideal B of an associative ring R with identity is called *principal* if there exists an element $\beta \in B$ such that every element of B can be written in at least one way in the form $\beta\alpha$, $\alpha \in R$. In this case we will write $B = (\beta)$.

If all the right ideals of the ring R are principal and R does not contain any divisors of zero, then every non-zero submodule of a free R-module will itself be a free R-module.

In fact, let us take a non-zero submodule U in the free R-module S with basis X. The set of elements $Y \subseteq U$ is called *admissible* if the following requirements are satisfied:

(1) the submodule $\{Y\}$ generated by the set Y is free and has Y as its basis;

(2) if X_y is the set of all elements of X which are contained in the expressions in the basis X for any elements of Y, then

$$\{X_y\} \cap U = \{Y\}.$$

The problem of the existence of admissible sets we leave open for the moment, but we note that if they exist and if we are given a chain of admissible sets, then their union will also be admissible. Therefore, by the Kuratowski–Zorn Theorem (I.6.3) there exist maximal sets amongst these admissible sets. Let Y be one of these.

The theorem will be proved, because of (1), if we show that $\{Y\} = U$.
Let

$$\{Y\} \subset U; \qquad\qquad (2)$$

this will also hold in the case when admissible sets do not exist, if we replace the submodule $\{Y\}$ by the zero submodule. We will show that (2) reduces to a contradiction.

By condition (2), in the expression for any element of U, lying outside $\{Y\}$, there must occur elements of X lying outside X_y. Let the least possible number of such elements be n, $n \geqslant 1$, and let there exist elements in $U \setminus \{Y\}$ in whose expressions the elements $x_1, x_2, \ldots, x_n$ of $X \setminus X_y$ occur and no others. The coefficients of x_n in the expressions for all these elements form, after we have adjoined zero to them, a right ideal of the ring R, i.e., by hypothesis, a principal right ideal (β).

We denote by z that one of the elements of $U \setminus \{Y\}$ considered, in whose expression the coefficient of x_n is exactly β, and we will show that, after we have adjoined the element z to Y we again obtain an admissible set, contradicting the fact that Y is maximal.

In fact, if condition 1) were not satisfied, then the elements of the submodule $\{Y, z\}$ would have non-unique expressions in terms of the elements of the set $Y \cup z$, and then we could find an element $\alpha \in R$ distinct from zero such that

$$z\alpha \in \{Y\}.$$

However, this is impossible, because in the expression for the element z there occur the elements $x_1, x_2, \ldots, x_n \in X \setminus X_Y$ with non-zero coefficients, and then, because the ring R has no divisors of zero, they also have non-zero coefficients in the expression for the element $z\alpha$.

On the other hand, to verify condition (2) we take any element $t \in \{X_{Y \cup z}\} \cap U$. In its expression in the basis X there occur some elements of X_Y, and also the elements $x_1, x_2, \ldots, x_n$, where the coefficient of x_n is contained in the right ideal (β), i.e. has the form β_γ, $\gamma \in R$. From this it follows that in the expression for the difference $t - z\gamma$ the element x_n does not occur, and then, because the number n is minimal, the elements $x_1, x_2, \ldots, x_{n-1}$ do not occur in it, i.e.

$$t - z\gamma \in \{X_Y\} \cap U = \{Y\},$$

whence

$$t \in \{Y, z\}.$$

Thus the theorem has been proved.

3. Every Abelian group is a module over the ring of integers, and this ring is a principal ideal ring (see II.9.3). By applying the results obtained above to this case and taking into account that the additive group of the ring of integers is an infinite cyclic group, we obtain:

Every free Abelian group (see III.7.10) *is the direct sum of infinite cyclic groups.* The number of these cyclic direct summands (or the power of the set of them) does not depend, by III.7.12, on the choice of the direct decomposition and is called the *rank* of this free Abelian group.

Every non-zero subgroup of a free Abelian group is itself free.

In a free Abelian group S of finite rank n the rank of every subgroup is finite and does not exceed n.

In fact, let $x_1, x_2, \ldots, x_n$ be the basis of the group S. In S we take any k elements $y_1, y_2, \ldots, y_k$, where $k > n$. Then

$$y_i = c_{i_1} x_1 + c_{i_2} x_2 + \ldots + c_{i_n} x_n, \quad i = 1, 2, \ldots, k.$$

The system of k integral n-dimensional vectors

$$(c_{i_1}, c_{i_2}, ..., c_{i_n}), \quad i = 1, 2, ..., k,$$

is linearly dependent, as we know, because $k > n$, and therefore it is possible to choose integers l_i, not all equal to zero, $i = 1, 2, ..., k$, such that

$$l_1 y_1 + l_2 y_2 + ... + l_k y_k = 0.$$

The elements $y_1, y_2, ..., y_k$ thus cannot be contained in the basis of any supgroup of the group S.

4. We will prove the following fundamental theorem on Abelian groups with a finite number of generators:

Every Abelian group with a finite number of generators is the direct sum of a finite number of cyclic groups.

The proof of this theorem, given below, is due to R. Rado [*J. Lond. math. Soc.* **26**, 74–75 (1951)].

Suppose that the Abelian group G has a system of n generators. We consider all possible such systems, assuming that there may occur in them elements which are equal to each other, and elements which are equal to zero. Let

$$a_1, a_2, ..., a_n \tag{3}$$

be one of these systems of generators, and we assume, if we denote by $o(a)$ the order of the element a, that

$$o(a_1) \leqslant o(a_2) \leqslant ... \leqslant o(a_n). \tag{4}$$

Thus, if any zeros occur in (3) then they stand at the beginning, and if there are any elements of infinite order, then they stand at the end.

The system (3) can be chosen in such a way that the system of numbers (4) will be minimal in the lexicographical ordering, i.e. if $b_1, b_2, ..., b_n$ is another system of generators and

$$o(b_1) \leqslant o(b_2) \leqslant ... \leqslant o(b_n),$$

then there is no i, $1 \leqslant i \leqslant n$, such that

$$o(b_1) = o(a_1), ..., o(b_{i-1}) = o(a_{i-1}), \quad o(b_i) < o(a_i).$$

We will show that if a system of generators (3) is chosen in the given way, then the group G will be the direct sum of the cyclic subgroups $\{a_1\}, \{a_2\}, ..., \{a_n\}$. If this is not so, then the expression for the elements of the group G in the form of a sum of elements of the given cyclic subgroups will not be unique, and therefore we obtain an equation

$$k_1 a_1 + k_2 a_2 + \ldots + k_n a_n = 0, \tag{5}$$

in which not all the summands are equal to zero. Let

$$k_1 a_1 = \ldots = k_{j-1} a_{j-1} = 0, \tag{6}$$

but $k_j a_j \neq 0$, $j \geqslant 1$; we can assume, however, that

$$0 < k_j < o(a_j). \tag{7}$$

We denote by k the greatest common divisor of the numbers $k_j, k_{j+1}, \ldots, k_n$, i.e.

$$k_i = k m_i, \quad i = j, \quad j+1, \ldots, n, \tag{8}$$

and the numbers $m_j, m_{j+1}, \ldots, m_n$ are all mutually prime. We will prove the following additional assertion:

5. *If we are given the Abelian group* $A = \{a_j, a_{j+1}, \ldots, a_n\}$ *and a system of mutually prime integers* $m_j, m_{j+1}, \ldots, m_n$, *then in A we can choose a new system of generators*

$$A = \{b_j, b_{j+1}, \ldots, b_n\}, \tag{9}$$

such that

$$b_j = m_j a_j + m_{j+1} a_{j+1} + \ldots + m_n a_n. \tag{10}$$

We will prove this by induction on the sum of the absolute values

$$m = |m_j| + |m_{j+1}| + \ldots + |m_n|,$$

because when $m = 1$ the assertion is trivial. If $m > 1$, then at least two numbers from the system of mutually prime numbers $m_j, m_{j+1}, \ldots, m_n$ must be distinct from zero. Suppose, for instance,

$$|m_j| \geqslant |m_{j+1}| > 0.$$

Then either $|m_j + m_{j+1}| < |m_j|$ or $|m_j - m_{j+1}| < |m_j|$, i.e. for one of the two signs it will be true that

$$|m_j \pm m_{j+1}| + |m_{j+1}| + \ldots + |m_n| < m. \tag{11}$$

Because

$$A = \{a_j, a_{j+1} \mp a_j, a_{j+2}, \ldots, a_n\},$$

then, using (11) and applying the inductive hypothesis, we obtain (9), where

$$b_j = (m_j \pm m_{j+1}) a_j + m_{j+1}(a_{j+1} \mp a_j) +$$

$$m_{j+2} a_{j+2} + \ldots + m_n a_n = m_j a_j + m_{j+1} a_{j+1} + \ldots + m_n a_n,$$

which is what we were required to prove.

6. We return to the proof of the fundamental theorem and by applying the assertion which we have just proved, we obtain a new system of generators for the group G,

$$G = \{a_1, \ldots, a_{j-1}, b_j, b_{j+1}, \ldots, b_n\},$$

where b_j satisfies equation (10). From (5), (6) and (8) it follows, however, that $kb_j = 0$, and therefore, because of (7),

$$o(b_j) \leqslant k \leqslant k_j < o(a_j),$$

which contradicts the choice of the system of generators (3). Hence the theorem has been proved.

7. *An infinite cyclic group cannot be decomposed as a direct sum* (see IV.3.10), because, by II.4.2, every two of its non-zero subgroups have non-zero intersection.

A finite cyclic group $\{a\}$ of order p^n, where p is a prime number, is indecomposable, because all its non-zero subgroups are exhausted by the cyclic subgroups of the elements $a, pa, p^2a, \ldots, p^{n-1}a$, which are embedded in one another. We will call such cyclic groups *primary*.

A finite cyclic group $\{a\}$, which has order

$$m = p_1^{n_1} p_2^{n_2} \ldots p_k^{n_k},$$

where $p_1, p_2, \ldots, p_k$ are distinct prime numbers and $k \geqslant 2$, can be decomposed into the direct sum of primary cyclic groups, which have respectively the orders $p_1^{n_1}, p_2^{n_2}, \ldots, p_k^{n_k}$,

In fact, we introduce the notation

$$q_i = p_1^{n_1} \ldots p_{i-1}^{n_{i-1}} p_{i+1}^{n_{i+1}} \ldots p_k^{n_k}, \quad i = 1, 2, \ldots, k.$$

Then the cyclic subgroup $\{q_i a\}$ has the order $p_i^{n_i}$, $i = 1, 2, \ldots, k$. The sum of these subgroups, by IV.3.2, will be their direct sum, because the orders of all the elements of the sum of the subgroups $\{q_j a\}, j \neq i$, are mutually prime to the number p_i, and therefore the intersection of this last sum with the subgroup $\{q_i a\}$ is equal to zero. Because, however, the order of the direct sum of a finite number of finite groups is equal to the product of the orders of the direct summands, then the order of the direct sum of all the subgroups $\{q_i a\}$, $i = 1, 2, \ldots, k$, is equal to m, i.e. this direct sum coincides with the whole group $\{a\}$.

From this, in view of IV.3.4, follows this strengthening of the fundamental theorem:

Every Abelian group with a finite number of generators is the direct sum of a finite number of indecomposable cyclic groups, some infinite, some finite primary.

8. In IV.4.5 we introduced the concept of an isomorphism of direct decompositions (the requirement of being "central" can, of course, be omitted for Abelian groups).

Every two decompositions of an Abelian group G with a finite number of generators into the direct sum of indecomposable cyclic groups are isomorphic.

In fact, suppose these decompositions are

$$G = \{a_1\} + \ldots + \{a_k\} + \{b_1\} + \ldots + \{b_s\},$$
$$G = \{a_1'\} + \ldots + \{a_l'\} + \{b_1'\} + \ldots + \{b_t'\}, \tag{12}$$

where the elements a have finite order, and the elements b have infinite order. We can verify without difficulty that in an Abelian group the totality of elements of finite order is a subgroup, which is called the *periodic part* of this group. If F is the periodic part of our group G, then

$$F = \{a_1\} + \ldots + \{a_k\} = \{a_1'\} + \ldots + \{a_l'\}, \tag{13}$$

because every element of G, in whose expression in one of the decompositions (12) at least one of the elements b occurs with coefficient distinct from zero, will certainly be of infinite order.

The group F is finite and therefore has principal series, and then the isomorphism of the direct decompositions (13) follows, by IV.4.6, from the Schmidt–Ore theorem. On the other hand, the free Abelian groups $\{b_1\} + \ldots + \{b_s\}$ and $\{b_1'\} + \ldots + \{b_t'\}$ of ranks s and t respectively are isomorphic, by IV.4.5, to the factor-group G/F, i.e. they are isomorphic to each other, and hence $s = t$ (see V.2.3).

Every two decompositions of an arbitrary Abelian group into the direct sum of indecomposable cyclic groups are isomorphic, if the group has such decompositions (possibly with an infinite set of direct summands).

Every subgroup of a direct sum of cyclic groups can itself be decomposed into the direct sum of cyclic groups [L. Ya. Kulikov, *Mat. Sb.* **16**, 129–162 (1945)].*

9. An Abelian group is called *primary* with respect to a prime number p or *p-primary* if the order of each of its elements is a power of the number p.

An element a of the p-primary Abelian group G has finite *height* $n, n \geqslant 0$, if the equation

$$p^k x = a$$

is soluble in G if, and only if, $k \leqslant n$.

   * Every periodic (see II.3.4) Abelian group can be decomposed into the direct sum of primary groups with respect to distinct prime numbers.

   A primary Abelian group G can be decomposed into the direct sum of cyclic groups if, and only if, it is the union of an ascending sequence

$$A_1 \subseteq A_2 \subseteq \ldots \subseteq A_n \subseteq \ldots$$

of its subgroups such that in each of them the elements distinct from zero have finite heights with a common bound (in G) [L. Ya. Kulikov, *ibid.*].

   Every primary Abelian group whose elements have a common bound can be decomposed into the direct sum of cyclic groups [Prüfer, *Math. Z.* **17**, 35–61 (1923)].

   Every countable primary Abelian group, all of whose non-zero elements have finite height, can be decomposed into the direct sum of cyclic groups [Prüfer, *ibid.*].*

§ 3. Vector spaces over skew fields

   1. We will study R-modules in the special case when the associative ring R is a skew field, not necessarily commutative. Every unital module over an associative skew field K is called a *vector* (or *linear*) *space* over this skew field. It is essential to bear in mind that the multiplication of elements of a vector space by elements of the skew field K is subject to the conditions (6)–(9) of V.1.4.

   The submodules (i.e. the K-admissible subgroups) of a vector space are called its *linear subspaces*. The *isomorphism* of vector spaces over a skew field K is always understood, corresponding to V.1.2, as a K-operator isomorphism.

   2. *For any subspace A of a vector space V over a skew field K there exists a complement, i.e. a subspace B of the space V such that*

$$A \cap B = 0, \quad \{A, B\} = V.$$

In other words, the space V will be the direct sum of the subspaces A and B,

$$V = A + B.$$

In fact, we consider all those subspaces of the vector space V whose intersections with A are equal to zero. The set M of all such subspaces is not empty, because it contains the zero subspace. Further, this set is partially ordered by set-theoretical inclusion, and it satisfies the conditions of the Kuratowski–Zorn theorem (see I.6.3).

In fact, if we are given any chain L in M, then the union C of the subspaces C_i forming this chain (i varies through some set of indices) will itself be a subspace in V: if $x, y \in C$, then there exist i and j such that $x \in C_i, y \in C_j$, and therefore, by letting, for instance, $C_i \subseteq C_j$, we obtain $x, y \in C_j$, i.e. $x + y \in C_j$ and, hence, $x + y \in C$; on the other hand, from $x \in C_i$ it follows that $x \alpha \in C_i$ for all $\alpha \in K$, and therefore $x \alpha \in C$. From $C_i \cap A = 0$ for all i it follows, obviously, that $C \cap A = 0$, and therefore the subspace C is the upper bound in the set M for the chain L.

Thus, there exist maximal elements in the set M. Let the subspace B be one of these maximal elements. Then $A \cap B = 0$, which follows from the definition of the set M. We will show that $\{A, B\} = V$.

If $x \in V$, $x \notin B$, then the subspace $\{B, x\}$ consists of all elements of the form $b + x\alpha$, where $b \in B$, $\alpha \in K$. This subspace is strictly greater than B, and therefore, because B is maximal in M, the intersection $A \cap \{B, x\}$ contains the elements $a = b + x\alpha$ distinct from zero. Because $\alpha \neq 0$ — otherwise it would be the case that $a \in B$, contradicting the equation $A \cap B = 0$ — then $x = a\alpha^{-1} - b\alpha^{-1} \in \{A, B\}$, which is what we were required to prove.

The complement for the subspace A can be chosen in the space V, generally speaking, in many ways. All these complements are, however, isomorphic to each other, because, by the isomorphism theorem in III.4.2. or by IV.4.5, all of them are isomorphic to the factor space V/A.

3. The concept of linear dependence, which plays a very important part in the theory of finite-dimensional vector spaces over a field, as studied in any course in higher algebra, also carries over to the general case now under consideration. In fact, a finite system of elements

$$a_1, a_2, \ldots, a_k \tag{1}$$

of the vector space V over the skew field K is said to be *linearly dependent* if there exist elements $\alpha_1, \alpha_2, \ldots, \alpha_k$ in K, not all equal to zero, such that

$$a_1\alpha_2 + a_2\alpha_2 + \ldots + a_k\alpha_k = 0,$$

and *linearly independent* otherwise. As usual, the linear dependence of the system (1) is equivalent to the fact that at least one of the elements of (1) can be expressed linearly in terms of the other elements of this system (with coefficients from the skew field K).

All the fundamental properties of linear dependence, which are established in a course in higher algebra can be extended without any difficulty to the case of arbitrary vector spaces over any associative skew field. Therefore we will not give the proofs of these properties and will limit ourselves merely to formulating the most important of them:

If in the vector space V over the skew field K we are given two finite systems of elements

$$a_1, a_2, \ldots, a_k$$

and

$$b_1, b_2, \ldots, b_l,$$

of which the first is linearly independent and, moreover, each of its elements can be expressed linearly in terms of the second system, then $k \leqslant l$.

From this it follows that *if in the vector space V over the skew field K we are given two finite linearly independent systems of elements where any element of either of these two systems can be expressed linearly in terms of the other system, then these two systems consist of exactly the same number of elements.*

4. Any, not necessarily finite, system of elements X of a vector space V over the skew field K is said to be *linearly dependent* if in X there is contained at least one finite linearly dependent subsystem of elements, and *linearly independent*, if all the finite subsystems of the system X are linearly independent. It is clear that every linearly independent system consists of distinct elements and that every part of it is itself linearly independent.

The space V has linearly independent subsets; such, for instance, are the subsets consisting of one non-zero element. The set M of all linearly independent subsets of the space V is partially ordered by inclusion, and satisfies the conditions of the Kuratowski–Zorn theorem (see I.5.3). In fact, if we are given a chain L in M, then the union X of the linearly independent subsets X_1, forming this chain, will itself be linearly independent: if we take a finite system of elements in X

$$x_1, x_2, \ldots, x_k, \tag{2}$$

then there exists a linearly independent subset X_j, contained in the chain L, which contains the whole system (2), and therefore the system (2) must be linearly independent. The subset X is, therefore, the upper bound of the chain L in the set M.

This proves that *the vector space V over the skew field K has maximal linearly independent subsets, where every linearly independent subset of space is contained in some maximal one.*

Every maximal linearly independent subset of a vector space V is called a *basis* of this space.

5. *A subset X, consisting of elements x_i (i varies through some set of indices) will be a basis of the vector space V over the skew field K if and only if every element a of V distinct from zero has a unique expression*

$$a = x_{i_1}\alpha^1 + x_{i_2}\alpha^2 + \ldots + x_{i_k}\alpha^k, \tag{3}$$

where $x_{i_1}, x_{i_2}, \ldots, x_{i_k} \in X$, $\alpha^1, \alpha^2, \ldots, \alpha^k$ are elements of the skew field K distinct from zero, and $k \geqslant 1$.

In fact, let X be a basis of the space V, but suppose that the element a of V, distinct from zero, does not have an expression of the form (3); from this, in particular, it follows that $a \notin X$. Then, by adjoining the element a to any finite subsystem of the set X, we obtain a linearly independent system, and therefore, by adjoining a to the whole basis X, we again obtain a linearly independent set, contrary to the definition of a basis. If, however, the element a has two distinct expressions in terms of the basis X, namely (3) and

$$a = x_{j_1}\beta^1 + x_{j_2}\beta^2 + \ldots + x_{j_l}\beta^l,$$

then the union of the finite subsystems $x_{i_1}, \ldots, x_{i_k}$ and $x_{j_1}, \ldots, x_{j_l}$ of the basis X will be linearly dependent, which again contradicts the definition of a basis. The verification of the converse assertion of the theorem is simple and is left to the reader.

As well as the expression (3) for all elements a of the vector space V we can, of course, also use the uniquely defined expression

$$a = \sum_{x_i \in X} x_i \alpha^i, \quad \alpha^i \in K, \tag{3'}$$

in which at most a finite number of the coefficients α^i are distinct from zero. By V.1.4 the addition of elements written in the form (3') is reduced to the addition of the coefficients for the individual x_i's, and the multiplication of the element a by the element β of the skew field K is equivalent to the multiplication of all the coefficients α^i from (3') by β on the right.

By IV.4.2 we can say that *the vector space V over the skew field K with basis X is the direct sum of the vector spaces xK, $x \in X$.*

6. *All bases of the vector space V over the skew field K have the same power.*

Let us, in fact, take the bases X and Y in the space V. If at least one of them, for instance X, is finite and consists of m elements, then, as follows from V.3.3, the basis Y is also finite and also consists of m elements.

Suppose, however, that both the bases X, Y are infinite and have respectively the powers m and n, where we suppose that $m < n$. Every element x of the basis X has, by V.3.5, an expression of the form (3) in terms of a finite system of elements Y_x from the basis Y. The union Y' of all such finite subsystems Y_x, where x varies through the whole basis X, will be a proper subset of the basis Y, because, as the union of a set of finite sets, having power m, it will itself have power m. Let y be any element of $Y \setminus Y'$. By V.3.5 it can be expressed linearly in terms of a finite system of elements $x_1, x_2, \ldots x_k$ of X, and therefore also in terms of a finite subsystem $\bigcup_{i=1}^{k} Y_{x_i}$ of the set Y', which, however, contradicts the linear independence of the basis Y. Thus the theorem has been proved.†

The power of any basis of a vector space V is called the *dimension* of this space. If, in particular, this power is finite, then we speak of a *finite-dimensional* space. Thus, the vector space xK is one-dimensional.

7. *For every power m, finite or infinite, there exists a vector space over the skew field K, having the dimension m.*

Let X be any set of power m. Then the direct sum of the one-dimensional vector spaces xK for all $x \in X$ (its existence follows from IV.5.5) will be the desired vector space. Here xK is the

---

† This result also follows from Fujiwara's first theorem (III.7.5), if we observe that a vector space over a skew field K is a free K-module (Ed.).

totality of elements of the form $x\alpha$, $\alpha \in K$, with the natural definitions of addition and multiplication by elements of K.

*Two vector spaces V and W over the skew field K are isomor-
phic if, and only if, they have the same dimension.*

In fact, if there exists an isomorphic mapping φ of the space V
onto the space W and if X is a basis of the space V, then $X\varphi$ will
be a basis of the space W. This proves one half of the theorem.

Suppose, on the other hand, that the spaces V and W have
respectively the bases X and Y, which have the same power.
We fix some one–one mapping φ of the basis X onto the basis Y

$$x\varphi \in Y \text{ for all } x \in X,$$

and in the following way we extend it to the whole space V:
if the element a of V has the expression (3') in terms of the basis
X, then we set

$$a\varphi = \sum_{x_i \in X} (x_i\varphi)\,\alpha^i.$$

We obviously obtain a one–one mapping of the space V onto
the whole space W; the fact that this mapping is an isomorphism follows from what was said in V.3.5.

We see that the theorems of the present section give a complete
description of all vector spaces over any skew field K.

§ 4. Rings of linear transformations

1. Operator endomorphisms of a vector space V over a skew
field K are called *linear transformations* of this space. By V.1.11
the linear transformations form a subring in the ring of all endomorphisms of an Abelian group V. We will denote the ring of
linear transformations by $R(V, K)$.

We wish to show that when this ring is given, both the skew
field K, and the space V itself, may be defined in terms of it.
In order to formulate this assertion more precisely, we introduce
the following concept, which is a generalization of the concept
of an isomorphism of two vector spaces over the same skew field.

Suppose that we are given the vector spaces V over the skew
field K and W over the skew field L. We will say that between
these spaces we can establish a *semi-linear correspondence* σ,
if there exists an isomorphism σ of the skew field K onto the skew

field L, and an isomorphism, which we also denote by σ, of the group V onto the group W, where for all $a \in V$, $\alpha \in K$

$$(a\alpha)\sigma = a\sigma \cdot \alpha\sigma.$$

Thus, if $K = L$ and σ is the identity automorphism of the skew field K, then the semi-linear correspondence reduces to an isomorphism of the vector spaces V and W over the skew field K.

2. *If the vector spaces V over the skew field K and W over the skew field L are related by a semi-linear correspondence σ, then the rings of linear transformations $R(V, K)$ and $R(W, L)$ of these spaces are isomorphic.*

In fact, let $\varphi \in R(V, K)$. Then $\sigma^{-1}\varphi\sigma$ will be a mapping of W into itself, which is a linear transformation, because, by taking into account that φ is a linear transformation, for any $b, b' \in W$, $\beta \in L$ we obtain

$$(b + b')(\sigma^{-1}\varphi\sigma) = b(\sigma^{-1}\varphi\sigma) + b'(\sigma^{-1}\varphi\sigma),$$

$$(b\beta)(\sigma^{-1}\varphi\sigma) = (b\sigma^{-1} \cdot \beta\sigma^{-1})\,\varphi\sigma = (b\sigma^{-1}\varphi \cdot \beta\sigma^{-1})\sigma = b(\sigma^{-1}\varphi\sigma) \cdot \beta.$$

The correspondence $\varphi \to \sigma^{-1}\varphi\,\sigma$ is a homomorphism of the ring $R(V, K)$ into the ring $R(W, L)$, because for any $b \in W$ and any φ, $\psi \in R(V, K)$

$$b[\sigma^{-1}(\varphi + \psi)\sigma] = b[\sigma^{-1}\varphi\sigma + \sigma^{-1}\psi\sigma],$$

$$b[\sigma^{-1}(\varphi\psi)\sigma] = b(\sigma^{-1}\varphi\sigma)(\sigma^{-1}\psi\sigma).$$

This will be a mapping onto the whole of the ring $R(W, L)$, for if $\varphi' \in R(W, L)$, then

$$\varphi' = \sigma^{-1}(\sigma\varphi'\sigma^{-1})\sigma, \qquad \sigma\varphi'\sigma^{-1} \in R(V, K).$$

This correspondence will, finally, be an isomorphism, because if the transformation $\sigma^{-1}\varphi\sigma$ is zero, i.e. for all $b \in W$

$$b(\sigma^{-1}\varphi\sigma) = 0,$$

then for all $a \in V$

$$a\varphi = (a\sigma)(\sigma^{-1}\varphi\sigma)\sigma^{-1} = 0\sigma^{-1} = 0,$$

i.e. the linear transformation φ will also be zero.

We will say that the isomorphism which we have constructed between the rings $R(V, K)$ and $R(W, L)$ is *induced* by the semi-linear correspondence σ.

3. The converse of this assertion is true (see, for instance, R. Baer's book, *Linear algebra and projective geometry*):

* Every isomorphism between the rings of linear transformations $R(V, K)$ and $R(W, L)$ is induced by a semi-linear correspondence between the spaces V and W.*

However, we will prove the following weaker assertion: *Giving, to within isomorphism, a ring of linear transformations $R(V, K)$ defines, also to within isomorphism, both the skew field K and the space V (i.e. it defines the dimension of this space).*

4. We fix a basis X with elements $x_i, i \in I$, in the space V. As usual, a linear transformation φ is completely defined, because of (2) from V.1.2, by giving the images $x_i\varphi$ of all the elements of the basis X. We compare with the transformation φ the infinite matrix whose rows and columns are numbered by all the possible indices $i \in I$, and in whose i-th column we place the coefficients of the expression for the element $x_i\varphi$ in basis X; it is clear that only a finite number of these coefficients are distinct from zero.

Conversely, every matrix of the given form, in each of whose columns there are only a finite number of non-zero elements, corresponds to some linear transformation. *The set K_I of all such matrices will be a ring with the usual definitions for the operations on matrices, and this ring will be anti-isomorphic to the ring $R(V, K)$* (see V.1.6). We will only verify the following two assertions:

If $A, B \in K_I$, then $AB \in K_I$. In fact, if $i \in I$ and the i-th column of the matrix B has non-zero elements only in the rows with the numbers $j_1, j_2, \ldots, j_n$, then we consider the columns with these numbers in the matrix A. Only a finite number of non-zero elements are contained in them, and they are situated in a finite number of rows, and therefore in the i-th column of the product AB there will only be a finite number of non-zero elements.

If $\varphi, \psi \in R(V, K)$ and the matrices $(\beta_{ji}), (\gamma_{kj}) \in K_I$ correspond to them, then the matrix $(\gamma_{kj})(\beta_{ji})$ corresponds to the product $\varphi\psi$.

In fact, for all $i \in I$ it follows from

$$x_i\varphi = \sum_{j \in I} x_j \beta_{ji},$$

$$x_j\psi = \sum_{k \in I} x_k \gamma_{kj}$$

that

$$x_i(\varphi\psi) = \sum_{j \in I} (x_j\psi)\beta_{ji} = \sum_{k \in I} x_k \Big(\sum_{j \in I} \gamma_{kj}\beta_{ji}\Big).$$

5. Thus we now need to prove that giving the ring K_I as an abstract ring determines both the skew field K (to within isomorphism) and the power of the index set I.

We fix a finite system of indices

$$j_1, j_2, \ldots, j_n \in_I, \quad n \geqslant 1, \tag{1}$$

and a system of non-zero elements $\lambda_t^s \in K$, $s, t = 1, 2, \ldots, n$, subject to the following conditions:

$$\lambda_s^s = 1; \quad \lambda_s^t = (\lambda_t^s)^{-1}; \quad \lambda_t^s\lambda_u^t = \lambda_u^s. \tag{2}$$

We denote by

$$S = S(j_1, j_2, \ldots, j_n; \lambda_t^s, s, t = 1, 2, \ldots, n) \tag{3}$$

the set of matrices from K_I, of which only the rows with the numbers from (1) can be non-zero, and where for $s, t = 1, 2, \ldots, n$ the j_s-th row is obtained by multiplying the j_t-th row on the left by λ_t^s.

The set S is a minimal right ideal of the ring K_I.

The assertion that S is a right ideal in K_I can be verified without difficulty. This ideal does not consist of zero alone—one row with an index from (1) can, obviously, be given arbitrarily in a matrix from S.

To prove that the ideal S is minimal we introduce a notation which we will also use in what follows: if $\alpha \in K$, then we denote by $(\alpha)_{ji}$ the matrix from K_I in whose (j, i)-th position there is the element α, and all of whose other elements are equal to zero.

We take any non-zero matrix A in S; let the element $\alpha \neq 0$ occur in its (j, i)-th position, where j is from the system (1). By multiplying A on the right by the matrix $(\alpha^{-1})_{ii}$, we obtain a matrix from S with a single non-zero column, namely the i-th, and which has unity in its (j, i) th-position. Finally by multiplying the matrix obtained on the right by some matrix from K_I, in which only the i-th row can be non-zero, we can obviously obtain any matrix from S.

The ideals of the form (3) *exhaust all the minimal right ideals of the ring K_I.*

In fact, we take an arbitrary non-zero right ideal T in K_I, and in it a matrix with non-zero i-th column. By multiplying this matrix on the right by $(1)_{ii}$, we obtain a matrix A from T which contains only this one non-zero i-th column. Suppose that the elements of this column distinct from zero are

$$\alpha_{j_1 i}, \alpha_{j_2 i}, \ldots, \alpha_{j_n i}.$$

We set

$$\lambda_t^s = \alpha_{j_s i}\alpha_{j_t i}^{-1}, \quad s, t = 1, 2, \ldots, n;$$

conditions (2) are satisfied. Now it is easy to see that the right ideal contained in T, generated by the matrix A, is the ideal S of (3).

6. *All the minimal right ideals of the ring K_I, regarded as right modules over K_I, are isomorphic to each other.*

In fact, suppose that S and S' are two ideals of the form (3). We choose the single indices, j and j', from the systems of indices (1) corresponding to these ideals. Every matrix of S is completely determined by its j-th row, which may be arbitrary; the same is true of S' and j'. Thus we obtain a one–one correspondence between S and S', if we relate to each other the matrices whose j-th and j'-th rows, respectively, coincide. This correspondence is in fact an isomorphism of the K_I-modules S and S'.

From this it follows that *the rings of operator endomorphisms of the minimal right ideals of the ring K_I, regarded as K_I-modules, are isomorphic to each other.* We will show that *these rings are anti-isomorphic to the skew field K.*

Without loss of generality we can consider an ideal S of the form (3) for which $n = 1$, i.e. the system (1) consists of one index j. It is clear that multiplication on the left of all elements of all matrices of S by the element $\alpha \in K$ will be a K_I-operator endomorphism of the ideal S.

Now let φ be any K_I-operator endomorphism of the ideal S. Because $(1)_{jj} \in S$, we can find $(1)_{jj}\varphi$. If this matrix, which consists of one non-zero j-th row, were to have an element distinct from zero in the (j, i)-th position, $j \neq i$, then we would have, contrary to the fact that the endomorphism φ is a K_I-operator,

$$((1)_{jj} \cdot (1)_{ii})\varphi = 0\varphi = 0,$$
$$((1)_{jj}\varphi) \cdot (1)_{ii} \neq 0.$$

Thus,

$$(1)_{jj}\varphi = (\alpha)_{jj}, \quad \alpha \in K.$$

However, every matrix A from S is equal to its product on the left by $(1)_{jj}$, and therefore

$$A\varphi = ((1)_{jj}A)\varphi = (1)_{jj}\varphi \cdot A = (\alpha)_{jj}A.$$

The last product, however, means that all the elements of the matrix A are multiplied on the left by α.

We have that all the K_I-operator endomorphisms of the ideal S are exhausted by multiplications on the left by elements of the skew field K. Here there corresponds to the sum of endomorphisms the sum of the corresponding elements of K, and to the product, because multiplication by $\alpha \in K$ is performed on the left, there corresponds the product of the elements of K in the opposite order.

This proves that the skew field K is determined to within isomorphism by giving the ring $R(V, K)$ as an abstract ring. In fact, the skew field K is anti-isomorphic to the ring of R' operator endomorphisms of any minimal right ideal of the ring $R'(= K_I)$, anti-isomorphic to the ring $R(V, K)$.

7. We turn to the problem of the cardinal number of the set of indices I. We suppose first that the set I is finite and consists of the indices $1, 2, \ldots, n$. The totality $S(j)$ of matrices of K_I, in which only the j-th row can be distinct from zero, $j = 1, 2, \ldots, n$, by V.4.5, will be a minimal right ideal of the ring K_I. These ideals form a direct sum (see IV.3.2), which coincides with the whole ring K_I, and therefore in K_I, as in a right K_I-module, we have the composition series of length n (see III.4.6)

$$O \subset S(1) \subset S(1) + S(2) \subset \ldots \subset \sum_{j=1}^{n} S(j) = K_I.$$

The number n is invariant, and thus determines, by the Jordan–Hölder theorem, the K_I-module K_I itself.

Now we consider the case of an infinite set I. We call a system of minimal right ideals of the ring K_I *independent* if the right ideal generated by all the ideals of this system is their direct sum. The system of ideals $S(j)$ (see above), taken for all $j \in I$, will be an independent system, and in fact a maximal one, because every ideal S of the form (3) is contained in the direct sum of the ideals

$S(j)$, where j is taken from the system (1), and therefore cannot be added to the system of all the ideals $S(j)$, $j \in I$, without violating its independence. The cardinal number of the system of ideals $S(j)$ clearly coincides with the cardinal number of the set I.

The cardinal number of any independent system of minimal right ideals of the ring K_I is not greater than the cardinal number of the set I.

In fact, if we are given a system of ideals of the form (3), then the set of indices connected with this system will be part of the set of all finite subsets of the (infinite) set I, and therefore its cardinal number does not exceed the cardinal number of the set I. On the other hand, from the same results on composition series (see III.4.6) it follows that an independent system of ideals of the form (3), connected with a given system of indices (1), may only be finite.

Thus, the cardinal number of the set I (i.e. the dimension of the vector space V) is also determined uniquely by giving the ring $R(V, K)$ as an abstract ring. In fact, this cardinal number is the maximal cardinal number of an independent system of minimal right ideals of a ring anti-isomorphic to the ring $R(V, K)$. The theorem has thus been proved.

8. If we take a set M in the ring R, then we will call the totality of those elements $r \in R$ such that $xr = 0$ for all $x \in M$ the *right annihilator* of this set. The right annihilator of any set will, obviously, be a right ideal of the ring R. In the same way we define the *left annihilator* of a set.

* An associative ring R will be isomorphic to the ring $R(V, K)$ of all linear transformations of some vector space V over some skew field K, if and only if it satisfies the following conditions: (1) R has an identity; (2) R has minimal one-sided ideals which are all contained in every non-zero two-sided ideal; (3) if the right annihilator of a left ideal is equal to zero, then this ideal contains all minimal left ideals; (4) the sum of any two right (left) annihilators is itself such an annihilator [Wolfson, *Amer. J. Math.* **75** 358–386 (1953)].*

§ 5. Simple rings. Jacobson's theorem

1. From what was said in II.7.9 it follows that the complete ring of matrices of a given order n over an associative skew field

K (i.e. the ring of all linear transformations of the n-dimensional vector space over K) will be a simple ring. Now we wish to study one rather wider class of simple associative rings.

We consider an arbitrary vector space V over an associative skew field K. The image $V\varphi$ of this space under the linear transformation φ will obviously be a linear subspace (see V.3.1). We will say that φ is a linear transformation of *finite rank* if the subspace $V\varphi$ is finite-dimensional. It is clear that the sum and difference of linear transformations of finite rank, and also the product of linear transformations, at least one of which is a transformation of finite rank, will themselves be transformations of finite rank, and therefore the set $R'(V, K)$ of all such transformations will be a subring and in fact an ideal of the ring of all linear transformations $R(V, K)$.

A subring R_0 of the ring $R(V, K)$ is called a *dense ring of linear transformations* if for any linearly independent system of elements $x_1, x_2, \ldots, x_n \in V$ and an arbitrary system of elements $y_1, y_2, \ldots, y_n \in V$ we can find a linear transformation φ in the ring R_0 such that

$$x_i \varphi = y_i, \quad i = 1, 2, \ldots, n.$$

2. *Every dense ring of linear transformations of finite rank is a simple ring.*

In fact, let R_0 be a dense ring of linear transformations of finite rank in the vector space V over the skew field K and let R_0 have a non-zero ideal A. We will prove that *for every finite dimensional subspace L we can find in the ideal A a projection of V onto L*, i.e. a transformation $a \in A$ such that $Va = L$ and for every $y \in L$ the equation $ya = y$ holds.

First let the subspace L be one-dimensional, $L = xK$, $x \neq 0$. We take $a \in A$, $a \neq 0$. The subspace Va is finite dimensional; let $y_1, y_2, \ldots, y_n$ be a basis for it. Then there exists an $x_1 \in V$ such that $x_1 a = y_1$. Because R_0 is dense there exists a $\varphi \in R_0$ such that

$$y_1 \varphi = x_1, \quad y_2 \varphi = \ldots = y_n \varphi = 0. \tag{1}$$

Because A is an ideal, $a\varphi = a' \in A$ and, by (1), $Va' = x_1 K$, where $x_1 a' = x_1$. In addition, there exist $\varphi_1, \varphi_2 \in R_0$ such that

$$x\varphi_1 = x_1, \quad x_1 \varphi_2 = x.$$

Therefore

$$V(\varphi_1 a' \varphi_2) = xK = L,$$
$$x(\varphi_1 a' \varphi_2) = x,$$

and because $\varphi_1 a' \varphi_2 \in A$, this will also be the desired projection.

Now suppose that our assertion has been proved for subspaces of dimension $n-1$ and let the subspace L be n-dimensional, $n > 1$. We take an $(n-1)$-dimensional subspace L' in it; by hypothesis, there exists a projection $a' \in A$ of the space V onto the subspace L'. Then $La' = L$. The kernel L'' of this transformation is a one-dimensional subspace, $L''a' = 0$, and

$$L = L' + L''.$$

There exists a projection $a'' \in A$ of the space V onto the space L''. Then

$$a = a' + a'' - a'a'' \in A$$

will be the desired projection of V onto L. In fact, for all $x \in V$

$$xa = xa' + xa'' - (xa')a'' \in L;$$

if $x \in L'$, then

$$xa = x + xa'' - xa'' = x;$$

if $x \in L''$, then $xa' = 0$ and

$$xa = xa'' = x.$$

The proof of the theorem can now be carried out without difficulty. For any $\varphi \in R_0$ the subspace $V\varphi$ is finite-dimensional and, by what has been proved, there exists an $a \in A$, which is a projection of V onto $V\varphi$. Therefore $\varphi a = \varphi$, whence $\varphi \in A$, i.e. $A = R_0$.

3. *Every dense ring of linear transformations of finite rank has minimal right ideals.*

In fact, let R_0 again be a dense ring of linear transformations of finite rank in the vector space V over the skew field K and let L be any one-dimensional subspace of V. By applying the assertion proved above to the case $A = R_0$, we can assert that there exists an $a \in R_0$ which is a projection of V onto L. We denote by L' the totality of those $y' \in V$ such that $y'a = 0$. Then $L \cap L' = 0$ and

$$V = L + L'. \tag{2}$$

We denote by A the totality of those $a' \in R_0$ such that $L'a' = 0$. It is clear that $a \in A$, i.e. A does not consist of zero alone, and that A will be a right ideal of the ring R_0. We will prove that this ideal is minimal. Let a_1 and a_2 be any non-zero elements of A. If $L = xK$, then $xa_1 \neq 0$, because otherwise we would have $Va_1 = 0$, i.e. $a_1 = 0$. Therefore, because the ring R_0 is dense, there exists $a\varphi \in R_0$ such that

$$(xa_1)\varphi = xa_2, \tag{3}$$

and because

$$L'a_1 = L'a_2 = 0,$$

then, by (2) and (3),

$$a_1\varphi = a_2,$$

i.e. the right ideal A is generated by an arbitrary non-zero element a_1 of A.

4. A converse of the results obtained is the following theorem of Jacobson [*Trans. Amer. math. Soc.* **57**, 228–245 (1945)]:

Every non-zero (see II.2.2) *simple ring R, which has minimal right ideals, is isomorphic to a dense ring of linear transformations of finite rank of some vector space over some skew field.*

We take a minimal right ideal A in our ring R. Multiplication of the ideal A on the right by an element $r \in R$ determines an endomorphism of the additive group of A. Because the sum (product) of elements of R corresponds to the sum (product) of the corresponding endomorphisms, we have a homomorphism of the ring R into the ring of endomorphisms of the additive group of A.

From the simplicity of the ring R it follows that this homomorphism will either be an isomorphism or else a mapping into zero. The latter case, however, is impossible. From $AR = 0$ (i.e. $ar = 0$ for all $a \in A$, $r \in R$) it would follow that $A^2 = 0$, and then the non-zero two-sided ideal

$$B = RA + A,$$

i.e. the totality of elements of the form

$$\sum_{i=1}^{n} r_i a_i + a, \quad r_i \in R, \quad a_i, a \in A, \quad i = 1, 2, ..., n$$

(for all possible natural numbers n) would have the property $B^2 = 0$. From the simplicity of the ring R it follows, however, that $B = R$, and then $R^2 = 0$ which contradicts the hypothesis that the ring R is non-zero.

5. We can assume, thus, that R is some ring of endomorphisms (i.e. a subring of the ring of all endomorphisms) of the additive ring of the ideal A. Because the right ideal A is minimal, in the group of A there are no non-trivial subgroups, admissible (see V.1.2) with respect to all the endomorphisms of R, i.e., as we say, the ring of endomorphisms R is *irreducible*.

SCHUR'S LEMMA. *If we are given some irreducible ring of endomorphisms R of the Abelian group A, then the set K of those endomorphisms of the group A which commute (in the sense of the multiplication of endomorphisms) with every endomorphism of R will be a skew field.*

It is clear, in fact, that K is a subring of the ring of all endomorphisms of the group A and contains the identity automorphism of the group A. Now let $\alpha \in K$ and $\alpha \neq 0$. Then $A\alpha \neq 0$ and because the subgroup $A\alpha$ admits multiplication on the right by all elements of R, and the ring of endomorphisms R is irreducible, then $A\alpha = A$. The kernel of the endomorphism α will be an R-admissible subgroup, i.e. in view of the irreducibility of the ring R, it will be equal to zero. The endomorphism α is thus an automorphism, and then there exists an inverse automorphism α^{-1} which commutes, like α, with all the endomorphisms of R; therefore $\alpha^{-1} \in K$.

By applying Schur's lemma to the theorem which we wish to prove, we find that the additive group of the ideal A is a vector space over the skew field K, and because every endomorphism of R commutes with each endomorphism of K, R will be some ring of linear transformations of this vector space.

6. *The ring R is a dense ring of linear transformations.*

First let there be given in A the elements a and a', where $a \neq 0$. The set aR is a right ideal of the ring R. If $aR = 0$, then the set of all $x \in A$ for which $xR = 0$ will not consist of zero alone, and because it is a right ideal in R, then, because A is minimal, it coincides with A. From this it follows, however, that $AR = 0$, which, as was shown in V.5.4, is impossible. Therefore $aR = A$, and then there exists an $r \in R$ such that $ar = a'$.

Now let there be given in A the elements $a_1, a_2, ..., a_n$ linearly independent over K and the arbitrary elements $a_1', a_2', ..., a_n'$, $n > 1$ We suppose that we have already proved the existence of elements $r_i \in R$, $i = 1, 2, ..., n$, such that

$$a_i r_i \neq 0, \quad a_j r_i = 0 \quad \text{when} \quad j = 1, ..., i-1, i+1, ..., n.$$

By what was proved above, there exist $r_i' \in R$, $i = 1, 2, ..., n$, such that

$$a_i r_i r_i' = a_i'.$$

Therefore the element

$$r = \sum_{i=1}^{n} r_i r_i' \in R$$

has the property that

$$a_i r = a_i', \quad i = 1, 2, ..., n.$$

7. Thus we need to prove that *for any linearly independent system of elements $a_1, a_2, ..., a_n \in A$, $n > 1$, over K there exists an element $r \in R$ such that*

$$a_1 r = ... = a_{n-1} r = 0, \quad a_n r \neq 0.$$

First let $n = 2$. We suppose that from $a_1 r = 0$ it always follows that $a_2 r = 0$. For every $a \in A$ there exists an $r \in R$ such that $a = a_1 r$. If also $a = a_1 r'$, then $a_1(r - r') = 0$, and therefore, by hypothesis, $a_2(r - r') = 0$ also, whence $a_2 r = a_2 r'$. Thus we define a single-valued mapping α of the group A into itself, if for $a = a_1 r$ we set

$$a\alpha = a_2 r.$$

The mapping α is an endomorphism of the group A, because from $a = a_1 r$, $b = a_1 r'$ it follows that $a + b = a_1(r + r')$ and therefore

$$(a + b)\alpha = a_2(r + r') = a_2 r + a_2 r' = a\alpha + b\alpha.$$

The endomorphism α commutes with every endomorphism $r_0 \in R$, because from $a = a_1 r$ it follows that $a r_0 = a_1(r r_0)$, whence

$$(a r_0)\alpha = a_2(r r_0) = (a\alpha) r_0.$$

This proves that $\alpha \in K$. Because

$$(a_1 \alpha) r = (a_1 r)\alpha = a_2 r, \quad r \in R$$

then

$$(a_1 \alpha - a_2) r = 0, \quad r \in R,$$

and therefore, as we know from V.5.6, $a_1\alpha - a_2 = 0$, which contradicts the fact that the system of elements a_1, a_2 is linearly independent over K.

8. Now let n be arbitrary and suppose that the assertion of V.5.7 has already been proved for $n-1$. Thus there exists an $r' \in R$ such that

$$a_1 r' = \ldots = a_{n-2} r' = 0, \quad a_n r' \neq 0;$$

we denote by R' the set of all such r'. If the elements $a_{n-1} r'$ and $a_n r'$ are linearly independent over K, then, by what has been proved, there exists an $r'' \in R$ such that

$$a_{n-1} r' r'' = 0, \quad ar' r'' \neq 0,$$

and we can set $r = r' r''$.

Suppose, however, that

$$a_{n-1} r' = (a_n r')\beta, \quad \beta \in K, \quad \beta \neq 0. \tag{4}$$

By using induction again, we can find an $r_0 \in R$ such that

$$a_1 r_0 = \ldots = a_{n-2} r_0 = 0, \quad (a_{n-1} - a_n \beta) r_0 \neq 0. \tag{5}$$

If $a_n r_0 = 0$, $a_{n-1} r_0 \neq 0$, then we can find an $r_1 \in R$ such that $a_{n-1} r_0 r_1 = a_{n-1} r'$, and then we can set $r = r' - r_0 r_1$, because $a_n r = a_n r' \neq 0$. If $a_{n-1} r_0 = 0$, $a_n r_0 \neq 0$, then it will be true that simply $r = r_0$. If $a_{n-1} r_0$ and $a_n r_0$ are linearly independent, then, because $r_0 \in R'$, the existence of the desired r has already been proved above.

It remains to consider the case

$$a_{n-1} r_0 = (a_n r_0)\gamma, \quad \gamma \in K, \quad \gamma \neq 0; \tag{6}$$

from (5) it follows that $\beta \neq \gamma$. There exists an $r_2 \in R$ such that

$$a_{n-1} r_0 r_2 = a_{n-1} r'. \tag{7}$$

Then, by (6), (7) and (4),

$$a_n r_0 r_2 = a_{n-1} r_0 \gamma^{-1} r_2 = (a_{n-1} r_0 r_2)\gamma^{-1} = a_{n-1} r' \gamma^{-1} = a_n r' \beta \gamma^{-1},$$

whence

$$a_n (r' \beta \gamma^{-1} - r_0 r_2) = 0. \tag{8}$$

Now we can set $r = r' - r_0 r_2$: it is clear that

$$a_1 r = \ldots = a_{n-1} r = 0;$$

if it were also true that $a_n r = 0$, then, in view of (8), we would have

$$a_n r' = a_n r' \beta \gamma^{-1},$$

and because $\beta \gamma^{-1} \neq 1$, we would obtain $a_n r' = 0$, which is not true.

9. *The ring R consists of linear transformations of finite rank.*

It is sufficient to prove that R contains at least one non-zero linear transformation of finite rank, because then the intersection of R with the ideal $R'(A, K)$ of the ring $R(A, K)$ (see V.5.1) will be an ideal of the ring R distinct from zero and, by the simplicity of the ring R, it will coincide with R.

We know from V.5.4 that $A^2 \neq 0$. From this and from the fact that the right ideal A is minimal it follows that for any given non-zero $a \in A$ it will be true that $aA = A$. In particular, there exists an $e \in A$, $e \neq 0$, such that $ae = a$. Hence,

$$a(e^2 - e) = 0,$$

and therefore $e^2 = e$, because the elements of A which annihilate a on the right form a right ideal; the element e is thus *idempotent*. It is clear that $A = eR$.

Now by considering e as a linear transformation belonging to the ring R of the vector space A over the skew field K, we can show that it is of finite rank. In fact, the subspace Ae is one-dimensional. For, if it were to contain the elements a' and a'' linearly independent over K, then, because e is idempotent,

$$a'e = a', \quad a''e = a''. \tag{9}$$

By V.5.7 there exists an $r \in R$ such that

$$a'r = 0, \quad a''r \neq 0.$$

Hence

$$a'(er) = 0, \quad a''(er) \neq 0,$$

i.e. $er \neq 0$. Because $er \in A$, the set of elements of A which annihilate a' on the right does not consist of zero alone. This set is a right ideal and therefore coincides with A, which, however, contradicts the first of the equations (9). Hence Jacobson's Theorem has been proved.

* If R_i, $i = 1, 2$, is a dense ring of linear transformations of finite rank in the vector space V_i over the skew field K_i and if there exists an isomorphism τ between the rings R_1 and R_2, then between the spaces V_1 and V_2 there exists a semi-linear correspondence σ (see V.4.1) such that for all $a \in V_1$, $r \in R_1$

$$(ar)\sigma = a\sigma \cdot r\tau.$$

The total rings of matrices of finite order over skew fields, and only these, are non-zero simple associative rings, satisfying the minimal condition for right ideals.*

§ 6. Linear algebras. The algebra of quaternions and the Cayley algebra

1. In the transition to operator rings (see V.1.7), it is natural to consider as a special case rings which admit as their ring of operators (see V.1.8) some associative skew field. Here, by taking into account what was said in V.1.9, we will assume that this skew field is commutative, i.e. that it is a field.

A ring R, which has the field P as its ring of operators, is called a *linear algebra* over the field P. Usually, however, we simply speak of an *algebra* over a field, because there is no risk of confusing this concept with the concept of a universal algebra. If here R is an associative skew field, then it is usual to speak of it as an (associative) *division algebra*.

In the non-associative case, in connection with the terminology introduced in II.6.1, we will call every division ring, which is an algebra over a given field, a *division algebra*. The concept of an *algebra with single-valued division* has a similar meaning. If, however, the algebra over a field is a skew field, then, as we will prove below, all this only means that in the centre of our skew field we single out some subfield; however, sometimes we will nevertheless speak of *an algebra with single-valued division and with an identity*.

All that was said in V.1.7 is also applicable to the case of algebras. Thus, *isomorphisms* and *homomorphisms* of algebras over the field P must be understood as their P-operator isomorphisms and homomorphisms. The P-admissible subrings of an algebra are called its *subalgebras*. By an *ideal* of an algebra we always mean a P-admissible ideal of it. The term *factor-algebra* is also understood in this sense.

The additive group of every algebra R over the field P is a vector space over this field, which follows immediately from the definition of an algebra. Vector spaces are much easier to study than, for instance, arbitrary Abelian groups without operators. For this reason the theory of algebras is in many respects simpler, and has been worked out considerably further, than the theory of rings without operators which is parallel to it.

2. In III.2.9 we introduced the concept of the centre of a ring; we recall that the identity of a ring, if it exists, is contained in its centre.

If the ring R has an identity e and if the subfield P, containing e, lies in the centre of the ring R, then R will be an algebra over P.

In fact, if the product of elements of R by elements of the field P is understood in the sense of multiplication as given in the ring R, then the fact that all the requirements given in the definition of an algebra are satisfied follows at once from the properties of the operations in the ring and the definition of the centre.

Thus the field of complex numbers is a division algebra over the field of real numbers. The ring of polynomials $P[x]$ over the field P will be an algebra over this field, because the polynomials of zero degree form a subfield in $P[x]$, which is isomorphic to the field P and which contains the identity of the ring. Every skew field will be an algebra over its centre, because the latter, as we showed in III.2.9, is a field.

If the algebra R over the field P has an identity e, then in the centre of this algebra there lies a subfield containing e and isomorphic to the field P.

To prove this we denote by P' the totality of elements of the form $e\alpha$, where $\alpha \in P$. By (7) and (8) of V.1.4 and (11) of V.1.7

$$e(\alpha \pm \beta) = e\alpha \pm e\beta,$$

$$e(\alpha\beta) = (ee)(\alpha\beta) = [(ee)\alpha]\beta = (e\alpha \cdot e)\beta = e\alpha \cdot e\beta.$$

From this it follows that the mapping $\alpha \to e\alpha$ will be a homomorphic mapping of P onto P', and in fact an isomorphism, because P is a field and, by (9) of V.1.4,

$$1 \to e \cdot 1 = e \neq 0,$$

where 1 is the identity of the field P.

We will show, finally, that the subfield P' is contained in the centre of the algebra R. In fact, for any $x, y \in R$

$$(e\alpha)x = (ex)\alpha = (xe)\alpha = x(e\alpha),$$

$$[(e\alpha)x]y = [(ex)\alpha]y = x\alpha \cdot y = (xy)\alpha = [e(xy)]\alpha = (e\alpha)(xy),$$

$$(xy)(e\alpha) = [(xy)e]\alpha = (xy)\alpha = x \cdot y\alpha = x[(ye)\alpha] = x[y(e\alpha)].$$

Thus the theorem is proved.

3. Let there be given an algebra R over the field P and let us choose in the additive vector space of this algebra a basis X, consisting of the elements x_i (where i varies through some index set). Every element a of R has a unique expression in the form (3′) of V.3.5, i.e. in the form

$$a = \sum_{x_i \in X} x_i \alpha^i, \ \alpha^i \in P,$$

where the addition of elements of R and their multiplication by an element β of the field P reduces to the addition of corresponding coefficients and to the multiplication of the coefficients by β.

If $x_i, x_j \in X$, then the product $x_i x_j$, which is an element of R, will also have an expression in terms of the basis X,

$$x_i x_j = \sum_{x_k \in X} x_k \varepsilon_{ij}^k, \tag{1}$$

where for given i and j only a finite number of coefficients ε_{ij}^k can be distinct from zero. *The system of elements ε_{ij}^k of the field P completely defines the multiplication in the algebra R.* In fact, for any $\alpha, \beta \in P$

$$(x_i\alpha)(x_j\beta) = (x_i x_j)(\alpha\beta) = \sum_{x_k \in X} x_k (\varepsilon_{ij}^k \alpha\beta).$$

If, however, we are given the arbitrary elements

$$a = \sum_{x_i \in X} x_i \alpha^i, \quad b = \sum_{x_j \in X} x_j \beta^j, \tag{2}$$

in R, then, by taking into account that only a finite number of the coefficients α^j and β^j can be distinct from zero, on the basis of the distributive laws we obtain

$$ab = \sum_{x_i \in X} \sum_{x_j \in X} (x_i\alpha^i)(x_j\beta^j) = \sum_{i,j,k} x_k (\varepsilon_{ij}^k \alpha^i \beta^j). \tag{3}$$

It is obvious that in the transition from the basis X to another basis of the algebra R the numbers ε_{ij}^k are altered, i.e. the algebra

R will be defined in this new basis by a "multiplication table" distinct from (1).

4. *If in the vector space V over the field P we choose a basis X, consisting of the elements x_i, $i \in I$, and in the field P we take the arbitrary elements ε_{ij}^k, $i, j, k \in I$, then there exists an algebra over the field P, which has V as its additive vector space and is given in the basis X by the multiplication table (1) with these coefficients ε_{ij}^k.*

In fact, if for any elements $a, b \in V$, written in the basis X in the form (2), we define their product by the formula (3) then, as is easy to verify, both the distributive laws, and the requirements (11) of V.1.7, will be satisfied, and the elements of the basis X will be multiplied together by (1).

It is clear that the algebra constructed in this way will be neither associative nor commutative in the general case (i.e. if the choice of the numbers ε_{ij}^k is not subject to any additional restrictions). By using the distributive laws, the expressions for elements of the algebra in terms of the basis and the property of multiplication in the field, it is easy to verify, that *if in the algebra R over the field P we choose a basis X, then for this algebra to be associative, commutative or Lie* (see II.2.3), *it is not only necessary* (which is obvious) *but sufficient that for any x_i, x_j, $x_k \in X$ the following equations, respectively, should be satisfied*

$$(x_i x_j) x_k = x_i (x_j x_k)$$

or

$$x_i x_j = x_j x_i,$$

or, finally,†

$$x_i^2 = 0, \qquad x_i x_j = -x_j x_i, \qquad (x_i x_j) x_k + (x_j x_k) x_i + (x_k x_i) x_j = 0.$$

5. We will apply the results of V.3.7 and V.6.4 to the construction of one special type of algebra. We take an arbitrary groupoid G and an arbitrary field P, and then we construct a vector space over P, which has the set G as its basis. By defining the product for elements of this basis as their product in the groupoid G, we obtain an algebra called the *groupoid algebra* of the groupoid G over the field P. The reader may wish to compare this concept with the concept of the integral groupoid of a ring in II.4.5.

---

† The first condition may be omitted when the characteristic of P is not two (Ed.).

The groupoid algebra will be associative if the groupoid G is a semigroup or, in particular, a group. In this case we speak of the *semigroup* or *group algebra* respectively.

Thus the algebra of polynomials $P[x]$ over the field P will be a semigroup algebra: its basis is the set of powers $x^0 = 1, x, x^2, ..., x^n, ...$ of the unknown x, which forms a semigroup under multiplication, isomorphic to the semigroup of non-negative integers.

6. If the additive vector space of the algebra R over the field P is finite-dimensional (see V.3.6), then the algebra itself is also called *finite-dimensional*; its *dimension* is sometimes also called its *rank*.

Thus the ring of matrices P over the field P (see II.2.6) is, by V.6.2, an algebra over this field, because the centre of the ring P_n contains the set of scalar matrices (see II.4.3), including the identity matrix and isomorphic to the field P. The algebra of matrices P_n here has finite dimension n^2, because its basis consists of the matrices e_{ij}, $i, j = 1, 2, ..., n$, which have 1 in the (i, j)-th position, and everywhere else have zero. The multiplication table of the algebra P_n in this basis is as follows:

$$e_{ij} \cdot e_{jk} = e_{ik},$$
$$e_{ij} \cdot e_{kl} = 0 \quad \text{when} \quad j \neq k.$$

7. As we have already noted in V.6.2, the field of complex numbers K is a division algebra over the field of real numbers or, as we will say, a *real* division algebra. This algebra has dimension 2, because the numbers 1 and i form its basis. The algebra K has the following multiplication table in this basis:

$$1^2 = 1, 1 \cdot i = i \cdot 1 = i, \quad i^2 = -1.$$

8. Now we will construct a four-dimensional associative division algebra Q, called the *algebra of quaternions*. This will be an algebra with the basis 1, i, j, k and the following multiplication table:

	1	i	j	k
1	1	i	j	k
i	i	-1	k	$-j$
j	j	$-k$	-1	$-i$
k	k	j	$-i$	-1

(4)

In this table, to find the product, for instance of i by j, we must take the intersection of the i-th row with the j-th column, i.e. $ij=k$.

From the table of multiplication (4) it follows at once that the element 1 is the identity of the algebra Q and that this algebra is non-commutative. *The algebra Q will, however, be associative*: because the elements i, j, k occur in the table of multiplication (4) symmetrically (to within sign), then, by V.6.4, it is sufficient to verify the validity of the equations

$$(ii)i = i(ii), \quad (ii)j = i(ij), \quad (ij)i = i(ji),$$
$$(ji)i = j(ii), \quad (ij)k = i(jk).$$

which we leave to the reader.

9. Every *quaternion* (i.e. element of the algebra Q) α has a unique expression

$$\alpha = a + ib + jc + kd$$

with real coefficients a, b, c, d. The quaternion

$$\bar{\alpha} = a - ib - jc - kd$$

is called the *conjugate* of the quaternion α. It is easy to verify that

$$\overline{\alpha\beta} = \bar{\beta}\bar{\alpha}, \quad \overline{\alpha+\beta} = \bar{\alpha} + \bar{\beta} \tag{5}$$

and that

$$\alpha\bar{\alpha} = \bar{\alpha}\alpha = a^2 + b^2 + c^2 + d^2. \tag{6}$$

The non-negative real number

$$n(\alpha) = \alpha\bar{\alpha} = \bar{\alpha}\alpha. \tag{7}$$

only equal to zero when $\alpha = 0$, and it is called the *norm* of the quaternion α. It is easy to verify that

$$n(\alpha\beta) = n(\alpha) \cdot n(\beta), \tag{8}$$

and therefore *the algebra of quaternions does not contain divisors of zero*. In fact, by (7) and (5),

$$n(\alpha\beta) = (\alpha\beta)(\overline{\alpha\beta}) = \alpha\beta\bar{\beta}\bar{\alpha} = (\alpha\bar{\alpha}) \cdot n(\beta) = n(\alpha) \cdot n(\beta).$$

If $\alpha \neq 0$ and therefore $n(\alpha) \neq 0$, then, by (7),

$$\alpha \cdot \left(\frac{1}{n(\alpha)} \bar{\alpha} \right) = \left(\frac{1}{n(\alpha)} \bar{\alpha} \right) \cdot \alpha = 1.$$

For every quaternion α distinct from zero there thus exists an inverse quaternion, and therefore *the algebra of quaternions is a skew field.*

10. We will construct, finally, one eight-dimensional real non-associative algebra with single-valued division and with an identity, called the *Cayley algebra.*

We consider all possible expressions of the form $\alpha + \beta e$, where α and β are quaternions, and e is a new symbol; in particular, when $\beta = 0$ we will simply write α instead of $\alpha + \beta e$, and when $\alpha = 0$, simply βe. By defining addition and multiplication by the real number a for the expressions under consideration by means of the equations

$$(\alpha + \beta e) + (\gamma + \delta e) = (\alpha + \gamma) + (\beta + \delta)e, \qquad (9)$$

$$(\alpha + \beta e)a = (\alpha a) + (\beta a)e, \qquad (10)$$

we obtain an eight-dimensional real vector space with basis

$$1, i, j, k, e, ie, je, ke. \qquad (11)$$

In this space we define multiplication by the equation

$$(\alpha + \beta e)(\gamma + \delta e) = (\alpha\gamma - \overline{\delta}\beta) + (\delta\alpha + \beta\overline{\gamma})e. \qquad (12)$$

It is easy to verify that this multiplication is distributive with respect to the addition (9), and also, by (10), the equations

$$[(\alpha + \beta e)(\gamma + \delta e)]a = [(\alpha + \beta e)a](\gamma + \delta e) =$$
$$(\alpha + \beta e)[(\gamma + \delta e)a].$$

are valid.

The multiplication table for the Cayley algebra which we have obtained in the basis (11) can be derived without difficulty from (12). It will be the following table:

	1	i	j	k	e	ie	je	ke
1	1	i	j	k	e	ie	je	ke
i	i	-1	k	$-j$	ie	$-e$	$-ke$	je
j	j	$-k$	-1	i	je	ke	$-e$	$-ie$
k	k	j	$-i$	-1	ke	$-je$	ie	$-e$
e	e	$-ie$	$-je$	$-ke$	-1	i	j	k
ie	ie	e	$-ke$	je	$-i$	-1	$-k$	j
je	je	ke	e	$-ie$	$-j$	k	-1	$-i$
ke	ke	$-je$	ie	e	$-k$	$-j$	i	-1

We see that the elements of the form $\alpha = \alpha + 0e$ form a sub-algebra in the Cayley algebra, isomorphic to the algebra of quaternions. On the other hand, from (9) and (12) it follows that in the expression $\alpha + \beta e$ for elements of the Cayley algebra both addition and multiplication can be understood in the sense of operations defined in this algebra. The Cayley algebra is neither commutative nor associative. Thus,

$$(ij)e = ke, \qquad i(je) = -ke.$$

11. If $\xi = \alpha + \beta e$ is an element of the Cayley algebra, then we call

$$\overline{\xi} = \overline{\alpha} - \beta e.$$

the *conjugate* of this element. On the basis of (12) and (5) it is easy to verify that for any elements ξ and η of the Cayley algebra

$$\overline{\xi\eta} = \overline{\eta}\,\overline{\xi}, \qquad \overline{\xi + \eta} = \overline{\xi} + \overline{\eta} \tag{13}$$

and that for $\xi = \alpha + \beta e$

$$\xi\overline{\xi} = \overline{\xi}\xi = \alpha\overline{\alpha} + \beta\overline{\beta} = n(\alpha) + n(\beta). \tag{14}$$

This non-negative real number, which is equal to zero only when $\xi = 0$, is called the *norm* of the element ξ and is denoted by $n(\xi)$.

If $\xi = \alpha + \beta e$, $\eta = \gamma + \delta e$, then from (12) and (14) it follows, because of (5), that

$$n(\xi\eta) = (\alpha\gamma - \overline{\delta}\beta)(\overline{\gamma\alpha} - \overline{\beta}\delta) + (\delta\alpha + \beta\overline{\gamma})(\overline{\alpha}\overline{\delta} + \gamma\overline{\beta}) =$$
$$n(\alpha)n(\gamma) + n(\beta)n(\delta) + n(\alpha)n(\delta) + n(\beta)n(\gamma) + a - b,$$

where

$$a = \delta\alpha\gamma\overline{\beta} + \beta\overline{\gamma\alpha}\overline{\delta},$$
$$b = \alpha\gamma\overline{\beta}\delta + \overline{\delta}\beta\overline{\gamma\alpha}.$$

Because, by (5), the second summands in the expressions for a and b are conjugate to the first summands, a and b will be real numbers. If $\delta = 0$, then, obviously, $a = b = 0$ and therefore $a - b = 0$. If, however, $\delta \neq 0$ and therefore $n(\delta) \neq 0$, then, because the number a is real,

$$an(\delta) = \overline{\delta}\alpha\delta = bn(\delta),$$

whence $a = b$, i.e. again $a - b = 0$.

Thus,

$$n(\xi) = [n(\alpha) + n(\beta)][n(\gamma) + n(\delta)] = n(\xi)n(\eta). \tag{15}$$

From this it follows that the *Cayley algebra does not contain divisors of zero.*

12. Equation (12) shows that the element $1 = 1 + 0e$ is the identity of the Cayley algebra.

On the other hand, if we are given the elements $\xi = \alpha + \beta e$ and $\eta = \gamma + \delta e$, where $\xi \neq 0$, then the equation

$$\xi \zeta = \eta \tag{16}$$

has a solution, which is unique because there are no divisors of zero. In fact,

$$\zeta = \frac{1}{n(\xi)} \bar{\xi} \eta = \frac{1}{n(\xi)} [(\bar{\alpha}\gamma + \bar{\delta}\beta) + (\delta\bar{\alpha} - \beta\bar{\gamma})e].$$

The reader can verify without difficulty, by using (12) and (5), that the element ζ in fact satisfies equation (16). In the same way, the unique solution of the equation

$$\zeta \xi = \eta, \quad \xi \neq 0,$$

is the element

$$\zeta = \frac{1}{n(\xi)} \eta \bar{\xi}.$$

We thus find that the *Cayley algebra is a (non-associative) skew field.*

§ 7. Alternative rings. Artin's theorem

1. The algebra of quaternions and the Cayley algebra should in no way be regarded as random examples of real division algebras—their fundamental role is established in many theorems, some of which will be proved or mentioned in the following section, and also in §§ 6 and 10 of the following chapter.

First we mention one simple classification of all rings. As we well know, the associative law connects three elements, and therefore *every ring, all of whose subrings generated by three elements are associative, will itself be associative.* A wider class of rings is formed by the *alternative rings,* i.e. those rings in which all the subring generated by two elements are associative. Even wider is the class of *power-associative rings,* i.e. those rings in which all the subrings generated by one element are associative; this class, of course, does not include all rings.

2. If a, b, c are elements of some ring R, then we call the element

$$[a, b, c] = (ab)c - a(bc) \qquad (1)$$

the *associator* of these elements. It is obvious that

$$[a, b, c] = 0$$

if, and only if, the associative law

$$(ab)c = a(bc)$$

is satisfied for the elements a, b, c.

From (1) it follows that

$$[a + a', b, c] = [a, b, c] + [a', b, c]; \qquad (2)$$

similar equations are also valid for the places occupied by the elements b and c in the associator. On the other hand,

$$[-a, b, c] = -[a, b, c].$$

On the basis of (1) it is easy to verify the following equation, which is valid for any elements $a, b, c, d \in R$:

$$[ab, c, d] - [a, bc, d] + [a, b, cd] = a[b, c, d] + [a, b, c]d. \qquad (3)$$

3. ARTIN'S THEOREM. *The ring R is alternative if, and only if, for any $a, b \in R$ the equations*

$$(aa)b = a(ab), \quad (ba)a = b(aa) \,\dagger \qquad (4)$$

hold.

It is obvious that in an alternative ring conditions (4) are satisfied. We will assume therefore that we are given a ring R, in which for any elements a and b the equations (4) are satisfied; these equations can be rewritten in the form

$$[a, a, b] = 0, \quad [b, a, a] = 0. \qquad (5)$$

4. *In the ring R for any a and b the equation*

$$[a, b, a] = 0 \qquad (6)$$

is valid.

In fact, by (5) and (2),

$$0 = [a, a + b, a + b] = [a, a, a] + [a, a, b] +$$
$$[a, b, a] + [a, b, b] = [a, b, a].$$

---

† The reader can take the identity (4) as the definition of an alternative ring and omit the proof of Artin's theorem without prejudice to what follows. We see that alternative rings form a primitive class of universal algebras (see III.6.3).

If in the ring R the elements a, b, c undergo some permutation, then the associator [a, b, c] is unaltered if this permutation is even, and changes its sign if the permutation is odd.

It is sufficient, as we know, simply to consider the case of transposing two elements. By (5) and (2)

$$0 = [a, b+c, b+c] = [a, b, b] + [a, b, c] + [a, c, b] +$$
$$[a, c, c] = [a, b, c] + [a, c, b],$$

whence

$$[a, b, c] = -[a, c, b].$$

In the same way we can prove the equations

$$[a, b, c] = -[b, a, c]$$

and, because of (6),

$$[a, b, c] = -[c, b, a].$$

5. If A, B, C are subsets of our ring R, then we agree to write

$$[A, B, C] = 0,$$

if $[a, b, c] = 0$ for all $a \in A, b \in B, c \in C$.

A subset A of the ring R is called an α-*set* if

$$[A, A, R] = 0, \tag{7}$$

and therefore, on the basis of what we proved above,

$$[A, R, A] = 0, \quad [R, A, A] = 0. \tag{8}$$

From (5) it follows that a set consisting of one element will be an α-set.

The subring of R generated by an α-set A will itself be an α-set, i.e., more concisely, it will be an α-subring.

In fact, from (2) it follows that, by adjoining to the set A all possible sums and differences of its elements, we again obtain an α-set. We will show that this is also true when we adjoin to A the products of all possible pairs of its elements. In fact, if $a_1, a_2, a_3, a_4 \in A$, then, by (3)

$$[a_1 a_2, x, a_3] - [a_1, a_2 x, a_3] + [a_1, a_2, x a_3] =$$
$$a_1[a_2, x, a_3] + [a_1, a_2, x]a_3,$$

whence, by (7) and (8),

$$[a_1 a_2, x, a_3] = 0. \tag{9}$$

In addition, again by (3),

$$[a_1a_2, x, a_3a_4] - [a_1, a_2x, a_3a_4] + [a_1, a_2, x(a_3a_4)] =$$
$$a_1[a_2, x, a_3a_4] + [a_1, a_2, x](a_3a_4),$$

whence, by (7), (8) and (9),

$$[a_1a_2, x, a_3a_4] = 0.$$

Thus if, starting with the set A, we adjoin alternately to the α-set which we have constructed either all the sums and differences of its elements, or else all products of pairs of its elements, we obtain an ascending sequence of α-sets in R. The union of this sequence will, of course, be an α-set and in addition it will coincide with the subring generated by the set A.

From this result it follows that *every subring of the ring R generated by one element will be an α-subring and therefore will be associative.*

6. If A and B are α-subrings of the ring R, then we denote by C the set of all elements c of R such that

$$[A, B, c] = 0.$$

It is clear that

$$C \supseteq (A \cup B) \tag{10}$$

and that C is closed with respect to addition and subtraction. *If $c \in C$, then for any $a' \in A$ and $b' \in B$ the inclusions*

$$a'c, ca', b'c, cb' \in C.$$

hold.

In fact, if $a \in A$, $b \in B$, then, by (3),

$$[aa', c, b] - [a, a'c, b] + [a, a', cb] = a[a', c, b] + [a, a', c]b,$$

$$[bc, a', a] - [b, ca', a] + [b, c, a'a] = b[c, a', a] + [b, c, a']a$$

or, by taking into account that A is an α-subring, and $c \in C$,

$$[a, a'c, b] = 0.$$

$$[b, ca', a] = 0.$$

i.e. $a'c \in C$, $ca' \in C$. In the same way we prove the other two inclusions.

By II.3.7 any element of the subring $\{A, B\}$ can be represented in the form of a sum of products of the form $w = x_1 x_2 \dots x_n$, where every $x_i, i = 1, 2, \ldots, n$, belongs to A or to B; we call n the *length* of this product, $n = l(w)$. In the product w there is some arrangement of brackets, in which every bracket is the product of precisely two smaller brackets. We will call the product w of length n a *normal element* if every bracket of length k, $2 \leqslant k \leqslant n$, which is part of this product, is the product of a bracket of length $k-1$ and an element from A or from B, on the left or on the right. Thus, the product $(ab)(b'a')$ will not be normal, and the product $b'[(ab)a']$ will be normal.

From what has been proved above, it follows, by (10), that every normal element w belongs to the set C, i.e. for all $a \in A$, $b \in B$

$$[a, b, w] = 0. \tag{11}$$

7. *Every product of normal elements can be represented as a sum of normal elements.*

It is sufficient to prove this for the product of two normal elements v and w. We will carry out the proof by induction with respect to the length of the element v, because when $l(v) = 1$ it is obvious that the product vw is normal.

If $v = v'a, l(v') = l(v) - 1, a \in A$, then

$$vw = (v'a)w = v'(aw) + [v', a, w] =$$
$$v'(aw) - [v', w, a] = v'(aw) - (v'w)a + v'(wa),$$

but each of the three summands in the sum obtained can be represented, by induction, as a sum of normal elements. The case $v = av'$ also reduces to this case:

$$vw = (av')w = a(v'w) + [a, v', w] =$$
$$a(v'w) - (v', a, w) = a(v'w) - (v'a)w + v'(aw).$$

From this it follows that *every element of* $\{A, B\}$ *can be represented as a sum of normal elements.*

8. *If v, w are normal elements, then for any $a \in A$, $b \in B$*

$$[a, v, w] = [b, v, w] = 0. \tag{12}$$

If $l(v) = 1$, then (12) follows from (11). We will therefore carry out the proof by induction with respect to the length of the element v. If $v = b'v'$, where $l(v') = l(v) - 1, b' \in B$, then, by (3),

$$[b'v', w, a] - [b', v'w, a] + [b', v', wa] =$$
$$b'[v', w, a] + [b', v', w]a.$$

Hence, by using induction, and also (11) and the result proved in the previous section, we obtain

$$[b'v', w, a] = [v, w, a] = [a, v, w] = 0.$$

In the cases $v = v'a'$, $v = a'v'$ and $v = v'b'$ we can also apply the identity (3), where as the elements a, b, c, d we must take, respectively, w, v', a', a or a, a', v', w, or, finally, v', b', w, a.

9. *If u, v, w are normal elements, then*

$$[u, v, w] = 0. \tag{13}$$

By (12) we can carry out the proof by induction with respect to the length of the element u. If $u = u'a$, $l(u') = l(u) - 1$, $a \in A$, then, by (3),

$$[u'a, v, w] - [u', av, w] + [u', a, vw] =$$
$$u'[a, v, w] + [u', a, v]w$$

or, by using induction and the result from V.7.7,

$$[u'a, v, w] = [u, v, w] = 0.$$

The other possible cases are considered in the same way.

Hence, by taking into account that every element of the subring $\{A, B\}$ is the sum of normal elements, we find that *the subring $\{A, B\}$ generated by the α-subrings A and B will be associative.* If we take as A and B subrings each of which is generated by one element, then, by the last result of V.7.5, we obtain that *every subring of the ring R, generated by two elements, is associative*, and this completes the proof of Artin's theorem.

* If the additive group of the ring R does not contain elements of finite order distinct from zero, then R will be power associative if, and only if, for every element a of R

$$(aa)a = a(aa),$$
$$[(aa)a]a = (aa)(aa).$$

[Albert, *Summa Bras. Math.* **2**, 21–33 (1948); see also A. T. Gainov, *Uspekhi mat. nauk* **12**, No 3, 141–146 (1957)].*

10. Now we will prove that the *Cayley algebra is alternative.*

By Artin's Theorem, it is sufficient to verify that in the Cayley algebra equations (4) are satisfied. We will verify at least the first of these. If

$$\xi = \alpha + \beta e, \quad \eta = \gamma + \delta e,$$

then, by (12) of V.6.10,

$$(\xi\xi)\eta = [(\alpha^2 - \overline{\beta}\beta)\gamma - \overline{\delta}(\beta\alpha + \beta\overline{\alpha})] + [\delta(\alpha^2 - \overline{\beta}\beta) + (\beta\alpha + \beta\overline{\alpha})\overline{\gamma}]e,$$

$$\xi(\xi\eta) = [\alpha\,(\alpha\gamma - \overline{\delta}\beta) - (\overline{\delta\alpha + \beta\overline{\gamma}})\beta] + [(\delta\alpha + \beta\overline{\gamma})\alpha + \beta\overline{(\alpha\gamma - \overline{\delta}\beta)}]e.$$

However, the right-hand sides of these equations will coincide, as it is easy to show on the basis of (5) from V.6.9, if we take into account that both $\alpha + \overline{\alpha}$ and $\overline{\beta}\beta = \beta\overline{\beta}$ are real numbers and therefore commute with any quaternion.

§ 8. A generalization of Frobenius' theorem

1. *The field of real numbers and the field of complex numbers are the only finite-dimensional real associative-commutative algebras without divisors of zero.*

The skew field of quaternions is the only finite-dimensional real associative, but not commutative algebra without divisors of zero.

The Cayley algebra is the only finite-dimensional real alternative, but not associative algebra without divisors of zero.

The first two theorems together are called *Frobenius' theorem*; all three theorems together we will call *the generalization of Frobenius' theorem.*

2. *First we will prove the following general theorem:*

Every finite dimensional algebra R without divisors of zero over an arbitrary field P is an algebra with single-valued division.

We will prove that at least the first of the equations

$$ax = b, \quad ya = b, \tag{1}$$

has a unique solution, where $a \neq 0$. We denote by aR the totality of elements of the form ar for all possible r from R. It is clear that aR will be a linear subspace of the additive vector space of the algebra R. If this subspace is distinct from the whole algebra R, then it has a strictly smaller dimension. Hence, taking any basis

$$x_1, x_2, \ldots, x_n$$

of the algebra R, we have that the elements

$$ax_1, ax_2, \ldots, ax_n$$

are linearly dependent, i.e. in the field P there exist elements $\alpha_1, \alpha_2, \ldots, \alpha_n$, not all equal to zero, such that

$$(ax_1)\alpha_1 + (ax_2)\alpha_2 + \ldots + (ax_n)\alpha_n = 0.$$

From this, however, it follows that

$$a(x_1\alpha_1 + x_2\alpha_2 + \ldots + x_n\alpha_n) = 0,$$

where both factors are distinct from zero, which contradicts the fact that there are no divisors of zero in the algebra R.

We have that $aR = R$. Thus there exists an element $r \in R$ such that

$$ar = b,$$

i.e. the first of the equations (1) is in fact soluble. The uniqueness of this solution follows from the fact that there are no divisors of zero in R. The theorem has thus been proved.

For what follows, we note that in an alternative algebra not only every subring generated by two elements but also every subalgebra with two generators is associative it is sufficient; to take into account how the elements of the given subalgebra are expressed in terms of elements of the subring generated by the same two generators.

Every alternative finite-dimensional algebra with single-valued division R over an arbitrary field P has an identity.

In the associative case the assertion of this theorem follows at once from II.2.10. If the algebra R is merely alternative, then every subalgebra of R with two generators will be an associative finite-dimensional algebra without divisors of zero, i.e., by the preceding theorem, a division algebra and thus it has an identity. Suppose, however, that two such subalgebras have different identities, e_1 and e_2. The subalgebra generated by these two elements will itself be an associative division algebra, and we arrive at a contradiction, because in an associative skew field there cannot be two different *idempotent elements*, i.e. elements equal to their own squares.

3. Now, starting on the proof of the generalization of Frobenius' theorem, we can assume that we are given a real alternative (in particular, associative or even associative-commutative) algebra with single-valued division R of finite dimension n, which has an identity.

As we proved in V.6.2, in the centre of the algebra R there is contained a subfield D, isomorphic to the field of real numbers—it will be the set of elements which are multiples of the identity 1 of the algebra R.

If the element a of the algebra R lies outside the subfield D, then the subalgebra $\{a\}$ generated by it contains this subfield and is isomorphic to the field of complex numbers.

In fact, because the algebra R is alternative, the subalgebra $\{a\}$ is associative, i.e. we can speak in the usual sense of powers of the element a. Because the algebra R has dimension n, then the elements

$$1, a, a^2, \ldots, a^n$$

are linearly dependent. Thus there exists a polynomial $f(x)$ with real coefficients, of degree not more than n, which vanishes for the element a. From the fundamental theorem of algebra for complex numbers it follows that $f(x)$ can be decomposed into linear and irreducible quadratic factors with real coefficients, and because there are no divisors of zero in the algebra R, the element a makes one of these factors vanish; we denote it by $\varphi(x)$.

Because a lies outside the subfield D and therefore cannot satisfy any equation of the first degree with real coefficients, then

$$\varphi(x) = x^2 + \beta x + \gamma, \quad \gamma \neq 0. \tag{2}$$

Thus,

$$a^2 + \beta a + \gamma = 0, \tag{3}$$

i.e. $\gamma \in \{a\}$ and therefore the whole subfield D is contained in the subalgebra $\{a\}$. From (3) it follows that the subalgebra is two-dimensional and that its basis consists of the elements 1 and a, where

$$a^2 = -\gamma - \beta a.$$

On the other hand, we denote by α the complex number which is a root of the quadratic trinomial (2). The number α is not real, and therefore the numbers 1, α form a basis for the algebra of complex numbers. The multiplication table defining the algebra of complex numbers in this basis obviously coincides with the multiplication table defining the subalgebra $\{a\}$ in the basis 1, a. From this, by V.6.3, it follows that the subalgebra $\{a\}$ is isomorphic to the field of complex numbers.

4. *If the elements a and b of the algebra R lie outside the sub-field D and generate different subalgebra $\{a\}$, $\{b\}$, then the sub-algebra $\{a, b\}$ is isomorphic to the algebra of quaternions.*

Because the subalgebra $\{a\}$ is isomorphic to the field of complex numbers, we can take a basis 1, i in it, where

$$i^2 = -1. \tag{4}$$

In the same way there exists a basis 1, j_0 in the subalgebra $\{b\}$, where

$$j_0^2 = -1. \tag{5}$$

It is clear that $\{i\} = \{a\}$, $\{j_0\} = \{b\}$, whence $\{i, j_0\} = \{a,b\}$ and, because $j_0 \notin \{a\}$, the elements 1, i, j_0 are linearly independent.

Each of the elements $i + j_0$, $i - j_0$ therefore lies outside the sub-field D and, hence, must satisfy some irreducible quadratic polynomial with real coefficients, and then it must be possible to express the squares of these elements in terms of their first powers and the identity. Hence there exist real numbers α, β, γ, δ such that

$$(i + j_0)^2 = -2 + (ij_0 + j_0i) = \alpha(i + j_0) + \beta, \tag{6}$$

$$(i - j_0)^2 = -2 - (ij_0 + j_0i) = \gamma(i - j_0) + \delta.$$

By adding these equations we obtain

$$-4 = (\alpha + \gamma)i + (\alpha - \gamma)j_0 + (\beta + \delta);$$

whence, because the elements 1, i, j_0 are linearly independent, it follows that $\alpha + \gamma = \alpha - \gamma = 0$, i.e. $\alpha = \gamma = 0$. From (6) we now have that the element $ij_0 + j_0i$ will be a real number, which we denote by 2μ; in fact,

$$ij_0 + j_0i = 2\mu = \beta + 2 = -(\delta + 2). \tag{7}$$

Because the quadratic trinomials which the elements $i + j_0$ and $i - j_0$ satisfy are irreducible, then, since $\alpha = \gamma = 0$, it follows that $\beta < 0$, $\delta < 0$, whence, by (7),

$$-1 < \mu < 1.$$

The number

$$\nu = \frac{1}{\sqrt{1 - \mu^2}}$$

will thus be a real number distinct from zero.

Now we consider the element

$$j = \mu\nu i + \nu j_0.$$

which lies in the subalgebra $\{a, b\}$. Because $\nu \neq 0$, the elements $1, i, j$ are linearly independent, and on the basis of (7) and (8) it is easy the verify the equations

$$j^2 = -1, \tag{9}$$

$$ij + ji = 0. \tag{10}$$

We introduce the notation

$$k = ij = -ji. \tag{11}$$

If the equation

$$k = \alpha + \beta i + \gamma j$$

with real coefficients α, β, γ were to hold, then, by multiplying both sides of it on the right by i, because of (11) we would arrive at the equation

$$j = \alpha i - \beta - \gamma k = \alpha i - \beta - \gamma(\alpha + \beta i + \gamma j).$$

However, by equating the coefficients of j here, we would obtain

$$1 = -\gamma^2,$$

which is impossible, because the number γ is real.

The elements $1, i, j, k$ thus turn out to be linearly independent. These elements lie in an associative subalgebra $\{a, b\}$ (because the algebra R is alternative) and in fact generate this subalgebra. Therefore, on the basis of (4), (9) and (11), we can verify without difficulty that for the elements $1, i, j, k$ all the equations (4) of V.6.8 are satisfied. Thus, for instance,

$$k^2 = (ij)(-ji) = -i(j^2)i = i^2 = -1,$$

$$jk = j(-ji) = -(j^2)i = i.$$

This shows that the elements $1, i, j, k$ form a basis for the subalgebra $\{a, b\}$ which they generate and that this subalgebra is isomorphic to the algebra of quaternions.

Thus the first of the theorems in V.8.1 has been proved.

5. If the proof of the second of the theorems of V.8.1 were our final aim, then we should have very little left to do. Suppose that the algebra R under consideration is associative and suppose that we have found a subalgebra $\{a, b\}$ in it isomorphic to the quaternions, and an element c lying outside it. We denote by 1, i, j, k the basis of the subalgebra $\{a, b\}$ with the usual multiplication table for the algebra of the quaternions—we will call such a basis *canonical*. In addition, the subalgebra $\{c\}$ by our hypotheses is isomorphic to the field of complex numbers and therefore it contains an element e such that

$$e^2 = -1,$$

where $\{e\} = \{c\}$.

By repeating the reasoning used in the derivation of equation (7), we can assert that there exist real numbers α, β, γ, such that

$$ie + ei = \alpha, \quad je + ej = \beta, \quad ke + ek = \gamma.$$

Hence, by using the fact that the algebra R is associative, we obtain

$$ek = (ei)j = \alpha j - i(ej) = \alpha j - \beta i + (ij)e =$$
$$\alpha j - \beta i + ke = \alpha j - \beta i + \gamma - ek,$$

i.e.

$$2ek = \alpha j - \beta i + \gamma,$$

or, after multiplication on the right by k,

$$-2e = \alpha i + \beta j + \gamma k.$$

However, this reduces to the inclusion $e \in \{a, b\}$, which is impossible. The second of the theorems in V.8.1 has been proved.

6. We return to the proof of the generalization of Frobenius' theorem.

If the elements a, b and c of the algebra R are such that $\{a, b\}$, $\{a, c\}$ and $\{b, c\}$ are distinct subalgebras, isomorphic to the skew field of quaternions, then the subalgebra $\{a, b, c\}$ is isomorphic to Cayley algebra.

Because the subalgebra $\{a, b\}$ is isomorphic to the skew field of quaternions, it has a canonical basis 1, i, j, k. On the other hand, in the subalgebra $\{c\}$ there is an element e_0 such that

$$e_0^2 = -1,$$

where $\{e_0\} = \{c\}$.

The subalgebra $\{i, e_0\}$ is isomorphic to the skew field of quaternions, because from $\{i\} = \{e_0\}$ it would follow that $c \in \{a, b\}$. Therefore, as we showed in V.8.4, there exists an element

$$e_1 = \alpha_1 i + \beta_1 e_0 \qquad (12)$$

with real α_1 and β_1, where $\beta_1 \neq 0$, such that the elements $1, i, e_1$, ie_1, form a canonical basis for the subalgebra $\{i, e_0\}$.

From $\{j\} = \{e_1\}$ it would follow, by (12), that $e_0 \in \{a, b\}$, which is impossible. Thus the subalgebra $\{j, e_1\}$ is isomorphic to the skew field of quaternions and therefore there exists in it an element

$$e_2 = \alpha_2 j + \beta_2 e_1 \tag{13}$$

with real α_2 and β_2, where $\beta_2 \neq 0$, such that the elements $1, j, e_2$, je_2 form a canonical basis for the subalgebra $\{j, e_2\}$.

We will show that *the subalgebra $\{i, e_2\}$ is also isomorphic to the skew field of quaternions and has the system of elements 1, i, e_2, ie_2 as its canonical basis.* In fact, from $\{i\} = \{e_2\}$ it would follow, by (13) and (12), that $e_1 \in \{a, b\}$, whence $e_1 \in \{a, b\}$, which is impossible. This proves the first assertion. In addition, because we already know that

$$i^2 = e_2^2 = -1,$$

then for the proof of the second assertion it is sufficient, as we know from V.8.4, to establish the validity of the equation

$$ie_2 + e_2 i = 0.$$

However, by taking into account that the equations

$$ij + ji = 0, \quad ie_1 + e_1 i = 0$$

hold, we obtain

$$ie_2 + e_2 i = i(\alpha_2 j + \beta_2 e_1) + (\alpha_2 j + \beta_2 e_1)i =$$
$$\alpha_2(ij + ji) + \beta_2(ie_1 + e_1 i) = 0.$$

7. As above, the subalgebra $\{k, e_2\}$ is isomorphic to the skew field of quaternions and has a canonical basis $1, k, e, ke$, where

$$e = \alpha_3 k + \beta_3 e_2 \tag{14}$$

with real α_3 and β_3, where $\beta_3 \neq 0$. We note that $\{k, e_2\} = \{k, e\}$. In the same way as in the preceding section, we can verify that the subalgebras $\{i, e\}$ and $\{j, e\}$ are also isomorphic to the skew field of quaternions and have as their canonical bases respectively the systems of elements $1, i, e, ie$ and $1, j, e, je$.

8. *The system of elements*

$$1, i, j, k, e, ie, je, ke \tag{15}$$

is linearly independent.

In fact, if it were linearly dependent, then in the subalgebra $\{i, j\} = \{a, b\}$ there would exist elements u, v, where $v \neq 0$, such that

$$u = ve. \qquad (16)$$

Because the subalgebra $\{v\}$ is isomorphic to the field of complex or real numbers, the element v^{-1} is contained in it and therefore in the associative subalgebra $\{v, e\}$. Hence

$$v^{-1}(ve) = (v^{-1}v)e = e,$$

i.e. from (16) we would obtain

$$e = v^{-1}u \in \{a, b\},$$

which is impossible.

9. *For the elements* (15) *the table of multiplication for the Cayley algebra is satisfied* (see V.6.10).

We know that the systems of elements

$$(1, i, j, k), \qquad (1, i, e, ie), \qquad (1, j, e, je), \qquad (1, k, e, ke) \qquad (17)$$

are canonical bases for the subalgebras which they generate. Because of this it remains to verify very little in the given table. We will show how this is done in some typical cases.

Because the subalgebra $\{e + i, j\}$ is associative, then

$$[j(e + i)](e + i) = j[(e + i)(e + i)],$$

whence, by using what was said above about the systems (17), we obtain

$$-j + (je)i - ke - j = -2j,$$

i.e.

$$(je)i = ke. \qquad (18)$$

Further, from the equation

$$(e + i)[j(e + i)] = [(e + i)j](e + i)$$

we have, by using (18), that

$$i(je) = -ke. \qquad (19)$$

Finally, from the fact that the subalgebra $\{k, i + je\}$ is associative, there follows the equation

$$[(i + je)(i + je)]k = (i + je)[(i + je)k],$$

from which, by using equations (18), (19) and the equation

$$(je)k = - ie,$$

which is proved in the same way, we obtain

$$(je)(ie) = k.$$

In this way we show that the elements (15) form a basis for the subalgebra $\{a, b, c\}$ which they generate and that this subalgebra is isomorphic to the Cayley algebra.

We will agree to call the basis of the Cayley algebra which satisfies the multiplication table in V.6.10 *canonical*.

10. Finally, we suppose that the algebra R contains both a subalgebra which is isomorphic to the Cayley algebra and has as its canonical basis the system of elements

$$1, i, j, k, e, ie, je, ke,$$

and also some element which lies outside this subalgebra. Then, by generalizing the reasoning carried out in the preceding sections, we would find an element f in the algebra R such that each of the following systems of elements would generate a subalgebra isomorphic to the Cayley algebra and would be a canonical basis for it:

$$1, i, j, k, f, if, \qquad jf, kf;$$
$$1, i, e, ie, f, if, \qquad ef, (ie)f;$$
$$1, j, e, je, f, jf, \qquad ef, (je)f;$$
$$1, je, i, ke, f, \quad (je)f, if, (ke)f.$$

The corresponding constructions are very complicated, but present no serious difficulties and therefore can be left to the reader.

From the fact that the given bases are canonical there follow these equations:

$$e^2 = -1, \qquad\qquad (if)^2 = -1,$$
$$(jf)(if) = k, \qquad\quad k(if) = -jf,$$
$$e(if) = (ie)f, \qquad\quad (if)e = -(ie)f,$$
$$(jf)e = -(je)f, \qquad [(je)f]e = jf,$$
$$[(je)f](if) = -ke,$$

By using these equations, and the equation

$$(jf) \, [(e + if)(e + if)] = [(jf)(e + if)](e + if),$$

which is valid because the algebra R is alternative, we obtain

$$-2(jf) = [-(je)f + k](e + if) = -2(jf) + 2ke,$$

i.e. $ke = 0$, which is impossible.

The contradiction which we have obtained completes the proof of the generalization of Frobenius' theorem.

* Every alternative skew field is either associative or else, regarded as an algebra over its centre (see V.6.2), finite-dimensional, and in fact it has dimension eight and is the so-called Cayley-Dickson algebra, i.e. it is a generalization of the Cayley algebra to the case of an arbitrary base field [L. A. Skornyakov, *Ukr. mat. journal* **2**, No 1. 70–85 (1950); Bruck and Kleinfeld, *Proc. Amer. math. Soc.* **2**, 878–890 (1951)].*

11. Frobenius theorem cannot be generalized to the case of non-alternative algebras, because, for instance, there exist very many different finite-dimensional real power-associative algebras, which are algebras with single-valued division.

* The dimension of a finite-dimensional real algebra without divisors of zero can only take the values $n = 1, 2, 4$ or 8 [Milnor, *Bull. Amer. Math. Soc.* **64**, 87–89 (1958)].*

12. Reasoning parallel to that which we used in V.8.3 leads at once to the following theorem:

The only finite-dimensional power-associative algebra over the field of complex numbers, having an identity, but not containing divisors of zero, is the field of complex numbers itself.

§ 9. The Birkhoff–Witt theorem on Lie algebras

1. In II.2.3 we proved that by replacing the operation of multiplication ab in the associative ring R by the commutator operation

$$a \circ b = ab - ba,$$

we obtain the Lie ring $L(R)$.

If the ring R is a Σ-operator ring (see V.1.7), then the ring $L(R)$ will be a Σ-operator ring.

Because the given rings have the same additive group, we need only verify that condition (11) of V.1.7 is true. If $a, b \in R$, $\alpha \in \Sigma$, then

$$(a \circ b)\alpha = (ab - ba)\alpha = (ab)\alpha - (ba)\alpha$$
$$= (a\alpha)b - b(a\alpha) = (a\alpha) \circ b.$$

In the same way we can also verify the equation

$$(a \circ b)\alpha = a \circ (b\alpha).$$

In particular, *if R is an algebra over the field P, then L(R) will also be an algebra over the same field.*

2. For the case of algebras a converse of the result in II.2.3 is the following theorem [Birkhoff, *Ann. of Math.* **38** 526–532 (1937); Witt, *J. reine und angew. Math.* **177**, 152–160 (1937)]:

For every Lie algebra L over any field P there exists an associative algebra R over the same field such that the algebra L can be isomorphically embedded in the algebra L(R).

Proof. We choose a basis for the algebra *L* over the field *P*. Assuming, by Zermelo's theorem (see I.6.3), that this basis is well ordered, we write it in the form

$$e_1, e_2, \ldots, e_\alpha, \ldots \tag{1}$$

If we use the symbol $\times$ to express multiplication in the algebra *L* then

$$e_\alpha \times e_\beta = \sum_\gamma c_{\alpha\beta}^\gamma e_\gamma ; \tag{2}$$

it is clear that for given α and β only a finite number of coefficients $c_{\alpha\beta}^\gamma$ can be distinct from zero.

Every ordered finite system of elements from the basis (1), not necessarily distinct, will be called a *word*. If we are given the word

$$w = e_{\alpha_1} e_{\alpha_2} \cdots e_{\alpha_k} \tag{3}$$

of *length k*, $k > 1$ — we write down the elements, forming this word, one after the other, not separating them by commas — then, as usual, we say that every pair e_{α_i}, e_{α_j} of elements occuring in it, for which $i < j$, but $\alpha_i > \alpha_j$ in the sense of the ordering of the basis (1), is *inverted* in this word.

In addition, we will consider the *sums of words*, i.e. finite unordered systems of words, not necessarily distinct, taken with coefficients from the field *P* distinct from zero. In writing sums of words we will formally combine words by means of the sign $+$.

The greatest length of the words occuring in a given sum of words *s* will be called the *degree* of this sum. If *n* is the degree of the sum of words *s*, then we denote by l_i, $i = n, n-1, \ldots, 2$, the total number of inversions in words of length *i* contained in

s; if in s a word of length i does not occur at all, then we set $l_i = 0$. It is clear that l_1 need not be considered. The symbol

$$\sigma = (l_n, l_{n-1}, \ldots, l_2) \tag{4}$$

is called the *height* of the sum of words s.

3. Assuming that n is fixed, we introduce a lexicographic ordering in the set of heights of the form (4), i.e. of the degree n: if

$$\sigma' = (l'_n, l'_{n-1}, \ldots, l'_2),$$

then we will assume that $\sigma < \sigma'$ if there is an i such that $l_i < l'_i$ but $l_n = l'_n, \ldots, l_{i+1} = l'_{i+1}$ (when $i < n$).

The lexicographic ordering of the heights of the degree n makes the set of these heights a well ordered set.

It is obvious that this will be a linear ordering. We consider the strictly decreasing sequence of heights

$$\sigma_1 > \sigma_2 > \ldots > \sigma_k > \ldots \tag{5}$$

where

$$\sigma_k = (l_{kn}, l_{k,n-1}, \ldots, l_{k2}), \qquad k = 1, 2 \ldots$$

It is clear that

$$l_{1n} \geqslant l_{2n} \geqslant \ldots \geqslant l_{kn} \geqslant \ldots,$$

and therefore there exists a k_1, such that

$$l_{k_1 n} = l_{k_1+1, n} = \ldots$$

From this it follows that

$$l_{k_1, n-1} \geqslant l_{k_1+1, n-1} \geqslant \ldots,$$

and therefore there exists a k_2, $k_2 \geqslant k_1$, such that

$$l_{k_2, n-1} = l_{k_2+1, n-1} = \ldots$$

Continuing for $n-2, \ldots, 2$, we prove that the sequence (5) breaks off.

4. Suppose that in the sum of words s there occurs the word $w = w_1 e_\beta e_\alpha w_2$, with coefficient $a \in P$, where $\beta > \alpha$ in the sense of the ordering of the basis (1), and w_1, w_2 are words, one or both of which may be absent. We will call the replacement in s of the summand aw by the sum of words

$$a w_1 e_\alpha e_\beta w_2 + \sum_\gamma (a c_{\beta\alpha}^\gamma) w_1 e_\gamma w_2$$

a *reduction* of the sum of words s. A reduction obviously does not alter the degree of the sum of words s, but lowers its height.

From this it follows, because the set of heights is well ordered, that every sum of words s can, by successive reductions, be made a sum of words of height $(0, 0, ..., 0)$, i.e. a sum of words without inversion or, as we will say, of *normal words*. In the sum of words obtained we then reduce similar terms, which may, of course, lower the degree of this sum, but does not violate its property of being a sum of normal words, and in this way we reduce the sum of words s *to normal form*.

5. LEMMA. *Every sum of words can be reduced to a unique normal form, which does not depend on the successive reductions which are performed.*

The assertion of the lemma is satisfied for sums of height $(0, 0, ..., 0)$, because in this case we only need to reduce similar terms. This enables us to carry out the proof by induction with respect to the well ordered set of heights.

Suppose that the sum of words s is reduced by two sequences of reductions respectively to the normal forms s_1 and s_2. If both chains of reductions begin with the same reduction, which carries s into s', then, because the height of the sum s' is less than the height of the sum s, we can use induction, and therefore $s_1 = s_2$.

On the other hand, suppose that the first reductions of both chains of reductions are with respect to different words of the sum s, where they carry s respectively into s' and s''. In the sum s' we can carry out the first reduction of the second chain of reductions, after which we arrive at some sum of words s'''; we obtain the same sum of words s''' by carrying out the first reduction of the first chain in s''. By reducing s''' in some way to a normal form s_3 and taking into account that the heights of the sums s' and s'' are less than the height of the sum s, we find that $s_1 = s_3$, $s_2 = s_3$, i.e. $s_1 = s_2$.

The same reasoning is applicable to the case when the first reductions of both chains of reductions relate to the given two positions of the word

$$w_1 e_\beta e_\alpha w_3 e_\delta e_\gamma w_2, \qquad \beta > \alpha, \ \delta > \gamma, \qquad (6)$$

whose coefficient we omit; the word w_3 may, of course, be absent. In this case, however, for the transition from the sums s' and s'' to the same sum s''' it is necessary to carry out the first reduction of the second (first) chain in all the words of the sum s' (of the sum s''), which appear, instead of the word (6).

6. It remains to consider the case when the first reduction of both chains of reductions relates to the given two positions of the word

$$w_1 e_\gamma e_\beta e_\alpha w_2, \quad \gamma > \beta > \alpha. \tag{7}$$

As above, let s' and s'' be the sums of words obtained after these first reductions. If the first reduction of the first chain relates to the position (γ, β), then in the word of the same length, which appears instead of the word (7) after this reduction, we can carry out yet another reduction in the position (γ, α), and then in the position (β, α). As a result from the sum s' we arrive at the sum s_1''', which will differ from the original sum s in that instead of the word (7) we have the sum

$$w_1 e_\alpha e_\beta e_\gamma w_2 + \sum_\delta c_{\gamma\beta}^\delta w_1 e_\delta e_\alpha w_2 +$$

$$\sum_\delta c_{\gamma\alpha}^\delta w_1 e_\beta e_\delta w_2 + \sum_\delta c_{\beta\alpha}^\delta w_1 e_\delta e_\gamma w_2. \tag{8}$$

In the same way, from the sum s'' we can go over, by several reductions, to the sum s_2''', which differs from the sum s in that the word (7) is replaced by the sum

$$w_1 e_\alpha e_\beta e_\gamma w_2 + \sum_\delta c_{\beta\alpha}^\delta w_1 e_\gamma e_\delta w_2 +$$

$$\sum_\delta c_{\gamma\alpha}^\delta w_1 e_\delta e_\beta w_2 + \sum_\delta c_{\gamma\beta}^\delta w_1 e_\alpha e_\delta w_2. \tag{9}$$

7. We compare the sums (8) and (9). They contain, respectively, the summands

$$c_{\gamma\beta}^\delta w_1 e_\delta e_\alpha w_2 \quad \text{and} \quad c_{\gamma\beta}^\delta w_1 e_\alpha e_\delta w_2. \tag{10}$$

If $\delta = \alpha$, then the summands (10) coincide. If $\delta > \alpha$, then it is possible to make a reduction in the first of these summands, which reduces it to the second summand, to which is added the sum $\sum_\varepsilon c_{\gamma\beta}^\delta c_{\delta\alpha}^\varepsilon w_1 e_\varepsilon w_2$. If, however, $\alpha > \delta$, then a reduction in the second of the summands (10) reduces it to the sum of the first summand and the sum $\sum_\varepsilon c_{\gamma\beta}^\delta c_{\alpha\delta}^\varepsilon w_1 e_\varepsilon w_2$.

Similar reasoning is applicable to the other summands of the sums (8) and (9). From this it follows that these sums, after corresponding reductions, can be reduced to sums—we denote them by (8′) and (9′)—which differ from each other only by words of the form $w_1 e_\varepsilon w_2$. It is easy to see, however, that the sum of the coefficients for the given word $w_1 e_\varepsilon w_2$ in the sum (8′) is equal to

$$\sum_{\delta > \alpha} c_{\gamma\beta}^{\delta} c_{\delta\alpha}^{\varepsilon} + \sum_{\delta < \beta} c_{\gamma\alpha}^{\delta} c_{\beta\delta}^{\varepsilon} + \sum_{\delta > \gamma} c_{\beta\alpha}^{\delta} c_{\delta\gamma}^{\varepsilon}, \tag{11}$$

and in the sum (9′) to

$$\sum_{\delta < \alpha} c_{\gamma\beta}^{\delta} c_{\alpha\delta}^{\varepsilon} + \sum_{\delta > \beta} c_{\gamma\alpha}^{\delta} c_{\delta\beta}^{\varepsilon} + \sum_{\delta < \gamma} c_{\beta\alpha}^{\delta} c_{\gamma\delta}^{\varepsilon}. \tag{12}$$

These two sums of coefficients are equal to each other. In fact, by applying to the equation valid in the algebra L

$$(e_\gamma \times e_\beta) \times e_\alpha + (e_\beta \times e_\alpha) \times e_\gamma + (e_\alpha \times e_\gamma) \times e_\beta = 0$$

the multiplication table (2) and equating the coefficient of e_ε to zero, we obtain the equation

$$\sum_{\delta} (c_{\gamma\beta}^{\delta} c_{\delta\alpha}^{\varepsilon} + c_{\beta\alpha}^{\delta} c_{\delta\gamma}^{\varepsilon} + c_{\alpha\gamma}^{\delta} c_{\delta\beta}^{\varepsilon}) = 0.$$

From this it follows that the difference of the sums (11) and (12) is equal to zero, if we take into account that for any α, β and δ there follows from

$$e_\alpha \times e_\beta = -e_\beta \times e_\alpha$$

the equation

$$c_{\alpha\beta}^{\delta} = -c_{\beta\alpha}^{\delta}, \tag{13}$$

and from

$$e_\alpha \times e_\alpha = 0$$

the equation

$$c_{\alpha\alpha}^{\delta} = 0.$$

Now we can assert that there exist chains of reductions which reduce the sums of words s_1''' and s_2''' to the same normal from s_3. The remaining reasoning is carried out in the same way as in the preceding cases. The proof of the lemma is now complete.

8. Now we construct over the field P an algebra R, whose basis is the set of all normal words (see V.9.4). The product of the normal words w_1 and w_2 will be assumed to be the normal form to which the word $w_1 w_2$ can be reduced. By the lemma this product is unique and associative.

We go on from the associative algebra R which we have obtained to the corresponding Lie algebra $L(R)$, denoting multiplication in the latter by the symbol $\circ$. We will find a subalgebra of it generated by all the elements e_α, which, being normal words, are contained in the basis of the algebras R and $L(R)$. For this we will show that for any α and β

$$e_\alpha \circ e_\beta = e_\alpha \times e_\beta.$$

In fact, if $\alpha = \beta$, then

$$e_\alpha \circ e_\alpha = 0 = e_\alpha \times e_\alpha,$$

If $\alpha > \beta$, then, by (2),

$$e_\alpha \circ e_\beta = e_\alpha e_\beta - e_\beta e_\alpha = e_\beta e_\alpha + \sum_\gamma c^\gamma_{\alpha\beta} e_\gamma - e_\beta e_\alpha =$$
$$\sum_\gamma c^\gamma_{\alpha\beta} e_\gamma = e_\alpha \times e_\beta.$$

If $\alpha < \beta$, then, by (13),

$$e_\alpha \circ e_\beta = e_\alpha e_\beta - e_\beta e_\alpha = e_\alpha e_\beta - e_\alpha e_\beta - \sum_\gamma c^\gamma_{\beta\alpha} e_\gamma =$$
$$\sum_\gamma c^\gamma_{\alpha\beta} e_\gamma = e_\alpha \times e_\beta.$$

Thus in the algebra $L(R)$ we have found a subalgebra isomorphic to the algebra L. The Birkhoff–Witt theorem has thus been proved.

* If L is a finite-dimensional Lie algebra over a field of characteristic zero (see III.2.11), then there exists a finite-dimensional associative algebra R over the same field such that L can be isomorphically embedded in $L(R)$ [I. D. Ado, *Izv. Kaz. fiz.-mat. o-va* 7, 1–43 (1934–1935); see also I. D. Ado, *Uspekhi mat. nauk* 2: No. 6 159–173 (1947); Harish–Chandra, *Ann. of Math.* 50, 68–76 (1949)].

A theorem analogous to the Birkhoff–Witt theorem is valid for Lie rings without operators [C. R. Lazard, C. R. *Paris* 234, No. 8 788–791 (1952),]. This theorem cannot be extended to a Lie ring with an arbitrary domain of operators [A. I. Shirshov, *Uspekhi mat. nauk* 8, No. 5 173–175 (1953)].*

§ 10. Derivations. Differential rings

1. In V.1.7, in introducing the concept of an operator ring, we did not use endomorphisms of the ring R, i.e. not those endo-

morphisms φ of the additive group of this ring which satisfy the condition

$$(ab)\,\varphi = a\varphi \cdot b\varphi, \qquad a, b \in R,$$

but those endomorphisms φ of the additive group which commute with all right and left multiplications, i.e. which satisfy the condition

$$(ab)\varphi = (a\varphi)b = a(b\varphi), \qquad a, b \in R.$$

The choice of these particular transformations can, of course, be justified on historical grounds. However, in many problems it is essential to use also those endomorphisms δ of the additive group of the ring R for which the condition

$$(ab)\,\delta = (a\delta)b + a(b\delta), \qquad a, b \in R \qquad (1)$$

is satisfied. This condition is analogous to the rule for the differentiation of a product, and because δ, as an endomorphism of the additive group of the ring R, also satisfies the condition

$$(a+b)\,\delta = a\delta + b\delta, \qquad a, b \in R, \qquad (2)$$

which is analogous to the rule for the differentiation of a sum; δ is called a *derivation*, or a *differentiation* of the ring R.

If the ring R is an operator ring, in particular if it is an algebra over some field, then in the definition of a derivation it is natural to suppose that δ is an operator endomorphism of the additive group. In other words, δ must satisfy, in addition to the conditions (1) and (2), the condition

$$(a\alpha)\,\delta = (a\delta)\,\alpha, \qquad (3)$$

where $a \in R$, and α is an arbitrary operator.

The zero endomorphism of any ring R (see III.3.7) is obviously a derivation of R. An example of a non-trivial derivation is the ordinary differentiation in the ring of polynomials $P[x]$ of one unknown over the field P.

2. If G is an arbitrary Abelian group, then its ring of endomorphisms (III.3.8) is associative. By replacing the operation of multiplication in this ring by the operation

$$\varphi \circ \psi = \varphi\psi - \psi\varphi,$$

we obtain, by II.2.3, a Lie ring, which we call *the Lie ring of endomorphisms* of the Abelian group G.

The totality of derivations of an arbitrary ring R is a subring in the Lie ring of endomorphisms of the additive group of the ring R.

In fact, if δ_1 and δ_2 are derivations of the ring R, then the endomorphism $\delta_1 + \delta_2$ of the additive group will also be derivations, because for any $a, b \in R$

$$(ab)(\delta_1 + \delta_2) = (ab)\,\delta_1 + (ab)\,\delta_2 = (a\delta_1)b + a(b\delta_1) + (a\delta_2)b + a(b\delta_2) =$$

$$(a\delta_1 + a\delta_2)b + a(b\delta_1 + b\delta_2) =$$

$$[a(\delta_1 + \delta_2)]b + a[b(\delta_1 + \delta_2)].$$

We have already noted above, in addition, that the zero endomorphism is a derivation. The endomorphism $-\delta$, the additive inverse of the derivation δ, will itself be a derivation, because for $a, b \in R$

$$(ab)(-\delta) = -[(ab)\,\delta] = -[(a\delta)b + a(b\delta)] =$$

$$[a(-\delta)]b + a[b(-\delta)].$$

Finally, the Lie product

$$\delta_1 \circ \delta_2 = \delta_1\delta_2 - \delta_2\delta_1$$

of the derivations δ_1, δ_2 will itself be a derivation, because for $a, b \in R$

$$(ab)(\delta_1 \circ \delta_2) = (ab)(\delta_1\delta_2 - \delta_2\delta_1) = [(ab)\,\delta_1]\,\delta_2 - [(ab)\delta_2]\,\delta_1 =$$

$$[(a\delta_1)b + a(b\delta_1)]\,\delta_2 - [(a\delta_2)b + a(b\delta_2)]\,\delta_1 =$$

$$[(a\delta_1)b]\,\delta_2 + [a(b\delta_1)]\,\delta_2 - [(a\delta_2)b]\,\delta_1 - [a(b\delta_2)]\,\delta_1 =$$

$$[(a\delta_1)\,\delta_2]b + (a\delta_1)(b\delta_2) + (a\delta_2)(b\delta_1) + a[(b\delta_1)\,\delta_2] - [(a\delta_2)\,\delta_1]b -$$

$$(a\delta_2)(b\delta_1) - (a\delta_1)(b\delta_2) - a[(b\delta_2)\delta_1] =$$

$$[a(\delta_1 \circ \delta_2)]b + a[b(\delta_1 \circ \delta_2)].$$

Thus the theorem has been proved.

We note that if R is an algebra over the field P, then the ring of operator endomorphisms of the additive group of the ring R will also be an algebra over P: if φ is such an endomorphism, $\alpha \in P$ and $a \in R$, then it is necessary to set

$$a(\varphi\alpha) = (a\varphi)\alpha = (a\alpha)\varphi. \tag{4}$$

The Lie ring of operator endomorphisms of the additive group of the ring R will also be an algebra over P, because, by (4),

$$a[(\varphi_1 \circ \varphi_2)\alpha] = [a(\varphi_1\varphi_2 - \varphi_2\varphi_1)]\alpha =$$
$$[a(\varphi_1\alpha)]\varphi_2 - (a\varphi_2)(\varphi_1\alpha) = a[(\varphi_1\alpha)\circ\varphi_2],$$

i.e.

$$(\varphi_1 \circ \varphi_2)\alpha = (\varphi_1\alpha)\circ\varphi_2$$

and, similarly,

$$(\varphi_1 \circ \varphi_2)\alpha = \varphi_1 \circ (\varphi_2\alpha).$$

Finally, *the Lie ring of derivations of the algebra R will be a sub-algebra of this Lie algebra of endomorphisms*, because if δ is a derivation and $\alpha \in P$, then for $a, b \in R$

$$(ab)(\delta\alpha) = [(ab)\delta]\alpha = [(a\delta)b + a(b\delta)]\alpha = [a(\delta\alpha)]b + a[b(\delta\alpha)].$$

This remark carries over, obviously, to the case of a ring with an arbitrary system of operators.

3. Let there be given an associative ring R. If $r \in R$, then we define a mapping δ_r by setting for all $a \in R$

$$a\delta_r = ar - ra. \tag{5}$$

This mapping will be a derivation, because for $a, b \in R$

$$(a+b)\delta_r = (a+b)r - r(a+b) = a\delta_r + b\delta_r,$$
$$(ab)\delta_r = abr - rab = abr - rab + arb - arb =$$
$$(a\delta_r)b + a(b\delta_r).$$

It is called the *inner derivation* of the ring R defined by the element r. It is clear that amongst the associative rings only the associative-commutative rings do not have inner derivations distinct from the zero endomorphism.

4. If R is a Lie ring and $r \in R$, then right multiplication by r, i.e. the mapping δ_r defined by the equation

$$a\delta_r = ar, \tag{6}$$

where $a \in R$, is a derivation of the ring R. In fact, from V.1.6 we know that δ_r will be an endomorphism of the additive group of the ring R. On the other hand, if $a, b \in R$. then by using the

Jacobi identity and the anti-commutative law (see II.2.2), we obtain:

$$(ab)\,\delta_r = (ab)\,r = -(br)a - (ra)\,b = (ar)\,b + a(br) =$$
$$(a\delta_r)\,b + a(b\delta_r).$$

The derivation δ_r is called the *inner derivation* of the Lie ring R defined by the element r. It is obvious that amongst the Lie rings only the zero rings do not have inner derivations distinct from the zero endomorphism ω.

The inner derivations form an ideal in the Lie ring of all derivations of a Lie ring R, because

$$\delta_r - \delta_s = \delta_{r-s},$$
$$\delta_r \circ \delta' = \delta_{r\delta'},$$

where $r,\ s \in R,\ \delta'$ *is an arbitrary derivation.*

In fact, if $a \in R$, then

$$a(\delta_r - \delta_s) = ar - as = a\delta_{r-s},$$
$$a(\delta_r \circ \delta') = a(\delta_r\delta' - \delta'\delta_r) = (ar)\,\delta' - (a\delta')\,r =$$
$$(a\delta')\,r + a(r\delta') - (a\delta')\,r = a\delta_{r\delta'}.$$

The mapping

$$r \to \delta_r, \quad r \in R,$$

is a homomorphism of the Lie ring R onto the Lie ring of its inner derivations.

In fact, if $a,\ r,\ s \in R$, then

$$a\delta_{r+s} = a(r+s) = ar + as = a\delta_r + a\delta_s = a\,(\delta_r + \delta_s).$$
$$a\delta_{rs} = a(rs) = -(rs)\,a = (sa)\,r + (ar)\,s = (ar)\,s - (as)\,r =$$
$$a(\delta_r\delta_s - \delta_s\delta_r) = a(\delta_r \circ \delta_s).$$

The kernel of this homomorphism is obviously the set of annihilators of the ring R (see V.1.9).

The results of this section are very similar to the results of III.3.2 on the inner automorphisms of groups.

5. If R is an associative ring, and L is the Lie ring related to it in the sense of II.2.3, then *every derivation δ of the ring R will also be a derivation in L.* In fact,

$$(a \circ b)\,\delta = (ab - ba)\,\delta = (a\delta)\,b + a(b\delta) - (b\delta)\,a - b(a\delta) =$$
$$(a\delta \circ b) + (a \circ b\delta).$$

The converse, generally speaking, is not true. However, *the inner derivations of the ring R will also be inner derivations in the ring L and conversely.* In fact, (5) can be rewritten in the form

$$a\delta_r = a \circ r;$$

on the other hand, (6) must now be expressible in the form

$$a\delta_r = a \circ r;$$

and therefore

$$a\delta_r = ar - ra.$$

From the results of this and the preceding sections it follows that *the inner derivations of an associative ring R form an ideal in the* Lie *ring of all derivations of the ring R.*

We note that all the results obtained in these last sections are valid for rings with arbitrary domain of operators and, in particular, for algebras.

* The concept of an inner derivation can be extended from the case of associative and Lie rings to the case of arbitrary rings, in such a way that the inner derivations form an ideal in the Lie ring of all derivations [Schafer, *Bull. Amer. math. Soc.* **55**, 769–776 (1949)]*.

6. Completely analogous to the concept of an operator ring is the concept of a differential ring. A ring R is called a *differential ring with system of derivations* Δ, if there is given a set Δ and with every element $\delta \in \Delta$ we associate some derivation of the ring R; here it is not assumed that distinct elements of Δ are necessarily associated with distinct derivations. We note, without formulating it precisely, that we could regard Δ as a Lie ring and define the concept of a differential ring with the Lie ring of derivations Δ.

If R is a differential ring with system of derivations Δ, then by a *differential subring* (*ideal*) of the ring R we understand a subring (ideal) A of R such that for all $a \in A$, $\delta \in \Delta$

$$a\delta \in A.$$

In a natural way we can also define the concepts of *isomorphism* and *homomorphism* of differential rings with the same system of derivations Δ.

7. We consider a differential ring R with one derivation δ, and we agree to use the notation usual in courses on mathematical analysis: if $a \in R$, then

$$a\delta = a'.$$

The equations (1) and (2) can now be rewritten in the form

$$(ab)' = a'b + ab', \tag{7}$$

$$(a + b)' = a' + b', \tag{8}$$

whence, in particular,

$$0' = 0, \tag{9}$$

$$(-a)' = -a'. \tag{10}$$

If the ring R has an identity e, then, by (7), for $a \in R$

$$a' = (ae)' = a'e + ae' = a' + ae',$$

i.e. $ae' = 0$. A ring with identity cannot, however, have any annihilator distinct from zero, and therefore

$$e' = 0. \tag{11}$$

Let R be a field, $a, b \in R$, $a \neq 0$ and let c be the solution of the equation $ax = b$. Then

$$b' = (ac)' = a'c + ac',$$

whence

$$c' = a^{-1}b' - a^{-1}a'c = a^{-2}(ab' - a'b). \tag{12}$$

8. An element a of the ring R is called *constant* with respect to the derivation under consideration if

$$a' = 0.$$

From (7)–(11) it follows that *the constants form a subring in R, containing the identity if R is a ring with identity.* Thus, in the ring of integers there are no derivations distinct from the zero endomorphisms. The same is true for the field of rational numbers, because, by (12), *in a field the constants form a subfield.*

9. Let R be an associative-commutative differential ring with one derivation. We consider the ring of polynomials

$$\overline{R} = R[x, x', x'', \ldots, x^{(n)}, \ldots]$$

over the ring R in a countable set of unknowns (see II.2.7). Letting

$$(x)' = x', (x^{(n)})' = x^{(n+1)}, \quad n = 1, 2, \ldots,$$

we can, by operating on (7) and (8) and using the uniqueness of the expression for an element from $\overline{R}$ in the form of a polynomial, extend the derivation given in R to the whole ring $\overline{R}$. It is left to the reader to verify that here all the requirements included in the definition of a derivation are satisfied.

In the differential ring $\overline{R}$ obtained, the differential subring generated by the subring R and the element x coincides with the whole ring $\overline{R}$. For this reason the ring $\overline{R}$, with the derivation which we have introduces, is called *the ring of differential polynomials over the ring R in one unknown x*.

This construction can be extended without difficulty to the case of several unknowns, and also several derivations.

* The ring $\overline{R}$ does not contain any constants different from the constants of the ring R. In particular, if the ring R is considered with the zero derivation, then R will also be the subring of constants of the ring $\overline{R}$.*

CHAPTER SIX

ORDERED AND TOPOLOGICAL GROUPS AND RINGS. NORMED RINGS

§ 1. Ordered groups

1. As a rule, the fundamental algebraic structures with which we usually have to deal in mathematics are not groups, rings and fields in their simple form. The operator groups and rings and the differential rings which we have already considered are an approximation to the concrete algebraic systems which one encounters in non-algebraic studies. In the present chapter we will proceed by other methods, but in the same direction. We begin by considering ordered structures.

The additive groups of integers, rational numbers and real numbers are at the same time both groups and linearly ordered sets (see I.4.1). The additive group of real functions of a real variable x, defined for all values of x, becomes a partially ordered set if we assume that $f \leqslant g$ if and only if $f(x) \leqslant g(x)$ for all values of x.

In all these groups the ordering and the group operation are connected in the following way: an inequality between elements of the group is not violated if we add the same element to both sides of it. This leads to the following definition, which we state in multiplicative form:

A groupoid G is said to be *linearly ordered* (respectively, *partially ordered*) if there is given for its elements a linear (respectively, partial) ordering, where from $a \leqslant b$ it follows that $ax \leqslant bx$ and $xa \leqslant xb$ for all $x \in G$.

From this definition it follows that if for the elements a, b, c, d of the partially (in particular, linearly) ordered groupoid G the inequalities

$$a \leqslant b, \ c \leqslant d,$$

hold, then

$$ac \leqslant bd. \tag{1}$$

It is obvious that if A is a subgroupoid of the groupoid G, then a partial ordering of the groupoid G induces a partial ordering in A.

The partially ordered groupoids G and G' are called *isomorphic* if there exists a one–one mapping of G onto G', which is an isomorphism both in the sense of the algebraic operation and in the sense of the partial ordering (see II.4.1 and I.4.3). Every groupoid can be regarded as partially ordered by considering its trivial partial ordering (see I.4.1).

2. A *monotonic transformation* of the partially ordered set M is a mapping φ of the set M into itself such that it always follows from $a \leqslant b$ that $a\varphi \leqslant b\varphi$. The product of monotonic transformations will itself be monotonic, i.e. these transformations form a subsemigroup in the symmetric semigroup on the set M (see II.1.8), and in fact a subsemigroup with identity, because the identity transformation is monotonic.

If φ, ψ are monotonic transformations of the set M, then we set $\varphi \leqslant \psi$ if $x\varphi \leqslant x\psi$ for all $x \in M$. This gives a partial ordering for the semigroup of monotonic transformations: if χ is any monotonic transformation, then from $x\varphi \leqslant x\psi$ it follows that $x(\varphi\chi) \leqslant x(\psi\chi)$ for all $x \in M$, i.e. $\varphi\chi \leqslant \psi\chi$; on the other hand, from $(x\chi)\varphi \leqslant (x\chi)\psi$ for all $x \in M$ it follows that $x(\chi\varphi) \leqslant x(\chi\psi)$, i.e. $\chi\varphi \leqslant \chi\psi$.

The following theorem of Krishnan is true [*Bull. Soc. Math. Fr.* **78**, 235–263 (1950)]:

Every partially ordered semigroup G with identity can be isomorphically embedded in the partially ordered semigroup of monotonic transformations of the partially ordered set G into itself.

In fact, we set up a correspondence between every element $a \in G$ and the transformation φ_a, by letting, for all $x \in G$

$$x\varphi_a = xa.$$

Because it follows from $x \leqslant y$ that $xa \leqslant ya$, then the transformation φ_a is monotonic. On the other hand, from II.4.6 we know that because there exists in G an identity transformation, $a \to \varphi_a$, $a \in G$, is an isomorphic mapping of the semigroup G into the symmetric semigroup on G, i.e., hence, into the semigroup of monotonic transformations of the set G. Finally, if $a \leqslant b$, then for all x it will be true that $xa \leqslant xb$, i.e. $\varphi_a \leqslant \varphi_b$; conversely, it follows from $\varphi_a \leqslant \varphi_b$ that, in particular, $1 \cdot a \leqslant 1 \cdot b$, i.e. $a \leqslant b$. Thus the theorem has been proved.

From this theorem it follows that *every partially ordered group G can be isomorphically embedded in the partially ordered group of monotonic permutations of the partially ordered set G into itself.*

3. An element a of a partially ordered group G is called *positive* if $a \geqslant 1$ (or, in the additive notation, if $a \geqslant 0$), and *negative* if $a \leqslant 1$. In a linearly ordered group every element is either positive or negative.

From (1) it follows that the product of positive elements of a partially ordered group G is positive, i.e. the positive elements form a subsemigroup in G, which we call the *semigroup of positive elements* of the partially ordered group G. In addition, the negative elements also form a subsemigroup.

The partial ordering of a group G is completely determined by giving the semigroup of positive elements, because $a \leqslant b$ if and only if $1 \leqslant ba^{-1}$.

A subsemigroup P of the group G will be a semigroup of positive elements for some partial ordering of the group G if and only if the following conditions are satisfied:

    (1) $1 \in P$;
    (2) if $a \in P$ and $a^{-1} \in P$, then $a = 1$;
    (3) *if* $a \in P$, $x \in G$, *then* $x^{-1}ax \in P$.

In fact, if P is the semigroup of positive elements for a partially ordered group G, then (1) $1 \leqslant 1$; (2) from $a^{-1} \geqslant 1$ it follows that $1 \geqslant a$, and because it is given that $a \geqslant 1$, $a = 1$; (3) from $a \geqslant 1$ it follows that $x^{-1}ax \geqslant x^{-1}x = 1$.

Conversely, let the subsemigroup P of the group G have the properties (1)–(3). We set $a \leqslant b$, if $ba^{-1} \in P$, and therefore, by (3), $a^{-1}b = a^{-1}(ba^{-1})a \in P$. This will be a partial ordering of the group G:

    $a \leqslant a$, because, by (1), $aa^{-1} = 1 \in P$;
    if $a \leqslant b$ and $b \leqslant a$, i.e. $ba^{-1} \in P$ and $ab^{-1} = (ba^{-1})^{-1} \in P$, then by (2), $ba^{-1} = 1$, i.e. $b = a$;
    if $a \leqslant b$ and $b \leqslant c$, i.e. $ba^{-1} \in P$ and $cb^{-1} \in P$, then $ca^{-1} = (cb^{-1})(ba^{-1}) \in P$, i.e. $a \leqslant c$;
    finally, if $a \leqslant b$, i.e. $ba^{-1} \in P$, then $(bx)(ax)^{-1} = ba^{-1} \in P$, i.e.

$ax \leqslant bx$, and, by (3), $(xb)(xa)^{-1} = x(ba^{-1})x^{-1} \in P$, i.e. $xa \leqslant xb$.

In this partial ordering the elements of P will be positive, and only these elements, because $a \geqslant 1$ if and only if $a \cdot 1^{-1} = a \in P$. Thus the theorem has been proved.

A subsemigroup P of the group G defines a linear ordering of this group if, and only if, in addition to the conditions (1)–(3), *it also satisfies the condition*

(4) *for any* $a \in G$ *either* $a \in P$, *or* $a^{-1} \in P$.

In fact, if the group G is linearly ordered and the element a is not positive, then $a < 1$, from which it follows that $1 < a^{-1}$, i.e. the element a^{-1} is positive. Conversely, suppose that the subsemigroup P satisfies the conditions (1)–(4) and $a, b \in G$. If $ba^{-1} \in P$, then $a \leqslant b$ in the sense of the partial ordering defined by the semigroup P. If, however, $ba^{-1} \notin P$, then, by (4), $(ba^{-1})^{-1} = ab^{-1} \in P$, i.e. $b \leqslant a$.

* A partially ordered set M is called *directed* if for any $a, b \in M$ there exists an element $c \in M$ such that

$$a \leqslant c, \quad b \leqslant c.$$

Thus we can speak of a *directed group*. A partially ordered group will be directed if, and only if, it coincides with the subgroup generated by all its positive elements.*

4. In a partially ordered group G it follows from $a \geqslant 1$ that $a^n \geqslant 1$ for all natural n. Therefore, by the property (2) of the semigroup of positive elements, *every strictly positive element a* (i.e. such that $a > 1$) *must have infinite order*: if $a^n = 1$, $n > 1$, then $a^{n-1} = a^{-1}$. From this it follows (for the definition see II.3.4) that:

Every linearly ordered group is torsion free.

A periodic group does not admit any partial orderings except the trivial one.

5. If in the group G we are given two partial orderings with the semigroups of positive elements P_1 and P_2, respectively, then the second partial ordering is called an *extension* of the first if $P_2 \supset P_1$, i.e. if from $a \leqslant b$ in the first ordering the same inequality always follows in the second ordering.

The set of all subsemigroups of the group G which satisfy the conditions (1)–(3) of VI.1.3 is partially ordered by inclusion. The union of any chain of such subsemigroups will itself be a subsemigroup with the properties (1)–(3), and therefore, by the Kuratowski–Zorn theorem, every subsemigroup with the properties (1)–(3) is contained in such a maximal subsemigroup, i.e. *every partial ordering of the group G can be extended to a maximal partial ordering (not necessarily a proper extension).*

If the group G admits linear orderings, then each of its linear orderings is maximal.

We add to this obvious assertion one criterion for determining when all the maximal orderings of the group G are linear [Ohnishi, *Osaka Math. J.* **2**, 161–164 (1950)].

6. We begin with some remarks on the subsemigroups of the group G which have the properties (1)–(3). If P is such a subsemigroup, then the set P^{-1} of all elements p^{-1}, where $p \in P$, will obviously also be a subsemigroup with the properties (1)–(3). We note that

$$P \cap P^{-1} = 1, \qquad (2)$$

because otherwise the property (2) will be violated.

LEMMA 1. *If P and Q are subsemigroups of the group G with the properties* (1)–(3), *and*

$$P \cap Q^{-1} = 1, \qquad (3)$$

then the set PQ of all elements of the group G which can be represented in the form pq, $p \in P$, $q \in Q$ will itself be a subsemigroup with the properties (1)–(3).

In fact,

$$(p_1 q_1)(p_2 q_2) = (p_1 \cdot q_1 p_2 q_1^{-1})(q_1 q_2) = p_3 q_3, \qquad (4)$$

where $p_3 \in P$, $q_3 \in Q$. This proves that PQ is a subsemigroup.

In addition, $1 = 1 \cdot 1 \in PQ$. On the other hand, if $pq = 1$, then $p = q^{-1}$, whence, by (3), it follows that $p = q = 1$. From

$$(p_1 q_1)(p_2 q_2) = 1$$

it will therefore follow (see (4)) that $p_3 = q_3 = 1$, i.e., because the subsemigroups P and Q have the property (2),

$$q_1 = q_2 = p_1 = q_1 p_2 q_1^{-1} = p_2 = 1.$$

Finally, for any $x \in G$

$$x^{-1}(pq)x = (x^{-1}px)(x^{-1}qx) = p'q' \in PQ.$$

The lemma has therefore been proved.

The intersection of any system of subsemigroups of the group G which have the properties (1)–(3) will itself obviously be a subsemigroup with the same properties. From this it follows that if the element a is in general contained in at least one such subsemigroup, then there exists a minimal subsemigroup with the properties (1)–(3) containing the element a; we denote it by P_a.

7. *All the maximal orderings of a group G are linear if, and only if*:

I. P_a *exists for every* $a \in G$.

II. *If* $b, c \in P_a$, $a \in G$, *and* $b \neq 1$, $c \neq 1$, *then*

$$P_b \cap P_c \neq 1.$$

Proof. If the group G admits a linear ordering with the semigroup of positive elements P, then $a \in P$ or $a \in P^{-1}$, and therefore the property I is satisfied.

Now let every partial ordering of the group G be extended to a linear one. If $b, c \in P_a, b \neq 1, c \neq 1$, but $P_b \cap P_c = 1$, then, by Lemma 1, $P_b P_c^{-1}$ will be a subsemigroup with the properties (1)–(3). The partial ordering defined by this subsemigroup can, by hypothesis, be extended to a linear one, defined by the subsemigroup of positive elements P. Thus

$$b \in P, \quad c^{-1} \in P$$

and therefore $c \in P^{-1}$. We arrive at a contradiction to the fact that either $a \in P$, i.e. $P_a \subseteq P$, and therefore $P_a \cap P^{-1} = 1$, or else $a \in P^{-1}$, i.e. $P_a \subseteq P^{-1}$, and then $P_a \cap P = 1$. This proves that the property II is also satisfied.

Now we suppose that the group G has the properties I and II and that in G we take the element a and a subsemigroup P with the properties (1)–(3).

LEMMA 2. *If* $P \cap P_a \neq 1$, *then* $P \cap P_a^{-1} = 1$.

In fact, let $x \in P \cap P_a$, $x \neq 1$, and also $y \in P \cap P_a^{-1}$, $y \neq 1$. Then $x^{-1} \in P_a^{-1}$, $y \in P_a^{-1} = P_{a^{-1}}$, and therefore, by II,

$$P_{x^{-1}} \cap P_y \neq 1.$$

However, $x^{-1} \in P^{-1}$, $y \in P$, i.e. $P_{x^{-1}} \subseteq P^{-1}$, $P_y \subseteq P$, and therefore $P^{-1} \cap P \neq 1$, which contradicts (2). The Lemma has now been proved.

To complete the proof of the theorem we take any subsemigroup P in the group G which defines a maximal ordering. If this ordering is not linear, then the condition (4) of VI.1.3 is not satisfied, i.e. there exists an element $a \in G$ such that $a \notin P$ and $a^{-1} \notin P$. By virtue of condition I the subsemigroup P_a exists, where, by Lemma 2, we can assume (if necessary, replacing a by a^{-1}) that $P \cap P_a^{-1} = 1$. Therefore, by Lemma 1, the product PP_a will be a subsemigroup with the properties (1)–(3), which is strictly greater than P, which, however, contradicts the choice of the subsemigroup P. Thus the theorem has been proved.

8. From the criterion we have proved there follows this theorem by E. P. Shimbireva [*Mat. Sb.* **20**, 145–178 (1947)]:

All the maximal orderings of an Abelian group without torsion are linear.

In fact, if a is an element of the torsion-free Abelian group G which is distinct from 1, then the subsemigroup P_a consists of all the powers $a^n, n = 0, 1, 2, \ldots$ Because, in addition, $P_1 = 1$ always, condition I is satisfied. Condition II is also satisfied, because if $b = a^k, c = a^l, k \geqslant 1, l \geqslant 1$, then $a^{kl} \neq 1$ and $a^{kl} \in P_b \cap P_c$.

A special case of this theorem is Levi's theorem [*Rend. Palermo* **35**, 225–236 (1913)]:

Every torsion-free Abelian group can be linearly ordered.

* There exist, in various forms, necessary and sufficient conditions for a group to be linearly ordered [Iwasawa, *J. Math. Soc. Jap.* **1**, 1–9 (1948); A. I. Mal'cev, *Izv. AN SSSR*, seria matem. **13**, 473–482 (1949); V. D. Podderyugin, *Izv. AN SSSR*, seria matem. **21**, 199–208 (1957)].*

§ 2. Ordered rings

1. All the ordered groups listed in the second paragraph of VI.1.1 are the additive groups of certain rings or fields. These examples of ordered rings (fields) suggest the following definition, which could be formulated at once for any group with multi-operators (see III.2.1):

A ring R is called *linearly* (*partially*) *ordered*, if its additive group is linearly (partially) ordered (see VI.1.1), and therefore, by VI.1.3, we can speak of its positive elements if, in addition, the product of positive elements is positive, i.e. from $a \geqslant 0$, $b \geqslant 0$ it follows that $ab \geqslant 0$.

From this definition if follows that the trivial partial ordering of the additive group of any ring will be a (trivial) partial ordering of the ring itself.

The requirement for the product of positive elements, included in our definition, is obviously equivalent to the fact that if $a \leqslant b$ and $c \geqslant 0$, then $ac \leqslant bc$ and $ca \leqslant cb$. We note further that because from $a \geqslant 0$ it follows that $-a \leqslant 0$ — it is sufficient to add $-a$ to both sides of the first inequality—and, conversely, from $a \leqslant 0$ it follows that $-a \geqslant 0$, then the following *sign rule* is true:

if $a \leqslant 0$, $b \geqslant 0$, then $ab \leqslant 0$ and $ba \leqslant 0$;

if $a \leqslant 0$, $b \leqslant 0$, then $ab \geqslant 0$.

From this it follows that it would be impossible to define an ordered ring as a ring in which there is given an ordering with respect to which both the additive group and the multiplicative groupoid of this ring are ordered in the sense of VI.1.1.

We note that in the case of rings without divisors of zero the condition for the product of positive elements included in the definition of an ordered ring can be altered to the following: the product of strictly positive elements is strictly positive, i.e. from $a > 0$, $b > 0$ it follows that $ab > 0$. This is equivalent to the fact that if $a < b$ and $c > 0$, then $ac < bc$ and $ca < cb$.

We mention, finally, that an *isomorphism* of ordered rings is defined in essentially the same way as in VI.1.1 for ordered groupoids.

2. By VI.1.3 any partial ordering of a ring R is determined by the additive semigroup of positive elements P: $a \leqslant b$ if, and only if, $b - a \in P$. From VI.1.3 and the definition of an ordered ring it follows that:

A subsemigroup P of the additive group of a ring R is a semigroup of positive elements for some partial ordering of this ring if, and only if, the following conditions are satisfied:

(1') $0 \in P$;

(2') if $a \in P$ and $-a \in P$, then $a = 0$;

(3') if $a \in P$ and $b \in P$, then $ab \in P$.

A partial ordering of the ring R defined by an additive semigroup P with the properties (1')–(3') *will be linear if, and only if, this condition is also satisfied*:

(4') *for any $a \in R$ either $a \in P$ or $-a \in P$.*

3. If $a_1, a_2, \ldots, a_n$ are elements of the ring R distinct from zero, then by a *product* of them we will now mean every product (in the non-associative case, with some arrangement of the brackets), every factor of which is one of the a_i, $i = 1, 2, \ldots, n$, where every a_i may occur in this product several times, including the case when it does not occur at all. A product of the elements $a_1, a_2, \ldots, a_n$ will be called *even* if every a_i, $i = 1, 2, \ldots, n$, occurs in it an even number of times. Finally, in speaking of the *sum of products* of several elements we will mean that all these products occur in the sum under consideration with the plus sign.

The following theorem is true [see R. E. Johnson, *Proc. Amer. math. Soc.* **3**, 414–416 (1952); V. D. Podderyugin, *Uspekhi mat. nauk* **9**, No. 4, 211–216 (1954)]:

The ring R is a ring without divisors of zero, admitting a linear ordering, if, and only if, every sum of even products of its elements is distinct from zero.

In fact, let R be a linearly ordered ring without divisors of zero, and let there be given some even product of its elements. This product is unaltered if all the negative factors occurring in it are replaced by their additive inverses, and therefore it is equal to the product of strictly positive elements, i.e., because there are no divisors of zero, it will itself be strictly positive. Hence every sum of even products will be strictly positive and therefore distinct from zero.

4. Now let the ring R be such that any sum of even products of its elements is distinct from zero. Then R cannot contain divisors of zero, because from $ab = 0$, $a \neq 0$, $b \neq 0$, it would follow that the even product $(ab)(ab)$ would be equal to zero.

We will call a subset Q of our ring R regular if it satisfies the following requirements:

(a) $0 \notin Q$;

(b) if $a \in Q$, then $-a \notin Q$;

(c) if $a_1, a_2, \ldots, a_n \in Q$, $n \geqslant 0$, and $x_1, x_2, \ldots, x_k$ are elements of R distinct from zero, $k \geqslant 0$, where $n + k > 0$, and σ is some sum of products of all these elements, then there exists at least one way of replacing the elements x_j by elements x_j', where

$$x_j' = x_j \text{ or } x_j' = -x_j, \, j = 1, 2, \ldots, k, \tag{1}$$

after which the sum σ will be distinct from zero.

LEMMA 1. *The empty set is regular.*

In fact, suppose that the sum σ of products of the elements $x_1, x_2, \ldots, x_k \in R$, $k \geqslant 1$, which are distinct from zero, remain equal to zero for any method of replacement of the form (1).

If the element x_1 occurs in every term of this sum an odd number of times, then σx_1 will be a sum each of whose terms contains the factor x_1 an even number of times, and this sum will again remain equal to zero, whatever replacement of the form (1) we make.

On the other hand, suppose that some terms of the sum σ contain the factor x_1 an even number of times, and others an odd number of times. We denote the sum of the first by σ_1, and the sum of the second by σ_2:

$$\sigma = \sigma_1 + \sigma_2.$$

Thus the sum $\sigma_1 + \sigma_2$ is equal to zero after any replacement of the form (1). This is consequently true also for the sum obtained from it after x_1 has been replaced by $-x_1$ — this sum can obviously be written in the form $\sigma_1 - \sigma_2$, —and therefore also for the sum $2\sigma_1$, every term of which contains the factor x_1 an even number of times.

By performing these transformations successively for each of the elements $x_1, x_2, \ldots, x_k$ we finally reduce a sum of even products of these elements to zero, which, however, contradicts our assertion. The lemma has thus been proved.

LEMMA 2. *If the regular set Q contains neither the element a nor the element $-a$, where $a \neq 0$, then at least one of the unions $Q \cup a$, $Q \cup (-a)$ will be regular.*

Suppose, in fact, that there exists a sum σ_1 of products of certain elements of Q, the element a and the elements

$$x_1, x_2, \ldots, x_k, \tag{2}$$

distinct from zero, which is equal to zero, whatever replacement of the elements (2) of the form (1) we make. On the other hand, suppose that there exists a sum σ_2 of products of certain elements of Q, the element a and the elements

$$y_1, y_2, \ldots, y_l, \tag{3}$$

distinct from zero, which remains equal to zero if the element a is replaced by $-a$, and the elements (3) undergo a replacement of the form (1). Then $\sigma_1 \sigma_2$ will be a sum of products of certain elements of Q and the elements

$$a, x_1, x_2, \ldots, x_k, \quad y_1, y_2, \ldots, y_l, \tag{4}$$

which is equal to zero for every replacement of the form (1) applied to the elements (4). However, this contradicts the fact that the set Q is regular. Thus the lemma has been proved.

5. The union of every chain of regular subsets of our ring R will obviously be regular. Therefore, by the Kuratowski–Zorn theorem, there exist maximal regular subsets in R. Let Q be one of these. By Lemma 2, for every $a \in R$, $a \neq 0$, either a or $-a$ belongs to Q.

If $a, b \in Q$, then $a + b \in Q$ also. In fact, $a + b \neq 0$ because of (b) from the definition of a regular set. If the set Q were to contain the element $c = -(a + b)$, then the equation

$$a + b + c = 0$$

would hold, which contradicts the fact the set Q is regular.

If $a, b \in Q$, then $ab \in Q$. In fact, $ab \neq 0$ because of (a) from the definition of a directed set and the fact that there are no divisors of zero. If the set Q were to contain the element $d = -ab$, then the equation

$$ab + d = 0$$

would hold, which contradicts the fact that the set Q is regular.

From this it follows that the union $P = Q \cup 0$ will be an additive subsemigroup of the ring R, satisfying all the conditions (1')–(4') of VI.2.2. This proves the theorem in VI.2.3.

6. From this theorem it follows that:

A commutative-associative ring is an integral domain admitting a linear ordering if, and only if, no sum of squares of its elements distinct from zero is equal to zero.

From this it follows that the field of complex numbers does not admit a linear ordering: in this field the equation

$$1^2 + i^2 = 0$$

holds.

* The field of power series over an ordered field P (see II.5.7), and therefore also the field of rational fractions over such a field P, can be linearly ordered.*

7. *If the linearly ordered ring R has an identity, then it has a subring isomorphic to the ring of integers with its usual ordering.*

In fact, the identity must be strictly positive, because it coincides with its own square. Hence all positive multiples of the identity are also strictly positive, and they are all distinct by virtue of VI.1.4.

From this it follows that *the usual ordering of the ring of integers is its only possible linear ordering.*

* The ring of integers is the only linearly ordered ring without divisors of zero and with an identity, ordered by a subset whose positive elements are well ordered (see I.5.4).*

8. *The ordering of the integral domain* R *can be extended, and in a unique way, to its quotient field* $\overline{R}$.

First we suppose that the ordering of the ring R has already been extended to the field $\overline{R}$. If $a/b > 0$, then, because it follows from $b \neq 0$ that $b^2 > 0$, we have that

$$\frac{a}{b} \cdot b^2 = ab > 0.$$

Conversely, if $ab > 0$ in R, then, because $(b^{-1})^2 > 0$, it will be true that

$$ab \cdot (b^{-1})^2 = \frac{a}{b} > 0.$$

From this it follows that any possible extension of the ordering from R to $\overline{R}$ is unique.

For the proof of the existence of such an extension, we assume that $a/b > 0$ if, and only if, $ab > 0$. If $a/b = c/d$, i.e. $ad = bc$ (see II.5.2), then $abd^2 = b^2cd$. Therefore, because $d^2 > 0$, $b^2 > 0$, it will follow from $ab > 0$ that $cd > 0$, i.e. $c/d > 0$; our definition of a strictly positive element in the field $\overline{R}$ is thus legitimate.

If $a, b \in R$, where $a \neq 0$, $b \neq 0$, then only one of the elements ab, $(-a)b$ will be strictly positive in R, and therefore either $a/b > 0$, or else $-(a/b) = (-a)/b > 0$ (see II.5.4), and these cases are mutually exclusive.

If $a/b > 0$, $c/d > 0$, i.e. $ab > 0$, $cd > 0$, then $abd^2 > 0$, $b^2cd > 0$, whence

$$(ad + bc)bd = abd^2 + b^2cd > 0,$$

i.e. (see II.5.4)

$$\frac{a}{b} + \frac{c}{d} > 0.$$

With the same hypotheses it will be true that

$$(ac)(bd) = (ab)(cd) > 0,$$

i.e. (see II.5.2)

$$\frac{a}{b} \cdot \frac{c}{d} > 0.$$

This proves that the set P, consisting of zero and all the strictly positive elements of the field $\overline{R}$, satisfies all the conditions of VI.2.2, i.e. it determines a linear ordering in $\overline{R}$. This ordering is an extension of the given linear ordering of the ring R, because by II.5.2,

$$a = \frac{ab}{b}, \quad b \neq 0,$$

but from $a > 0$ it follows that $(ab)b = ab^2 > 0$ and conversely.

From this theorem and VI.2.7 it follows that *the usual ordering of the field of rational numbers is its only possible linear ordering.*

Because the additive group of any linearly ordered skew field K is, by VI.1.4, torsion free, then K will be a skew field of characteristic zero (see III.2.11), i.e., by what was said above, *every linearly ordered skew field K contains as its prime subfield the field of rational numbers with the usual ordering.*

9. *The ordered set Q of strictly positive elements of any linearly ordered associative skew field K forms a linearly ordered group with respect to multiplication.*

In fact, from VI.2.7 we know that the identity of the skew field K belongs to Q. In addition, if $a \in Q$, i.e. $a > 0$, then $a^{-1} \in Q$ also, because from $a^{-1} < 0$ it would follow, by VI.2.1, that $aa^{-1} = 1 < 0$. The set Q is thus a multiplicative group. The remaining assertions of the theorem follow from the definition of an ordering of a ring without divisors of zero (see VI.2.1).

* Every linearly ordered group can be isomorphically embedded in a linearly ordered multiplicative group of strictly positive elements of some linearly ordered associative skew field [A. I. Mal'cev, *Dokl. AN SSSR* **60**, 1499–1501 (1948); Neumann, *Trans. Amer. math. Soc.* **66**, 202–252 (1949)].*

§ 3. Archimedean groups and rings

1. A subset N of a partially ordered set M is called *convex* if, together with all its comparable elements a and b, $a < b$, it also contains all the elements x of the set M which satisfy the inequalities $a \leqslant x \leqslant b$.

A subgroup A of a partially ordered group G will be convex if, and only if, together with every positive element a in it, it contains all positive elements x of the group G which satisfy the inequality $x \leqslant a$.

In fact the inequalities $a \leqslant x \leqslant b$ and $1 \leqslant a^{-1}x \leqslant a^{-1}b$ are equivalent.

Let G and G' be partially ordered groups, P and P' their semigroups of positive elements, and φ a mapping of G onto G'. We will call the mapping φ a *monotonic homomorphism* if it is a homomorphism in the set-theoretical sense and if, in addition, $P\varphi = P'$. In this we do not assume, of course, that P is a complete set of inverse images for P' — it is sufficient to recall (2) of VI.1.3.

The kernel A of a monotonic homomorphism φ is a convex normal subgroup.

In fact, suppose that $a \in A$, $a \geqslant 1$ and $x \in G$, $1 \leqslant x \leqslant a$. From $x \geqslant 1$ and from the definition of the homomorphism φ it follows that

$$x\varphi \geqslant 1'. \tag{1}$$

On the other hand, because $x^{-1}a \geqslant 1$ and $a\varphi = 1'$, then

$$1' \leqslant (x^{-1}a)\varphi = (x\varphi)^{-1}(a\varphi) = (x\varphi)^{-1}. \tag{2}$$

From (1) and (2) it follows that $x\varphi = 1'$, i.e. $x \in A$.

If A is a convex normal subgroup of the partially ordered group G, then the factor-group $G' = G/A$ can be partially ordered in such a way that the natural homomorphism of G onto G' will be a monotonic homomorphism.

In fact, if P is the semigroup of positive elements of the group G, then we denote by P' the totality of cosets with respect to A which contain at least one element of P. The theorem will be proved if we can show that P' is a subsemigroup of the group G' and has the properties (1)–(3) of VI.1.3. It is only necessary, however, to verify the property (2), because the remaining assertions are obvious.

Let $p \in P$, i.e. $pA \in P'$, and in addition let $(pA)^{-1} = p^{-1}A \in P'$. Thus there exists an element $p_0 = p^{-1}a$ such that $p_0 \in P$, $a \in A$. Therefore $pp_0 = a$, i.e. $a \geqslant 1$, and because $1 \leqslant p_0$, then

$$p \leqslant pp_0 = a.$$

Hence, because of the inequality $1 \leqslant p$ and the fact that A is convex, it follows that $p \in A$, i.e. $pA = A$, which is what we were required to prove.

2. The group G itself and the identity subgroup E are convex subgroups of any partially ordered group G. From the definition of a convex subgroup it follows that the intersection of any set of convex subgroups and also the union of any chain of convex subgroups will itself be convex.

The convex subgroups of a linearly ordered group G form a chain with respect to set-theoretical inclusion.

In fact, suppose that we take the convex subgroups A and B in the group G, where B contains the element b which lies outside A; without loss of generality we can assume that $b > 1$. If there were to exist an element a in A such that $b < a$, then, because A is convex, it would follow that $b \in A$, contrary to our assumption. Thus all the positive elements of the subgroup A are less than b, i.e., because B is convex, they all belong to B, and therefore $A \subset B$. Thus the theorem has been proved.

If a is a strictly positive element of a linearly ordered group G, then the set A, consisting of all the elements x such that $1 \leqslant x \leqslant a^n$ for some natural n, and their inverses, will be the minimal convex subgroup containing the element a.

All the given elements must in fact belong to every convex subgroup containing a. In addition, let

$$\left. \begin{array}{l} 1 \leqslant x \leqslant a^k, \\ 1 \leqslant y \leqslant a^l \end{array} \right\} \tag{3}$$

for some natural k and l. Then, by (1) from VI.1.1,

$$1 \leqslant xy \leqslant a^{k+1},$$

i.e. $xy \in A$, and therefore $(xy)^{-1} = y^{-1}x^{-1} \in A$. On the other hand, it follows from (3) that

$$a^{-l} \leqslant y^{-1} \leqslant 1,$$

and therefore

$$a^{-l} \leqslant xy^{-1} \leqslant a^k.$$

Thus, if $1 \leqslant xy^{-1}$, then $xy^{-1} \in A$. If, however, $xy^{-1} < 1$, then

$$1 < (xy^{-1})^{-1} \leqslant a^l,$$

i.e. $(xy^{-1})^{-1} \in A$, and then $xy^{-1} \in A$. Now it is obvious that A is a subgroup, which contains a and is convex.

3. Two strictly positive elements a and b of a linearly ordered group G are said to belong to the same *Archimedean class if they* generate the same convex subgroup of the group G. All the strictly positive elements are thus decomposed into non-intersecting Archimedean classes. It is convenient also to assume that the element 1 forms a separate Archimedean class.

The set of Archimedean classes of the group G is linearly ordered with respect to the natural linear ordering of the jumps (i.e. pairs of neighbouring elements) in the chain of convex subgroups of the group G.

A linearly ordered group G is called *Archimedean* if there are no convex subgroups in it distinct from G and E. From the last of the theorems of VI.3.2 it follows that:

A linearly ordered group G will be Archimedean if, and only if, for any pair a, b of its strictly positive elements it is possible to find a natural number $n = n(a, b)$ such that $a^n > b$.

Examples of Archimedean groups are the subgroups of the additive group of real numbers with their natural ordering.

4. HÖLDER'S THEOREM. *Every Archimedean group is commutative and is isomorphic to some subgroup of the additive group of real numbers with its natural ordering.*

Let the Archimedean group G have a minimal strictly positive element a. If b is any strictly positive element of G, then there exists a natural number n such that

$$a^n \leqslant b < a^{n+1}.$$

Hence

$$1 \leqslant ba^{-n} < a,$$

and therefore $ba^{-n} = 1$, i.e. $b = a^n$. All the strictly positive elements of the group G are thus powers of the element a, and because, by VI.1.1,

$$1 < a < a^2 < \dots < a^n < \dots,$$

G is isomorphic to the additive group of integers with its natural ordering.

Now we suppose that amongst the strictly positive elements of the Archimedean group G there is no minimal one. In this case for every $a > 1$ there exists $ab > 1$ such that $b^2 \leqslant a$. In fact, there exists an element c such that

$$1 < c < a,$$

whence $1 < c^{-1}a$. If $c^2 \leqslant a$, then $b = c$. If $c^2 > a$, then $1 > c^{-1}ac^{-1}$, i.e. $a > (c^{-1}a)^2$ and therefore $b = c^{-1}a$.

To prove the commutativity of the group G it is sufficient to show that any pair of its strictly positive elements a, b commute. If $ab \neq ba$, then without loss of generality we can assume that

$$c = a^{-1}b^{-1}ab > 1.$$

As we have proved, there exists an element d such that $1 < d$ and $d^2 \leqslant c$. We can assume here that $d < a$ and $d < b$, and therefore there exist natural numbers k and l such that

$$d^k \leqslant a < d^{k+1}, \qquad d^l \leqslant b < d^{l+1}.$$

Hence

$$ab < d^{k+l+2},$$

$$a^{-1}b^{-1} \leqslant d^{-(k+l)}.$$

i.e.

$$c < d^2,$$

and because, by hypothesis, $d^2 \leqslant c$, we arrive at a contradiction. We have thus proved that the group G is commutative.

5. We will find it convenient now to change to the additive notation for the operation in the group G. We fix some strictly positive element e in G and relate to every element $a \in G$ the class U_a of all rational numbers m/n, $n > 0$, for which

$$me \leqslant na. \tag{4}$$

If $m/n \in U_a$ and $p/q \leqslant m/n$, then $p/q \in U_a$, because from (4) and $pn \leqslant qm$ it follows that

$$(pn)e \leqslant (qm)e \leqslant (qn)a,$$

whence

$$pe \leqslant qa.$$

In particular, if $m/n \in U_a$ and $p/q = m/n$, then $p/q \in U_a$, i.e. the class U_a can in fact be regarded as a set of rational numbers.

The class U_a does not contain all the rational numbers: because the group G is Archimedean there exists a natural number m such that $me > a$, and therefore $m \notin U_a$. The class U_a is thus the first class of some section in the system of rational numbers, i.e. it determines, by the Dedekind theory of real numbers, some real number α. We set

$$\alpha = a\theta.$$

6. If $a \leqslant b$, then $a\theta \leqslant b\theta$, because from (4) and $a \leqslant b$ it follows that

$$me \leqslant nb,$$

i.e. $U_a \subseteq U_b$.

We will prove, in addition, that

$$(a + b)\theta = a\theta + b\theta. \tag{5}$$

In fact, if

$$\frac{m}{n} \in U_a, \qquad \frac{p}{q} \in U_b,$$

i.e.

$$me \leqslant na, \qquad pe \leqslant qb,$$

then

$$(mq + np)e \leqslant nq(a + b),$$

whence

$$\frac{mq + np}{nq} = \frac{m}{n} + \frac{p}{q} \in U_{a+b}.$$

On the other hand, in the same way we can show that if

$$\frac{m}{n} \notin U_a, \qquad \frac{p}{q} \notin U_b,$$

then also

$$\frac{m}{n} + \frac{p}{q} \notin U_{a+b},$$

from this follows (5).

The mapping θ is thus a monotonic homomorphism of the group G onto some subgroup of the additive group of real numbers. Under this homomorphism only the zero of the group G is carried into the zero: if $a > 0$, then, because the group G is Archimedean, there exists a natural number m such that $ma > e$, i.e. $1/m \in U_a$, and therefore $a\theta > 0$. The homomorphism θ will thus be an isomorphism, which preserves the order relation, and so the theorem has been proved.

We note that the subgroup $G\theta$ of the additive group of real numbers, onto which the additive group G is mapped by our isomorphism, contains the number 1, because $e\theta = 1$.

7. LEMMA. *If A and B are subgroups of the additive group of real numbers with its natural ordering, and φ is a monotonic homomorphism of A onto B, then there exists a real number r, $r \geqslant 0$, such that for all $a \in A$*

$$a\varphi = ar. \tag{6}$$

In fact, if there exists an $a \in A$, $a > 0$, such that $a\varphi = 0$, then $(na)\varphi = 0$ also for all natural n, i.e. $B = A\varphi = 0$. In this case $r = 0$.

Therefore we suppose that φ is an isomorphism. If $a_1, a_2 \in A$, $a_1 > 0$, $a_2 > 0$, then $a_1\varphi > 0$, $a_2\varphi > 0$ also. If $a_1\varphi/a_2\varphi < a_1/a_2$, then there exists a positive rational number $\dfrac{m}{n}$ such that

$$\frac{a_1\varphi}{a_2\varphi} < \frac{m}{n} < \frac{a_1}{a_2}. \tag{7}$$

Hence $na_1 > ma_2$, i.e. $n(a_1\varphi) > m(a_2\varphi)$, although from (7) it follows that $n(a_1\varphi) < m(a_2\varphi)$. We arrive at the same contradiction from the hypothesis that $a_1\varphi/a_2\varphi > a_1/a_2$. Thus

$$\frac{a_1\varphi}{a_2\varphi} = \frac{a_1}{a_2},$$

and then

$$r = \frac{a\varphi}{a}, \quad a \in A, \quad a > 0.$$

In fact, if $a' < 0$, then

$$a'\varphi = -(-a')\varphi = -(-a')r = a'r,$$

i.e. the number r satisfies the condition (6) for all the elements of A. The lemma has thus been proved.

We will call a homomorphism φ of a linearly ordered group G onto a linearly ordered group G' an *inverse homomorphism* if from $a \in G$, $a \geqslant 0$, it follows that $a\varphi \leqslant 0$. *The lemma which we have proved is also true if φ is an inverse homomorphism; in this case, however, $r \leqslant 0$.*

In fact, if φ is an inverse homomorphism of A onto B, then the mapping $-\varphi$, where

$$a(-\varphi) = -a\varphi, \qquad a \in A,$$

will be a monotonic homomorphism. Thus there exists a real number $r \geqslant 0$ such that

$$a(-\varphi) = ar, \qquad a \in A,$$

but then

$$a\varphi = -[a(-\varphi)] = -ar = a(-r), \qquad a \in A,$$

where $-r \leqslant 0$.

8. A linearly ordered ring R is called *Archimedean* if its additive group is Archimedean. The following theorem is true [Ya. V. Chion, *Uspekhi mat. nauk* **9**, No. 4, 237–242 (1954); Tallini, *Atti Accad. Naz. Lincei, Rend.* **18**, 367–373 (1955)]:

Every Archimedean ring R is associative and commutative. Moreover, it is either a zero ring on some subgroup of the additive group of real numbers, or else it is isomorphic to some subring of the field of real numbers with its natural ordering.

In fact, on the basis of Hölder's theorem (see VI.3.4) we can assume that the additive group of the ring R is a subgroup of the additive group of real numbers. However, multiplication in R will not, generally speaking, coincide with the ordinary multiplication of real numbers and, to distinguish it from the latter, we will denote it by $a \cdot b$.

If $a \in R$, then the mapping $x \to x \cdot a$, $x \in R$, will be an endomorphism of the additive group of the ring R, monotonic if $a \geqslant 0$ and inverse if $a \leqslant 0$. Therefore, by VI.3.7, there exists a real number r_a such that

$$x \cdot a = x r_a, \qquad x \in R,$$

where from $a \geqslant 0$ it follows that $r_a \geqslant 0$.

Because for all $x \in R$

$$x \cdot (a + b) = x \cdot a + x \cdot b = x r_a + x r_b = x(r_a + r_b),$$

i.e. $r_{a+b} = r_a + r_b$, the mapping $a \to r_a$ will be a monotonic homomorphism of the additive group of the ring R into the additive group of real numbers. Therefore, by the lemma, there exists a real number s, $s \geqslant 0$, such that for all $a \in R$

$$r_a = as.$$

If $s = 0$, then $r_a = 0$ for all a, i.e. R will be a zero ring. If, however, $s > 0$, then the mapping $a \to r_a$ will be a monotonic isomorphism of the additive group. In addition it follows from

$$a \cdot b = ar_b = a(bs) = (ab)s$$

that

$$r_{a \cdot b} = (a \cdot b)s = [(ab)s]s = (as)(bs) = r_a r_b.$$

Thus when $s > 0$ the correspondence $a \to r_a$ maps the ring R monotonically and isomorphically onto some subring of the field of real numbers with its natural ordering. Thus the theorem has been proved.

§ 4. Normed rings

1. In the field of real numbers there is defined the concept of the absolute value, in the field of complex numbers the concept of the modulus. Recalling the usual properties of these concepts and taking into account, in particular, that both the absolute value and the modulus are non-negative real numbers, and that the field of real numbers is linearly ordered, we arrive at the following general definition:

Let W be a linearly ordered ring (see VI.2.1). A ring R will be called *a normed ring with values of the norm in the ring W,* if to every element $a \in R$ we can relate some element $w(a) \in W$—the *norm*† of the element a — where the following conditions are satisfied:

1. $w(0) = 0$; $w(a) > 0$ when $a \neq 0$;
2. $w(ab) = w(a)w(b)$;
3. $w(a - b) \leqslant w(a) + w(b)$.

From 3 and 1 it follows that for all $b \in R$ it will be true that $w(-b) \leqslant w(b)$, and because $b = -(-b)$, then

3_1. $w(-b) = w(b)$, $b \in R$.

From which it follows that

3_2. $w(a + b) \leqslant w(a) + w(b)$.

In addition to the fields of real and complex numbers, *as examples of normed skew fields with real norms we can take the skew field of quaternions and the Cayley algebra.* In fact, in these

---

† When W is the field of real numbers, the norm defined above is also called a *valuation* (Ed.).

skew fields, as the norm of the element α we can take the square root of the norm $n(\alpha)$, which was introduced respectively in V.6.9 and V.6.11. The norm defined in this way will coincide with the length of the vector α respectively in four-and eight-dimensional Euclidean space, and therefore condition 3 is satisfied. The fact that condition 1 is satisfied is obvious, and the validity of condition 2 follows from equations (8) and (15) of § 6 of Chapter V.

Every linearly ordered ring R can be normed with values of the norm in the ring R itself.

In fact, we call the positive one of the elements a and $-a$ the *absolute value* $|a|$ of the element $a \in R$. The absolute value satisfies the requirements included in the definition of a norm. In fact, it is obvious that condition 1 is satisfied. Condition 2 follows easily from the *sign rule* (see VI.2.1):

if $a \geqslant 0$, $b \geqslant 0$, then $|a| \cdot |b| = ab = |ab|$;

if $a \leqslant 0$, $b \geqslant 0$, then $|a| \cdot |b| = (-a)b = -ab = |ab|$;

if $a \leqslant 0$, $b \leqslant 0$, then $|a| \cdot |b| = (-a)(-b) = ab = |ab|$.

We will show that condition 3 is also satisfied. If $a \geqslant b \geqslant 0$, then $b \geqslant -b$ and $a + b \geqslant a - b$, and therefore

$$|a - b| = a - b \leqslant a + b = |a| + |b|.$$

If $a \geqslant 0 \geqslant b$, then

$$|a - b| = a - b = a + (-b) = |a| + |b|.$$

If $0 \geqslant a \geqslant b$, then $-a \geqslant a$ and $-a - b \geqslant a - b$, and therefore

$$|a - b| = a - b \leqslant -a - b = |a| + |b|.$$

If $b \geqslant a \geqslant 0$, then $a \geqslant -a$ and $a + b \geqslant b - a$, and therefore

$$|a - b| = -(a - b) = b - a \leqslant a + b = |a| + |b|.$$

If $b \geqslant 0 \geqslant a$, then

$$|a - b| = b - a = b + (-a) = |a| + |b|.$$

If, finally, $0 \geqslant b \geqslant a$, then $b \leqslant -b$ and $b - a \leqslant -a - b$, and therefore

$$|a - b| = b - a \leqslant -a - b = |a| + |b|.$$

The theorem has thus been proved.

2. In all the examples considered above, all the positive elements of the ring W are norms for some elements of the ring R. In this case we will say that W is the *ring of values* of the norm.

Let R be a normed ring with ring of values W. *If the ring R has an identity* 1, *then* $w(1)$ *is the identity of the ring.* W. In fact, if $a \in R$, then

$$w(a) = w(a \cdot 1) = w(a) \cdot w(1),$$

i.e. $w(1)$ is an identity for all the positive elements of W, and therefore also for the elements which are their additive inverses.

Either both the rings R and W have divisors of zero or neither R nor W has divisors of zero.

In fact, if $a, b \in R$, $a \neq 0$, $b \neq 0$, but $ab = 0$, then $w(a) > 0$, $w(b) > 0$, but

$$w(a)w(b) = w(ab) = 0,$$

Conversely, if the ring W has divisors of zero, then we can find strictly positive elements α, β, in W such that $\alpha\beta = 0$. Then in R there exist elements a, b such that $w(a) = \alpha$, $w(b) = \beta$, and therefore $a \neq 0$, $b \neq 0$. However,

$$w(ab) = w(a) w(b) = \alpha\beta = 0,$$

whence $ab = 0$.

If the ring R is commutative or associative, then the same is true for the ring W.

In fact the validity of the commutative or associative law for positive elements of the ring W follows at once from condition 2 in the definition of a normed ring, and all the other elements of the ring W are the additive inverse of positive elements.

From these considerations there follows this assertion:

If R is a division ring (or a ring with single-valued division, or a skew field), then this is also true for W.

3. If a linearly ordered ring W has an identity 1, then any ring R admits the following *trivial norm* with values in W:

$$w(0) = 0, \quad w(a) = 1 \quad \text{for all} \quad a \in R, \quad a \neq 0.$$

It is clear that all the conditions 1–3 of VI.4.1 are satisfied. The following condition, which is stronger than condition 3, is also satisfied:

3′. $w(a - b) \leqslant \max\ (w(a),\ w(b))$.

From this, as before, it follows that

$3'_1$. $w(-b) = w(b)$,

and therefore

$$w(a + b) = w[a - (- b)] \leqslant \max(w(a), w(- b)) = \max(w(a), w(b)),$$

i.e.

$3_2'.$ $w(a + b) \leqslant \max(w(a), w(b)).$

A norm which is subject to the conditions 1, 2 and 3′ is called *non-Archimedean*, as opposed to an *Archimedean norm*, for which the condition 3′, is not satisfied and only condition 3 holds. The usual norms for the fields of real and complex numbers, the skew field of quaternions and the Cayley algebra, mentioned in VI.4.1, are Archimedean. So also is the norm of a linearly ordered ring mentioned in VI.4.1.

4. In the definition of a non-Archimedean norm, i.e. in the axioms 1, 2 and 3′ we only used the ordering and multiplication of positive elements of the ring W. This definition can therefore be carried over literally to the case of a norm of a ring R with elements in some linearly ordered multiplicative groupoid G with zero, i.e. with an element 0 such that for all $x \in G$, $0 \leqslant x$,

$$x \cdot 0 = 0 \cdot x = 0.$$

It will in fact be in this sense that in future we will understand a *non-Archimedean norm*† of the ring R. Here we will speak of a normed ring R with *groupoid of values* G, if every element of G is the norm of some element of R.

Let there be given in the ring R a non-Archimedean norm $w(a)$ with groupoid of values G. In this case, results similar to those mentioned in VI.4.2 hold, and they are proved by the same reasoning. We may note, however, that in the case we are considering the norm defines a homomorphism of the multiplicative groupoid of the ring R onto the groupoid G.

If the ring R has an identity 1, then $w(1)$ is an identity of the groupoid G.

The ring R and the groupoid G either both have divisors of zero or do not have divisors of zero—the meaning of the concept of a divisor of zero in a groupoid with zero is obvious.

If the ring R is associative, then the groupoid G will be a semigroup. From the commutativity of the ring R follows the commutativity of G.

---

† A norm with values in an ordered group is also called a *valuation* (cf footnote p. 292 (Ed.).

If R is an associative skew field, then the elements of G distinct from zero form a group with respect to the multiplication given in G.

5. Let R be a linearly ordered ring, and G the ordered set of Archimedean classes of its additive group (see VI.3.3); the class which contains the element $a \in R$, $a \geqslant 0$, will be denoted by $\overline{a}$. If $a, b \in R$, $a \geqslant 0$, $b \geqslant 0$, whence $ab \geqslant 0$, then we set

$$\overline{a}\overline{b} = \overline{ab}. \tag{1}$$

The equation (1) *makes the set G a linearly ordered groupoid with zero*, called *the groupoid of Archimedean classes* of the ring R.

In fact, if $\overline{a}_1 = \overline{a}_2$, then let, for instance, $a_1 \leqslant a_2$. However, there exists a natural number n such that $a_2 \leqslant na_1$, and therefore, because $b \geqslant 0$,

$$a_1 b \leqslant a_2 b \leqslant n(a_1 b),$$

whence $\overline{a_1 b} = \overline{a_2 b}$. This proves that the equation (1) defines in fact a multiplication in the set G.

In addition, if $\overline{a}_1 < \overline{a}_2$, then $a_1 < a_2$, and therefore for any $b \geqslant 0$

$$a_1 b \leqslant a_2 b, \quad ba_1 \leqslant ba_2,$$

whence for any $\overline{b} \in G$

$$\overline{a}_1 \overline{b} \leqslant \overline{a}_2 \overline{b}, \quad \overline{b}\overline{a}_1 \leqslant \overline{b}\overline{a}_2.$$

Thus the groupoid G is linearly ordered (see VI.1.1).

Finally, the class $\overline{0}$ will obviously be the zero of the linearly ordered groupoid G.

The following theorem is true [Ya. V. Chion, *Izv. AN SSSR, seria matem.* **21**, 311–328 (1957)]:

Every linearly ordered ring R admits a non-Archimedean norm with its groupoid of Archimedean classes as its groupoid of values.

In fact, for every $a \in R$ we take as $w(a)$ the Archimedean class to which the absolute value $|a|$ belongs (see VI.4.1). Condition 1 is obviously satisfied, the validity of condition 2 follows from the validity of this condition for the absolute value and from equation (1). We will show that condition 3' is also satisfied. In fact, because $|-b| = |b|$ and by VI.4.1,

$$|a - b| = |a + (-b)| \leqslant |a| + |b| \leqslant 2 \max(|a|, |b|),$$

and therefore

$$\overline{|a - b|} \leqslant \max(\overline{|a|}, \overline{|b|}),$$

i.e.

$$w(a - b) \leqslant \max \, (w(a), \, w(b)).$$

6. Suppose that there is given in the ring R a non-Archimedean norm with values in the linearly ordered groupoid G with zero. In the groupoid G we change from the multiplicative notation, which we have used up to now, to the additive notation and, in addition, we change the ordering in G to the inverse ordering (cf. I.4.6). It is natural to denote the element 0 now by the symbol ∞, where for all $x \in G$

$$\infty \geqslant x, \, x + \infty = \infty + x = \infty. \tag{2}$$

The non-Archimedean norm given in the ring R is in this way transformed into the so-called *logarithmic norm* with values in the additive groupoid G, and the conditions 1, 2 and 3' take the form:

1_0. $w(0) = \infty$, $w(a) < \infty$ when $a \neq 0$;
2_0. $w(ab) = w(a) + w(b)$;
$3_0'$. $w(a - b) \geqslant \min(w(a), \, w(b))$.

It is also possible, of course, to make the opposite transition.

If in R there is given a non-Archimedean norm with (non-negative) real values, then the logarithmic norm obtained from it can also be regarded as real-valued, in fact with values in the ordered additive group of real numbers with the symbol ∞ adjoined. The transformation of the groupoid of values of the norm described above can be obtained in the case under consideration by replacing every positive real number α by the number $- \log \alpha$.

We take a field P and we consider as R any of the following three rings: *the ring of polynomials $P[x]$* (see II.2.7), *the ring of power series $P\{x\}$* (see II.2.8), *the field of Laurent series* (see II.5.7). If $a \in R$, $a \neq 0$, then let $w(a)$ be the exponent of the smallest power of the unknown x which occurs in the expression for the polynomial (series) a with coefficient distinct from zero; in addition, we set $w(0) = \infty$. *This introduces an integral-valued logarithmic norm in the ring R* — conditions 1_0, 2_0, $3_0'$ can be verified without difficulty.

7. Returning to the general concept of a norm (see VI.4.1), we note that sometimes the condition 2 is replaced by the weaker condition

2'. $w(ab) \leqslant w(a)w(b)$.

In this case we speak of a *pseudonorm*.

Important examples of pseudonormed rings are certain rings of functions. Thus we consider the ring of all continuous real functions $f(x)$, defined in the interval $[0, 1]$ of the real line. By letting

$$w(f) = \max_{x \in |0, 1|} |f(x)|,$$

we introduce a real-valued pseudonorm into this ring, because the conditions 1, 2' (but not 2) and 3 are satisfied.

§ 5. Valuated fields

1. Logarithmic norms are used essentially in the theory of fields and the theory of integral domains, and their applications are based, in particular, on the concepts and results presented in this section. Instead of "logarithmic norm" we shall use the term "valuation" which is more usual in this context.

Suppose that there is given in the field P a valuation (i.e. a logarithmic norm) w (see VI.4.6) with groupoid of values G. From the results of VI.4.4 and the definition of a valuation it follows that G will be an additively written linearly ordered Abelian group, with the symbol ∞ adjoined.

We denote by R_w the set of all those elements $a \in P$ for which $w(a) \geqslant 0$. By 1_0, 2_0 and $3_0'$, R_w will be a subring of the field P; it is called *the ring of the valuation* w in the field P.

Because the valuation w defines a homomorphic mapping of the multiplicative group of the field P onto the group G, the identity of the field P belongs to R_w.

Moreover, if $a \in P$, then $w(a) = 0$ if, and only if, both a and a^{-1} belong to R_w, i.e. if a is an invertible element of the ring R_w, because

$$w(1) = 0. \tag{1}$$

2. *Suppose that there are given in the field P the valuations w and w' with the groups of values G and G', with the symbol ∞ adjoined, respectively. The rings of these valuations, considered as subrings of the field P, coincide:*

$$R_w = R_{w'}, \tag{2}$$

if, and only if, there exists an isomorphic mapping φ of the ordered group G onto the ordered group G' such that for all the elements $a \in P$ distinct from zero

$$(w(a))\varphi = w'(a). \tag{3}$$

In fact, suppose that equation (2) holds and let $w(a) = 0$. Then, as we noted above, a will be an invertible element of the ring R_w and, hence, of the ring $R_{w'}$, i.e. $w'(a) = 0$. The converse assertion, of course, is also true.

Thus the valuations w and w' determine homomorphisms of the multiplicative group of the field P which have the same kernel. Therefore, by III.2.6, there exists an isomorphism φ of the group G onto the group G', satisfying the condition (3).

Finally, if $\alpha \in G$ and $\alpha \geqslant 0$, then in R there exists an element a such that $w(a) = \alpha$. From (2) it then follows that $w'(a) = \alpha\varphi \geqslant 0$ in G'. The isomorphism φ thus maps the positive elements of the group G onto the positive elements of G' and consequently all the requirements of the theorem are satisfied.

The converse assertion of the theorem is obvious.

3. We see that the study of all possible (non-Archimedean) valuations of a field P reduces to the study of all the subrings of this field which can be rings of valuations.

A subring R of the field P can be the ring of a valuation for this field if, and only if, for every $a \in P$, $a \neq 0$, at least one of the elements a, a^{-1} belongs to R.

On the one hand the assertion of the theorem is almost obvious: if $a \notin R_w$, i.e. $w(a) < 0$, then from (1) it follows that $w(a^{-1}) > 0$, and therefore $a^{-1} \in R_w$.

Now suppose that the subring R satisfies the hypothesis of the theorem. Thus it contains the identity of the field P. The set S of invertible elements of the ring R will obviously be a subgroup of the multiplicative group P^* of the field P. We denote by G the factor-group P^*/S, written additively.

Because the ring R does not contain any divisors of zero, the elements of R distinct from zero form a subsemigroup R^* of the group P^*. Because of the inclusion $S \subset R^*$ we can single out the subsemigroup $H = R^*/S$ in the group $G = P^*/S$. We will show that H is the semigroup of positive elements for some linear ordering of the group G, i.e. we verify the conditions (1)–(4) of VI.1.3.

In fact, condition (1) follows from the fact that the zero of the group G is the subgroup S contained in R^*. In addition, if $\alpha \in H$ and $-\alpha \in H$, then both the elements forming the coset α, and the elements inverse to them, belong to R^*, and then all these elements occur in S, i.e. α will be the zero of the group G; this proves condition (2). The validity of condition (3) is obvious. Finally, condition (4) follows from the hypothesis made with respect to the subring R in formulating the theorem.

Now we supplement the linearly ordered group G with the symbol ∞ with the properties (2) of VI.4.6. By letting $w(0) = \infty$, and by taking, for every $a \in P$, $a \neq 0$, $w(a)$ to be the element of the group G which, as a coset with respect to S, contains the element a, we obtain a valuation of the field P.

In fact, it is obvious that condition 1_0 is satisfied. The validity of condition 2_0 in the case when both the elements a, b are distinct from zero follows from the fact that the mapping $a \to w(a)$, $a \neq 0$, is a homomorphism of the group P^* onto the group G; if at least one of the elements a, b is equal to zero, then 2_0 follows, from (2) in VI.4.6.

Finally, we will verify condition $3_0'$. Because, by (1) and 2_0,

$$0 = w(1) = w(-1) + w(-1).$$

and the group G does not contain, by VI.1.4, any elements of finite order distinct from zero, then $w(-1) = 0$ and therefore, again by 2_0, for all $b \in P$

$$w(-b) = w(b).$$

Condition $3'_0$ is thus equivalent in our case to the condition

$$w(a+b) \geqslant \min(w(a), w(b)),$$

which will also be proved.

It is obviously satisfied if at least one of the elements a, b is equal to zero. If both of them are distinct from zero, then let, for instance, $w(b) \leqslant w(a)$, i.e. $a/b \in R$. Therefore, because the identity of the field P is contained in R, and $1 + a/b \in R$, i.e., by 2_0 and (1),

$$0 \leqslant w\left(1 + \frac{a}{b}\right) = w[(a+b)\,b^{-1}] = w(a+b) + w(b^{-1})$$

$$= w(a+b) - w(b).$$

Whence

$$w(a+b) \geqslant w(b) = \min(w(a), w(b)).$$

The theorem has thus been proved.

4. If in the field P there is given a valuation w with valuation ring R_w, then those elements $a \in P$ for which $w(a) > 0$ form an ideal I_w in R_w (see II.7.8), called the *ideal of the valuation w*. In fact, if a, $b \in I_w$, then from $3_0'$ it follows that $a - b \in I_w$; if $a \in I_w$, $x \in R_w$, i.e. $w(a) > 0$, $w(x) \geqslant 0$, then, by 2_0,

$$w(ax) = w(a) + w(x) > 0,$$

i.e. $ax \in I_w$.

Because, by VI.5.1, every element $a \in R_w$, $a \notin I_w$, has an inverse in R_w, the factor-ring R_w/I_w will be a field; it is called the *residue field* of the valuation w.

5. As an important example we will find all the non-trivial (non-Archimedean) valuations of the field of rational numbers. Let w be such a valuation and R_w and I_w respectively the ring and ideal of this valuation. Because $1 \in R_w$, $1 \notin I_w$, then the whole ring of integers C is contained in R_w, and the intersection $I_w \cap C$ will be the desired ideal in C. This intersection is distinct from zero, because otherwise all the non-zero integers would have inverses in the ring R_w, i.e. this ring would contain the whole field of rational numbers, which is impossible for a non-trivial valuation. Therefore, by II.7.8 and II.4.2, the ideal $I_w \cap C$ is the set (p) of integers which are multiples of some natural number p, $p > 1$.

Because the factor-ring R_w/I_w will be a field, the product of two integers lying outside (p) cannot be contained in (p). This is obviously equivalent to the assertion that *the number p must be prime*.

Every integer n, prime to p, lies outside the ideal I_w and therefore, by VI.5.1, has an inverse in the ring R_w, i.e. $n^{-1} \in R_w$. This proves that *the ring R_w contains the whole ring R_p of those rational numbers whose denominators are prime to p*.

In fact, it is even true that

$$R_w = R_p.$$

Indeed, if the ring R_w contains a rational number m/n such that $(m, p) = 1$, and $n \in (p)$, then $m \notin I_w$, i.e. $m^{-1} \in R_w$, and then

$$n^{-1} = \frac{m}{n} \cdot m^{-1} \in R_w,$$

i.e. the number n has an inverse in the ring R_w which contradicts the fact that $n \in I_w$.

Conversely, the subring R_p of the field of rational numbers for any prime p satisfies the hypothesis of the theorem VI.5.3.

Thus *the rings of valuations of the field of rational numbers are exhausted by the rings R_p, where p varies through all the prime numbers.*

6. We shall now determine a valuation of the field of rational numbers for which the valuation ring is R_p.

Every rational number a, $a \neq 0$, can be expressed in a unique way in the form

$$a = \frac{m}{n} p^k, \qquad (4)$$

where the numbers m and n are prime to each other and to p, and the integer k is greater than, equal to or less than zero. We set

$$w(a) = k, \quad a \neq 0; \qquad (5)$$

in addition, let

$$w(0) = \infty.$$

We obtain a valuation of the field of rational numbers with values in the ordered additive group of integers, with the symbol ∞ adjoined—the verification of the conditions 1_0, 2_0 and $3_0'$ presents no difficulties. This valuation is called the *p-adic valuation of the field of rational numbers.*

From (4) and (5) it follows that *the ring and ideal of the p-adic valuation are respectively the ring R_p and its ideal R_p', consisting of those rational numbers, the numerators of whose irreducible expressions are divisible by p.* We note that

$$R_p = \{R_p', C\}, \qquad (6)$$

where C is the ring of integers. In fact, if $m/n \in R_p$, then from $(n, p) = 1$ it follows that the numbers $sn, s = 0, 1, 2, \ldots, p-1$, lie in different cosets of the ring C with respect to the ideal (p). Then this is also true for the numbers $m + sn$, $s = 0, 1, 2, \ldots, p-1$, and therefore one of these numbers, say $m + tn$, is divisible by p. Then

$$\frac{m + tn}{n} \in R_p',$$

but

$$\frac{m}{n} = \frac{m + tn}{n} - t.$$

By using (6) and also the equation $R'_p \cap C = (p)$ and the fact that R'_p is an ideal in R_p, on the basis of the isomorphism theorem (see III.4.2) we have that

$$R_p/R'_p \simeq C/(p).$$

The field of residues of the p-adic valuation is thus isomorphic to the prime field C_p of characteristic p (see III.2.8 and III.2.11).

7. It is clear that the p-adic valuation of the field of rational numbers can also be considered not as a logarithmic norm, but as a non-Archimedean norm in the sense of VI.4.3. In order to make the transition inverse to that described in VI.4.3, it is sufficient to take any real number r, $r > 1$, and for the rational number a, written in the form (4), to set

$$w(a) = r^{-k},$$

assuming, besides, that $w(0) = 0$.

* For every Archimedean valuation w of the field of rational numbers we can find a real number α, $0 < \alpha \leqslant 1$ such that for all rational numbers a

$$w(a) = |a|^{\alpha},$$

where $|a|$ is the absolute value of the number α [Ostrowski, *Acta Math.* **41**, 271–284 (1918)].*

8. Suppose that there is given in the field P a real-valued norm w in the sense of VI.4.1. The sequence of elements

$$a_1, a_2 \ldots, a_n \ldots \tag{7}$$

of P is called a *fundamental sequence* if for any real number $\varepsilon > 0$ there exists a natural number $N = N(\varepsilon)$ such that

$$w(a_n - a_m) < \varepsilon \quad \text{when} \quad n, m > N.$$

A fundamental sequence (7) is said to be *convergent* if in the field P we can find an element a—the *limit* of this sequence—such that for every $\varepsilon > 0$ there exists a natural number $N = N(\varepsilon)$, which satisfies the condition

$$w(a_n - a) < \varepsilon \quad \text{when} \quad n > N.$$

A convergent sequence which has the limit 0 is called a *null sequence*.

A field P is said to be *complete* with respect to the norm w if each of its fundamental sequences is convergent.

* For every field P with a real-valued norm w there exists a *completion*, i.e. a field $\overline{P}$ with real-valued norm $\overline{w}$, complete with respect to this norm, such that $P \subseteq \overline{P}$, the norm $\overline{w}$ is an extension of the norm w and every element of the field $\overline{P}$ is the limit of some fundamental sequence of the field P.

If the field of rational numbers is normed by means of absolute values, then its completion is the field of real numbers, also with absolute values as its norm. If the field of rational numbers is considered with the p-adic valuation, then its completion is the field of p-adic numbers (see III.3.12). Here the value of the p-adic number distinct from zero, written in the form (17) of III.3.12, is the integer k.*

9. The normed fields P and P' with real-valued norms are called *isomorphic* if there exists an isomorphism between them under which null sequences of one of these fields are carried into null sequences of the other field and conversely.

* Every normed field with Archimedean real-valued norm is isomorphic to a subfield of the field of complex numbers, normed by means of the moduli of complex numbers [Ostrowski, *Acta Math.* **41**, 271–284 (1918)].*

§ 6. Albert's theorem on normed algebras

1. Let there be given in the field P a real-valued norm, which we will now denote by $|\alpha|$, $\alpha \in P$. Suppose, in addition, that R is an algebra over the field P and that in R, as a ring, there is given a real-valued norm w with the properties 1–3 of VI.4.1. We will call R a *normed algebra* if for any $a \in R$, $\alpha \in P$ the equation

$$w(\alpha a) = |\alpha| w(a) \tag{1}$$

is satisfied. The validity of this equation will also be assumed when we speak of a *pseudonormed algebra* (see VI.4.7).

2. *Every real finite-dimensional algebra R can be pseudonormed* [Albert, *Ann. of Math.* **48**, 495–501 (1947)].

In fact, let us take in the algebra R a basis x_i, $i = 1, 2, \ldots, n$, with the multiplication table

$$x_i x_j = \sum_{k=1}^{n} \varepsilon_{ij}^k x_k .$$

If μ is a real number distinct from zero, then the elements $y_i = \mu x_i$, $i = 1, 2, \ldots, n$, also form a basis for the algebra R, where

$$y_i y_j = \sum_{k=1}^{n} \delta_{ij}^k y_k,$$

and where

$$\delta_{ij}^k = \mu \varepsilon_{ij}^k.$$

We choose the number μ, as it is easy to do, in such a way that for all i, j, $k = 1, 2, \ldots, n$

$$|\delta_{ij}^k| \leqslant \frac{1}{n}, \tag{2}$$

where $|\delta|$ is the absolute value of the number δ. Then, by defining $w(a)$ for any element $a \in R$, written in the form $a = \sum_{i=1}^{n} \alpha_i y_i$, by the equation

$$w(a) = \sum_{i=1}^{n} |\alpha_i|,$$

we introduce a pseudonorm in the algebra R.

In fact, if

$$a = \sum_{i=1}^{n} \alpha_i y_i, \qquad b = \sum_{j=1}^{n} \beta_j y_j,$$

then

$$ab = \sum_{k=1}^{n} \left(\sum_{i,j=1}^{n} \delta_{ij}^k \alpha_i \beta_j \right) y_k,$$

and therefore, by (2),

$$w(ab) = \sum_{n=1}^{n} \left| \sum_{i,j=1}^{n} \delta_{ij}^k \alpha_i \beta_j \right| \leqslant \sum_{i,j,k=1}^{n} |\delta_{ij}^k| |\alpha_i| |\beta_j| \leqslant$$

$$\sum_{i,j=1}^{n} |\alpha_i| |\beta_j| = w(a) w(b).$$

This proves the validity of the condition 2′ of VI.4.7, and it is obvious that all the other conditions included in the definition of a pseudonorm are satisfied.

3. On the other hand, we have the following theorem of Albert [*Ann. of Math.* **48**, 495–501 (1947)]:

The fields of real and complex numbers, the skew field of quaternions, and the Cayley algebra are the only finite-dimensional real normed algebras with identity.

We note that the given four algebras in fact satisfy all the hypotheses of the theorem (see VI.4.1). On the other hand, *if a real-valued norm w is given in the ring R, then there are no divisors of zero in R*: if $a, b \in R$, $a \neq 0$, $b \neq 0$, $ab = 0$, then $w(a) \neq 0$, $w(b) \neq 0$, but $w(a)w(b) = w(ab) = 0$, which is impossible. Therefore, by the generalization of Frobenius' theorem (see V.8.1), we only have to prove the following assertion:

Every finite-dimensional real normed algebra K, which has an identity, is alternative.

4. We begin the proof with some remarks. First of all, we agree to denote the norm in the algebra K by $|a|$, where $a \in K$.

In addition, as we noted above, there are no divisors of zero in the algebra K, and therefore, by V.8.2, K will be an algebra with single-valued division. From this it follows that when $a \neq 0$, $a \in K$, right multiplication by the element a (see V.1.6), which is a linear transformation of the additive vector space of the algebra K, will be non-singular. We agree to denote this right multiplication by R_a; the identity linear transformation we will denote by E.

Finally, because the algebra K has an identity 1, then, by V.6.2, its centre contains a subfield D isomorphic to the field of real numbers; this will be the set of all elements of the form $\alpha \cdot 1 = \alpha$, where α is a real number.

LEMMA 1. *If $a \notin D$, then the linear transformation R_a does not have any real characteristic roots.*

In fact, if α is such a root, then the linear transformation $R_a - \alpha E = R_{a-\alpha}$ will be singular, i.e. as we noted above, $a - \alpha = 0$, whence $a = \alpha \in D$.

5. LEMMA 2. *If $a \notin D$ and $|a| = \alpha$, then the modulus of any characteristic root λ_0 of the linear transformation R_a is equal to α.*

In fact, let

$$\lambda_0 = \varrho \, (\cos \varphi + i \sin \varphi). \tag{3}$$

The linear tranformation $R_a - \lambda_0 E$ of the complex vector space, which is an extension of the real additive vector space of the algebra K, must be singular. Therefore in K there exist elements b and c such that

$$b + ci \neq 0,$$

whence

$$\delta = |b| + |c| > 0 \tag{4}$$

and

$$(b + ci)(R_a - \lambda_0 E) = 0.$$

Hence

$$(b + ci) R_a = \lambda_0(b + ci),$$

and therefore

$$(b + ci)R_a^m = \lambda_0^m (b + ci) \tag{5}$$

for all natural numbers m. Because R_a is a linear transformation of the real vector space K, then from (5) and (3) follow the equations

$$bR_a^m = \varrho^m (b \cos m\varphi - c \sin m\varphi),$$
$$cR_a^m = \varrho^m (b \sin m\varphi + c \cos m\varphi). \tag{6}$$

By using the definition of a normed algebra, in particular (1), and also (4) and the inequality $|\cos m\varphi| \leqslant 1$, $|\sin m\varphi| \leqslant 1$, we obtain from (6)

$$|b|\alpha^m = |bR_a^m| \leqslant \varrho^m \delta,$$
$$|c|\alpha^m = |cR_a^m| \leqslant \varrho^m \delta.$$

Hence, by (4), $\delta\alpha^m \leqslant 2\varrho^m \delta$, i.e. $(\alpha\varrho^{-1})^m \leqslant 2$, and because the number m is arbitrary, then $\alpha \leqslant \varrho$.

On the other hand, from (6) follow the equations

$$(b \cos m\varphi + c \sin m\varphi)R_a^m = \varrho^m b,$$
$$(c \cos m\varphi - b \sin m\varphi)R_a^m = \varrho^m c,$$

which reduce to the inequalities

$$\varrho^m|b| \leqslant \delta\alpha^m, \quad \varrho^m|c| \leqslant \delta\alpha^m.$$

Hence, $\varrho^m \delta \leqslant 2\delta\alpha^m$, i.e. $(\varrho\alpha^{-1})^m \leqslant 2$, and therefore $\varrho \leqslant \alpha$. As a result we obtain $\varrho = \alpha$, which is what we were required to prove.

6. LEMMA 3. *If $a \notin D$, then the characteristic polynomial of the linear transformation R_a is a power of an irreducible quadratic polynomial.*

In fact, if λ_0 is a characteristic root for R_a and $b = a + 1$, then $R_b = R_a + E$, and therefore the number $\lambda_0 + 1$ will be a characteristic root for R_b. Let $\alpha + \beta i$, $\gamma + \delta i$ be two characteristic roots of the transformation R_a. From Lemma 2 it follows that these roots have equal moduli, i.e.

$$\alpha^2 + \beta^2 = \gamma^2 + \delta^2.$$

By applying the same thing to the characteristic roots of the transformation R_b—it is clear that $b \notin D$—we obtain

$$(\alpha + 1)^2 + \beta^2 = (\gamma + 1)^2 + \delta^2.$$

Hence $2\alpha = 2\gamma$, i.e. $\alpha = \gamma$, and therefore $\beta^2 = \delta^2$, i.e. $\beta = \pm\delta$. These results together with Lemma 1 complete the proof of the lemma.

7. LEMMA 4. *If $a \notin D$, then the minimal polynomial of the linear transformation R_a is an irreducible quadratic polynomial.*

By Lemma 3, the characteristic polynomial of the transformation R_a has the form

$$\chi(\lambda) = (\lambda^2 - \alpha\lambda - \beta)^h,$$

where

$$\gamma = -\frac{\alpha^2}{4} - \beta > 0.$$

Therefore the minimal polynomial will be

$$\varphi(\lambda) = (\lambda^2 - \alpha\lambda - \beta)^k, \quad k \leqslant h,$$

i.e.

$$(R_a^2 - \alpha R_a - \beta E)^k = 0. \tag{7}$$

Let $k > 1$. If

$$b = \gamma^{-\frac{1}{2}}\left(a - \frac{\alpha}{2}\right),$$

so that $b \notin D$, then the equations

$$(R_a^2 - \alpha R_a - \beta E)^l = 0 \quad \text{and} \quad (R_b^2 + E)^l = 0$$

will be equivalent. Thus,

$$(R_b^2 + E)^k = 0, \quad (R_b^2 + E)^{k-1} \neq 0. \tag{8}$$

Because the number i is a characteristic root for the linear transformation R_b, then, by Lemma 2, $|b| = 1$. Therefore, by setting $S = R_b^2$, we obtain, for any $c \in K$,

$$|cS| = |(cb)b| = |c|.$$

Hence

$$|cS^m| = |c| \qquad (9)$$

for all $c \in K$ and all natural m.

If $T = (S + K)^{k-2}$ — here we use the fact that $k \geqslant 2$ — then, by (8),

$$T \neq 0, \quad T(S + E) \neq 0, \quad T(S + E)^2 = 0.$$

Thus there exists an element c' such that

$$c'(S + E)^{k-1} \neq 0,$$

i.e.

$$c = c'T \neq 0, \quad c(S + E) \neq 0, \quad c(S + E)^2 = 0. \qquad (10)$$

From the last equation it follows that

$$cS^2 = -c(2S + E),$$

i.e. when $m = 2$ the equation

$$cS^m = (-1)^{m-1}c[mS + (m - 1)E] \qquad (11)$$

is satisfied.

If equation (11) has already been proved for given m, then

$$cS^{m+1} = (-1)^{m-1}c[mS^2 + (m - 1)S] = (-1)^m c[2mS + mE -$$
$$(m - 1)S] = (-1)^m c[(m + 1)S + mE],$$

i.e. (11) is valid for all m. By making some changes in the way this equation is written, and taking the norms of both sides, we have, by (9), that

$$|c| = |mc(S + E) - c|. \qquad (12)$$

If

$$|c(S + E)| = \delta,$$

then, by (10), $\delta > 0$. However,

$$|mc(S + E) - c| \geqslant m\delta - |c|,$$

i.e., by (12), for all m the inequality

$$2|c| \geqslant m\delta,$$

is valid, which is impossible. This proves that $k = 1$, i.e. Lemma 4 is proved.

8. From this, by (7), there follows the equation

$$R_a^2 = \alpha R_a + \beta E,$$

i.e., because there exists an identity in the algebra K,

$$a^2 = \alpha a + \beta.$$

Therefore for any $b \in K$

$$(ba)a = bR_a^2 = b(\alpha R_a + \beta E) = \alpha ba + \beta b = b(\alpha a + \beta) = ba^2.$$

Thus the equation $(ba)a = b(aa)$ is proved for $a \notin D$; it is true, however, for $a \in D$ also, because D is contained in the centre of the algebra K. The equation $a(ab) = (aa)b$ can be verified in a similar way. By Artin's theorem (see V.7.3), this proves that the algebra K is alternative, i.e. it proves Albert's theorem.

* The fields of real and complex numbers, the skew field of quaternions and the Cayley algebra are the only real normed division algebras, having an identity; the fact that these algebras are finite-dimensional is not assumed [Albert, *Bull. Amer. Math. Soc.* **55**, 763–768 (1949); Wright, *Proc. nat. Acad. USA* **39**, 330–332 (1953)].

The fields of real and complex numbers and the skew field of quaternions are the only pseudonormed real associative algebras not containing an element x distinct from zero, for which there exists a sequence y_n, not a null sequence (see VI.5.8), such that at least one of the sequences xy_n or $y_n x$ is null [Kaplansky, *Duke Math. J.* **16**, 399–418 (1949)].

The field of complex numbers itself is the only pseudonormed complex associative division algebra [C. R. Mazur, *Paris*, **207**, 1025–1027 (1938); I. M. Gel'fand, *Mat. sb.* **9**, 3–24 (1941)].*

§ 7. Closure. Topological spaces

1. We will say that a *closure relation* is given in the partially ordered set M if we can relate to every element $a \in M$ a uniquely determined element $\bar{a} \in M$, called the *closure* of the element a, where for all a, $b \in M$ the following requirements are satisfied:

(1_0) $a \leqslant \bar{a}$;

(2_0) if $a \leqslant b$, then $\bar{a} \leqslant \bar{b}$;

(3_0) $\bar{\bar{a}} = \bar{a}$, i.e. the closure of any element coincides with its own closure.

An element a is called *closed* if it coincides with its own closure. By (3_0) the closures of all elements will be closed and, obviously, nothing else will be. On the other hand, it follows from (2_0) that $\bar{a}$ is contained in every closed element containing a, i.e.

the closure relation is determined uniquely by giving the system of closed elements.

In every partially ordered set we can define a *trivial closure* by letting $\overline{a} = a$ for all a.

2. A closure relation can be introduced, in particular, in the system $\overline{M}$ of all subsets of an arbitrary set M, partially ordered by set-theoretical inclusion. In fact in what follows it will be in this sense that we will speak of *a closure relation given in an arbitrary set M*. Clearly, the meaning of such concepts as *the closure of a subset* of M and *a closed subset* is completely defined; we keep, essentially, the method of formulating the conditions $(1_0)–(3_0)$ of VI.7.1.

We note that if a closure relation is given in the set M, then *the set M itself is closed*, being its own closure. On the other hand, *the intersection of any system of closed subsets in M is itself closed*.

In fact, suppose that a system of closed subsets A_α is given in M (α varies through some index set) and let

$$B = \bigcap_\alpha A_\alpha.$$

Then, by condition (2_0) of VI.7.1, it follows from $B \subseteq A_\alpha$ that $\overline{B} \subseteq \overline{A_\alpha} = A_\alpha$, i.e.

$$\overline{B} \subseteq \bigcap_\alpha A_\alpha = B.$$

Because, on the other hand, $B \subseteq \overline{B}$ by condition (1_0) of VI.7.1, then $\overline{B} = B$, which is what we were required to prove.

The following converse of the theorem is true:

In every set M we can give a closure by taking as the system of closed subsets any system of subsets Σ which contains M itself and also the intersection of any of its subsystems.

In fact, if we take as the closure $\overline{A}$ of any subset A of M the intersection of all the subsets in Σ which contain A—such sets exist, for instance M itself—then conditions $(1_0)–(3_0)$ will be satisfied, and the closed sets will be the sets of Σ and only these.

3. Two partially ordered sets with closures are naturally called *isomorphic* if between them there exists an isomorphic correspondence in the sense of I.4.3, under which the images and inverse images of closed elements are closed. In the same sense we can speak of the *isomorphic embedding* of one partially ordered set with closure in another.

* If M is a partially ordered set with closure, then in the partially ordered system $\overline{M}$ of all the subsets of the set M we can give a closure relation such that M is isomorphically embedded in $\overline{M}$.*

4. The concept of a set with a closure relation for its subsets, introduced in VI.7.2, is very wide. By imposing some additional restrictions on the closure relation, we arrive at the concept of a topological space, one of the most important general concepts in mathematics, which in many cases plays a role parallel to that of partially ordered sets.

We say that a *topology* is given in the set M or that M is a *topological space* if there is given in it a closure which satisfies, in addition to the conditions (1_0)–(3_0) (or the conditions equivalent to them, mentioned in the formulation of the theorem in VI.7.2), also the following additional conditions:

(4_0) the closure of the union of two (and therefore also any finite number of) subsets of M is equal to the union of the closures of these subsets,

$$\overline{A \cup B} = \overline{A} \cup \overline{B};$$

(5_0) every subset consisting of one element is closed.

In fact, *conditions* (1_0) *and* (2_0) *can be derived from conditions* (4_0) *and* (5_0). Thus, let A be any subset of M and $a \in A$. Then, by conditions (4_0) and (5_0)

$$\overline{A} = \overline{A \cup a} = \overline{A} \cup \overline{a} = \overline{A} \cup a,$$

i.e. $a \in \overline{A}$, from which the inclusion $A \subseteq \overline{A}$ follows, proving the condition (1_0). On the other hand, if the subsets A and B are such that $A \subseteq B$, then, by the condition (4_0),

$$\overline{B} = \overline{A \cup B} = \overline{A} \cup \overline{B},$$

i.e. $\overline{A} \subseteq \overline{B}$, which proves condition (2_0).

If the topological space M contains more than one element—only such spaces are of interest—*then its empty subset is closed.* In fact, it will be closed as the intersection of any two distinct elements of M, which, by condition (5_0), are closed subsets.

We note, finally, that, as follows from condition (4_0), *the union of any finite number of closed subsets of a topological space is closed.*

5. The system of all the closed subsets of a topological space M is partially ordered by inclusion. The system of all the complements in M of the closed subsets is also ordered by inclusion, i.e. the system of *open subsets*. We obtain an inverse isomorphism (see I.4.6) between these two partially ordered systems if we relate to every closed subset A the open subset $M \setminus A$. This gives us a method of dualizing the results which we know, relating to closed sets, leads to results relating to open sets.

Thus, taking into account that the complement of an intersection (or union) of a given system of subsets of any set is always the union (respectively intersection) of the complements of all these subsets, we find that *the union of any system of open subsets and the intersection of any finite number of open subsets will itself be open. On the other hand, both the space M itself and the empty subset are open*, because they are the complements of each other.

6. Every closure relation in the set M, and therefore also every topology is completely defined, as we know, by giving the system of all closed subsets. Hence we can also define a topology in M by giving the system of all open subsets. Taking into account that the union of any system of open sets is open, we can limit ourselves to giving only a system of open subsets Σ such that every (non-empty) open subset of the space M is the union of subsets from Σ. Such a system Σ, called *a complete system of neighbourhoods*† of the space M, is obviously not uniquely determined.

The subsets which form a given complete system of neighbourhoods Σ will be called *neighbourhoods*; all the neighbourhoods of Σ which contain a given element $a \in M$ form a *complete system of neighbourhoods of this element*.

Let the topology in M be given by a complete system of neighbourhoods Σ. Then *a subset A of M is open if, and only if, for every element $a \in A$ we can find a neighbourhood U from Σ such that $a \in U$ and $U \subseteq A$*—this follows from the fact that A is open if, and only if, it is the union of neighbourhoods from Σ.

On the other hand, *if A is an arbitrary subset of the space M, then its closure $\overline{A}$ consists of those, and only those, elements any neighbourhood of which contains at least one element of A.*

---

† This is usually called an *open neighbourhood base*. The term 'neighbourhood' is then given a wider meaning: any subset of M with an open subset containing a is called a neighbourhood of a. (Ed.).

LECTURES IN GENERAL ALGEBRA

In fact, if the element $x \notin \overline{A}$, then x is contained in the open set $M \setminus \overline{A}$, and therefore there exists a neighbourhood of the element x contained in $M \setminus \overline{A}$, i.e. having empty intersection with A. Conversely, if an element x has a neighbourhood U not containing elements of A, then A is contained in the closed set $M \setminus U$, and therefore, by condition (2_0) of VI.7.1,

$$\overline{A} \subseteq \overline{M \setminus U} = M \setminus U,$$

i.e. $x \notin \overline{A}$.

From this it follows that *a subset A of a topological space M is closed if, and only if, every element x, each of whose neighbourhoods contains at least one element of A, itself belongs to A.*

7. *A system Σ of subsets of the set M is a complete system of neighbourhoods for some topology given in M if, and only if,*

(α) *for any ordered pair of distinct elements a, b of M we can find a subset U, belonging to Σ, such that $a \in U$, $b \notin U$;*

(β) *for any two subsets U, V, belonging to Σ and containing some element a, we can always find a subset W in Σ such that $a \in W$ and $W \subseteq U \cap V$.*

Proof. Let Σ be a complete system of neighbourhoods of a topological space M. If a and b are distinct elements of M, then, because b is closed, the subset $M \setminus b$ is open and therefore is the union of neighbourhoods from Σ. Because $a \in M \setminus b$, then, by VI.7.6, we can find a neighbourhood U in Σ such that $a \in U$ and $U \subseteq M \setminus b$, and therefore $b \notin U$. This proves (α). On the other hand, if we are given the neighbourhoods U and V of the element a, then, by VI.7.5, their intersection $U \cap V$ is open, and because a is contained in this intersection, then, again by VI.7.6, there exists a neighbourhood W of the element a, contained in $U \cap V$.

Now suppose that an arbitrary system of subsets Σ is given in M, having the properties (α) and (β). For every subset $A \subseteq M$ we denote by $\overline{A}$ the set of those elements $x \in M$ such that every subset of Σ, containing x, contains at least one element of A, and we will show that this gives a topology in M. It is sufficient to show, by VI.7.4, that conditions (3_0), (4_0) and (5_0) are satisfied.

If $x \in \overline{\overline{A}}$, then any subset U of Σ, containing x, contains at least one element $y \in \overline{A}$, and therefore, again by the definition of $\overline{A}$, the subset U contains at least one element of A. From this it follows that $x \in \overline{A}$, i.e. $\overline{\overline{A}} \subseteq \overline{A}$. Because it is obvious, conversely, that $A \subseteq \overline{A}$, then $\overline{A} \subseteq \overline{\overline{A}}$ and therefore $\overline{\overline{A}} = \overline{A}$, i.e. condition (3_0) is proved.

In addition, if A and B are arbitrary subsets of M, and x is any element of the union $\overline{A} \cup \overline{B}$, then every subset of Σ, containing x, contains at least one element either of A or of B, i.e. at least one element of $A \cup B$, and therefore $x \in \overline{A \cup B}$. This proves that $\overline{A} \cup \overline{B} \subseteq \overline{A \cup B}$. On the other hand, if the element $y \in \overline{A \cup B}$, then any subset of Σ, containing y, contains at least one element of $A \cup B$. Let there exist two subsets U and V in Σ, containing y, such that U does not contain elements of A, and V does not contain elements of B. Then, by condition (β), we can find a subset W in Σ, containing y and lying in the intersection $U \cap V$, i.e. containing elements neither of A, nor of B, which is impossible. Thus, either all the subsets of Σ, containing y, contain elements of A, and then $y \in \overline{A}$, or else they all contain elements of B, and then $y \in \overline{B}$. From this it follows that $\overline{A \cup B} \subseteq \overline{A} \cup \overline{B}$. Thus the validity of condition (4_0) has also been proved.

Finally, condition (5_0) follows from the fact that for any element $b \in M$ its closure $\overline{b}$ consists of b alone, because, by condition (α), for any other element a we can find a subset of Σ which contains a, but does not contain b.

To complete the proof of the theorem, it remains to show that the system Σ is a complete system of neighbourhoods for the topology which we have constructed in the set M. If U *is* a subset from Σ, then its complement $M \setminus U$ will be closed, because any element of M, lying outside $M \setminus U$, is contained in U, i.e. it lies in a subset from Σ which contains no element of $M \setminus U$. This proves that U is open. On the other hand, let A be any open subset, and a an element of A. Then $M \setminus A$ is closed, $a \notin M \setminus A$, and therefore there exists a subset U from Σ, containing a, whose intersection with $M \setminus A$ is empty, i.e. $U \subseteq A$. The subset A can thus be regarded as the union of some system of subsets of Σ. This completes the proof of the theorem.

8. Two sets with closure, M and M', are called *isomorphic* if between them there exists a one–one correspondence χ, which preserves the closure relation, i.e. for all $A \subseteq M$

$$\overline{A}\chi = \overline{A\chi}.$$

The mapping χ here is called an *isomorphic mapping* or an *iso-*

morphism. The inverse mapping χ^{-1} will obviously also be an isomorphism.

The connection is obvious between this concept and the concept of an isomorphism for partially ordered sets with closure, introduced in VI.7.3. In the special case of topological spaces the term "isomorphism" is usually replaced by the term "homeomorphism"; we will not, however, make use of this special term.

Under an isomorphic correspondence between sets with closure, closed sets are mapped into closed sets and conversely, where, by VI.7.1, *this property can be taken as the definition of an isomorphism.* From this it follows that *in the case of topological spaces an isomorphism can be defined also as a one–one correspondence between these spaces, under which open sets are mapped into open sets and conversely.*

If in the topological spaces M and M' the topologies are given respectively by means of the complete systems of neighbourhoods Σ and Σ', then a one–one mapping χ of the space M onto the space M' will be an isomorphism if, and only if, for every element $a' \in M'$ and any neighbourhood U' of it there exists a neighbourhood U of the element $a'\chi^{-1} \in M$ such that $U\chi \subseteq U'$, and for every element $a \in M$ and any neighbourhood V of it there exists a neighbourhood V' of the element $a\chi$ such that $V'\chi^{-1} \subseteq V$.

In fact, let χ be an isomorphism and suppose, for instance, that we are given the element $a' \in M'$ and the neighbourhood U' of a'. Then the set $U'\chi^{-1} \subseteq M$ will be open, i.e. it contains a neighbourhood U of the element $a'\chi^{-1}$. It is clear that $U\chi \subseteq U'$.

Conversely, suppose that the mapping χ satisfies the conditions given in formulating the theorem, and suppose, for instance, that we are given an open subset A of the space M. If $a\chi$ is an arbitrary element of $A\chi$, then $a \in A$ and A contains some neighbourhood V of the element a. Then, by the hypothesis of the theorem, there exists a neighbourhood V' of the element $a\chi$ such that $V'\chi^{-1} \subseteq V$. Hence

$$V' = V'\chi^{-1}\chi \subseteq V\chi \subseteq A\chi.$$

This proves that $A\chi$ will be an open subset of the space M'. Thus the theorem has been proved.

By applying this theorem to the case when M and M' coincide, and χ is the identity mapping of the space M onto itself, i.e. $a\chi = a$ for all $a \in M$, we arrive at a condition of *equivalence* for two complete systems of neighbourhoods Σ and Σ' given in M, i.e. the condition that these two complete systems of neighbourhoods should define the same topology in M: *this will be true if, and only if, every neighbourhood of any element $a \in M$, taken in one of the systems Σ, Σ', contains some neighbourhood of the element a in the other system.*

9. A topology given in the set M *induces* a topology in every subset $A \subseteq M$. In fact, if the topology in M is given by a complete system of neighbourhoods Σ, then we denote by Σ_A the set of all intersection $U \cap A$, where $U \in \Sigma$. Since the conditions (α) and (β) of the theorem in VI.7.7 are valid for the system Σ it follows at once that analogous conditions are valid for the system Σ_A, i.e. this system is a complete system of neighbourhoods for some topology given in A.

If in the space M we are given another complete system of neighbourhoods Σ', equivalent to Σ, then the equivalence in A of the complete systems of neighbourhoods Σ_A and Σ'_A can be verified without difficulty on the basis of VI.7.8. Thus a topology in M determines a unique topology in the subset A. The topological space A obtained in this way is called a *subspace* of the space M.

From the definition of a subspace it follows at once that *the open or closed subsets of the subspace A of the space M will be the intersections with A of the open or closed subsets respectively of M, and only these.*

10. The trivial closure (see VI.7.1), introduced in the system of all subsets of an arbitrary set M, obviously satisfies the conditions (4_0) and (5_0) of VI.7.4, i.e. it gives a topology. This topology is called *discrete*; all the subsets of the set M will be both open and closed in this topology. Every set can thus be considered as a discrete topological space, and in finite sets, where every subset is the union of a finite number of elements, only the discrete topology is possible.

As our first example of a non-discrete topological space we have the *straight line*. By considering it as a numerical straight line and defining for every subset A the closure $\overline{A}$ as the set of numbers which are limits of convergent sequences of numbers in A, we obtain a topology—conditions (3_0)(4_0) and (5_0) can be verified without difficulty. One complete system of neighbourhoods for this natural topology of a straight line is the system of all (open) intervals. In what follows, when speaking of the numerical straight line as a topological space, we shall always mean that it has this natural topology.

The plane and in general every n-dimensional real Euclidean space is usually also regarded as a topological space. Topologies are introduced here in the same way as above in the case of a straight line, but by using coordinate-wise convergence. In the case of a plane, one system of neighbourhoods is the system of all (open) circles; an equivalent complete system of neighbourhoods will be the system of all (open) squares.

§ 8. Special types of topological spaces

1. As we know (see, for instance, VI.7.7), for any two distinct elements a, b of a topological space we can find an open subset U which contains the element a, but does not contain the element b. Stronger restrictions than this property enable us to introduce some special important types of topological spaces.

Thus, a topological space is called *Hausdorff* if for any two distinct elements a, b of it we can find open subsets U, V such that $a \in U$, $b \in V$ and the intersection $U \cap V$ is empty.

If the topology in M is given by the complete system of neighbourhoods Σ, then the space M will be Hausdorff if, and only if, the intersection of the closures of all the neighbourhoods of any element a contain only this element itself.

In fact, if the space M is Hausdorff, and the element b is distinct from a, then, by taking neighbourhoods U and V for a and b respectively such that $U \cap V$ is empty, we obtain that $\overline{U} \notin b$. On the other hand, if the space M satisfies the hypothesis given in the formulation of the theorem, and if we are given two distinct elements a and b in it, then there exists a neighbourhood U of the element a such that $b \notin \overline{U}$. Then the element b is contained in the open subset $V = M \setminus \overline{U}$, where $\overline{U} \cap V$ is empty.

2. A topological space is called *regular* if for any element a and any closed subset B, not containing a, we can find non-intersecting open subsets U, V such that $a \in U$, $B \subseteq V$.

It is clear that every regular space will be Hausdorff. All the spaces mentioned in VI.7.10 are regular.

If the topology in M is given by the complete system of neighbourhoods Σ, then the space M will be regular if, and only if, for

*every neighbourhood U of any element a we can find a neighbour-
hood V of this element whose closure $\overline{V}$ is contained in U.*

In fact, if the space M is regular and in it we take a neighbourhood U of some element a, then for a and the closed subset $M \setminus U$
we can find non-intersecting open subsets V and W such that
$a \in V$, $(M \setminus U) \subseteq W$. Then V contains some neighbourhood V_0
of the element a, where

$$\overline{V}_0 \subseteq \overline{V} \subseteq M \setminus W \subseteq M \setminus (M \setminus U) = U.$$

Conversely, suppose that the space M has the property mentioned in the formulation of the theorem, and suppose that we are
given the element a and the closed subset B in it, where $a \notin B$.
Then, by hypothesis, there exists a neighbourhood U of the
element a, the closure $\overline{U}$ of which is contained in the open subset
$M \setminus B$. The intersection of the open subsets U and $M \setminus \overline{U}$ is
empty, and because

$$M \setminus \overline{U} \supseteq M \setminus (M \setminus B) = B,$$

the regularity of the space M has been proved.

It is easy to verify that *the property that a topological space
should be Hausdorff or regular carries over to the subspaces of
this space.*

More specialized than the concept of a regular space is the
concept of a *normal* space: this is a topological space such that
for any of its non-intersecting closed sets A and B there exist
non-intersecting open sets U and V such that $A \subseteq U$, $B \subseteq V$.

* An intermediate class between regular and normal spaces
is that formed by the *completely regular* topological spaces, i.e.
spaces with the following property: for any element a and any
closed subset B not containing this element, we can define a continuous (in the sense of the topology of this space) real-valued
function f on this space such that $f(a) = 0$, $f(b) = 1$ for all
$b \in B$ and $0 \leqslant f(x) \leqslant 1$ for all x.*

3. A very important class of topological spaces is that formed
by the bicompact spaces. In fact, a space M is called *bicompact*†
if it satisfies any of the following conditions, whose equivalence
follows from what was said in VI.7.5:

I. From every system of open subsets whose union coincides

---

† Although the term *compact* is now more usual in English, the form
in the text has been kept to avoid all risk of confusion (Ed).

with M we can choose a finite subsystem such that the union of the subsets forming it coincides with M.

II. From every system of closed subsets whose intersection is empty we can choose a finite subsystem such that the intersection of the subsets forming it is empty.

As follows from the Heine–Borel theorem, which is proved in any course in mathematical analysis, any finite closed interval of the numerical straight line is a bicompact space.

* Each of the following two conditions is equivalent to the conditions I and II, and therefore can be used to define a bicompact space:

III. The union of every chain (see I.4.1) consisting of open subsets distinct from M is itself distinct from M.

IV. The intersection of every chain consisting of non-empty closed subsets is itself non-empty.*

4. A topological space is called *locally bicompact* if every element of this space is contained in an open subset whose closure is bicompact.

Every bicompact space is locally bicompact. An example of a locally bicompact but not bicompact space is the real line. In fact, every point of the real line has a neighbourhood which is a finite open interval. The closure of such a neighbourhood will be a closed interval, i.e., as we noted above, it is bicompact. On the other hand, the real line itself is not bicompact: it is the union of all its intervals of finite length, but it cannot be represented as the union of a finite number of such intervals.

As another example of a locally bicompact but not bicompact space we can take any infinite discrete space.

5. *Every closed subset of a bicompact space is bicompact, and one of a locally bicompact space is locally bicompact.*

First we note that if A is a closed subset of any topological space M, then every subset B of A, closed in the subspace A, will also be closed in M. In fact, if $\overline{B}$ is the closure of B in M, then, as follows from VI.7.9, $\overline{B} \cap A$ will be the closure of B in A, i.e., because B is closed in A,

$$\overline{B} \cap A = B. \tag{1}$$

However, because A is itself closed in M, then it follows from $B \subseteq A$ that $\overline{B} \subseteq A$, and therefore, by (1), $\overline{B} = B$.

Now it is clear that from the validity of the condition II of VI.8.3 in the bicompact space M follows the validity of this condition in every closed subspace of the space M. If the space M is locally bicompact and A is a closed subspace of it, then for every $a \in A$ there exists in M a neighbourhood U, whose closure $\overline{U}$ is bicompact. Then the intersection $U \cap A$ is a neighbourhood of a in A, and its closure in A is $\overline{U} \cap A$. This last intersection will, however, be bicompact, because it is closed in M (as the intersection of closed subsets) and is contained in the bicompact space $\overline{U}$.

* Every open subset of a locally bicompact (in particular, a bicompact) space is locally bicompact.

Every locally bicompact space is isomorphic to an open subspace of some bicompact space [P. S. Alexandrov, *Math. Ann.* **92**, 294–301 (1924)].*

6. A topological space M is called *disconnected* if it can be decomposed into two non-empty non-intersecting closed subsets (each of which will, obviously, also be open), and *connected* otherwise.

A topological space M is called *totally disconnected* if for any two distinct elements $a, b \in M$ there exists a decomposition of M into two non-intersecting closed subsets A, B such that $a \in A$, $b \in B$.

Every discrete space will, of course, be totally disconnected. An example of a non-discrete totally disconnected space is *the straight line of rational numbers*, i.e. the subspace of the real line consisting of the rational numbers. It is not discrete, because every neighbourhood on the real line contains an infinite number of rational numbers. On the other hand, if a and b are two distinct rational numbers, $a < b$, then there exists an irrational number α, situated between them, and we obtain the required decomposition by taking as A the set of rational numbers less than α, and as B the set of rational numbers greater than α.

We note that every subspace of a totally disconnected topological space is itself totally disconnected.

§ 9. Topological groups

1. The consideration of numerous examples of algebraic structures which are at the same time topological spaces (see VI.7.4) leads to the following definitions.

A groupoid G which is also a topological space is called a *topological groupoid* if multiplication in the groupoid G is *continuous* in the given topology, i.e. for any elements a, $b \in G$ and any neighbourhood W of the element ab (see VI.7.6) we can find neighbourhoods U and V of the elements a and b respectively such that $UV \subseteq W$ (where UV is the set of elements of G which can be represented in at least one way as a product uv, $u \in U$, $v \in V$).

A special case of a topological groupoid is a *topological semigroup*.

A group G is called a *topological group* if it is a topological semigroup and if, in addition, the operation of taking the inverse of an element is *continuous* in the given topology, i.e. for any element $a \in G$ and any neighbourhood V of the element a^{-1} there exists a neighbourhood U of the element a such that $U^{-1} \subseteq V$ (where U^{-1} is the set of elements of the form u^{-1} for all $u \in U$).

It is easy to verify, by applying the condition for the equivalence of complete systems of neighbourhoods in a topological space (see VI.7.8), that the property that the operation of multiplication (or the operation of passing to the inverse element) should be continuous does not depend on the choice of the complete system of neighbourhoods in G. The intuitive meaning of the continuity of an operation lies in the fact that to small variations in factors (or in an element) correspond small variations in the product (or in the inverse element).

Giving a topology in the group G which makes this group G a topological group is called *topologizing* it.

* There exist groups which are topological semigroups but not topological groups.

Every Hausdorff bicompact topological semigroup (see VI.8.1 and VI.8.3), in which the cancellation law is satisfied (see II.5.1), will be a group and in fact a topological group [see Arens, *Bull. Amer. math. Soc.* **53**, 623–630 (1947)].*

2. Every group can be regarded as a topological group with the discrete topology (see VI.7.10). A finite group obviously only admits the discrete topology. The problem of possible non-discrete topologies for any infinite group remains open.

* Every infinite Abelian group can be made a topological group with a non-discrete topology [Kertész and Szele, *Publ. Math.* **3**, 187–189 (1953)].*

3. *If A is an open subset of a topological group G and g is an element of G, then the sets Ag, gA, A^{-1} are also open.*

We will prove only the first of these assertions. If $b = ag$,

$a \in A$, then $a = bg^{-1}$. The existence of a neighbourhood U of the element b such that $Ug^{-1} \subseteq A$ (we recall that A is an open set) follows from the continuity of multiplication. Hence $U \subseteq Ag$, i.e. the set Ag contains, together with each of its elements b, also some neighbourhood of b, which is what we were required to prove.

If g is an element of the topological group G, then the mappings (for all $x \in G$)

$$x \to xg, \, x \to gx, \, x \to x^{-1}$$

are isomorphic mappings (see VI.7.8) *of G, as a topological space, onto itself.*

The fact that the mappings are one–one is obvious and therefore we can make use of the preceding theorem, taking into account that the inverse mapping for the *right translation* $x \to xg$ will be the right translation $x \to xg^{-1}$, and the mapping $x \to x^{-1}$ is its own inverse.

From this, by VI.7.8, it follows that *if A is a closed subset of the topological group G and g is an element of G, then the sets Ag, gA, A^{-1} are also closed.*

4. If a and b are elements of a topological group G, then the translation $x \to xa^{-1}b$, $x \in G$, carries a into b. From this, and from what we established above, it follows that to prove properties of the space of a topological group which are related to separate elements, it is sufficient to consider only one fixed element, for instance the identity. From this it follows that in giving the topology in a group there is no necessity to give the whole of the complete system of neighbourhoods, and we can limit ourselves to giving the *complete system of neighbourhoods of the identity* (see VI.7.6).

* A system Σ of subsets of a group G will be a complete system of neighbourhoods of the identity for some topology of this group if, and only if, the following conditions are satisfied:

(1) the intersection of all the sets in Σ contains only the identity of the group G;

(2) the intersection of any two sets of Σ contains some third set belonging to Σ;

(3) for every set U of Σ we can find a set V in Σ such that $VV^{-1} \subseteq U$;

(4) for every set U of Σ and every element $a \in U$, in Σ we can find a set V such that $Va \subseteq U$;

(5) for every set U of Σ and any element a of the group G we can find a set V in Σ such that $a^{-1}Va \subseteq U$.*

5. *The space of every topological group G is regular and, hence, Hausdorff* (see VI.8.1 and VI.8.2).

By using the criterion of regularity from VI.8.2 and taking into account what was said in the preceding section, we can take any neighbourhood U of the identity of the group G. Because $1 \cdot 1^{-1} = 1$, there exist neighbourhoods V_1 and V_2 of the elements 1 and 1^{-1} ($= 1$, obviously) such that $V_1V_2 \subseteq U$. In addition, there exists a neighbourhood V_3 of the identity such that $V_3^{-1} \subseteq V_2$. Finally, there exists a neighbourhood V of the identity lying in the intersection $V_1 \cap V_3$ (see VI.7.7). It is clear that

$$VV^{-1} \subseteq U. \tag{1}$$

Let $a \in \overline{V}$. Because the set aV is open, by VI.9.3, and contains the element $a = a \cdot 1$ of the closure of the set V, then, by VI.7.6, we can find an element b of V in aV. Let $b = ac$, $c \in V$. Hence, by (1),

$$a = bc^{-1} \in VV^{-1} \subseteq U,$$

i.e. $\overline{V} \subseteq U$, which is what we were required to prove.

* The space of every topological group is completely regular (see VI.8.2).

There exist topological groups whose spaces are not normal [A. A. Markov, *Izv. AN SSSR*, ser. matem. **9**, 3–64 (1945)].*

6. Every subgroup A of a topological group G will itself obviously be a topological group with respect to the topology induced in it (see VI.7.9) by the topology of the group G.

The closure $\overline{A}$ of a subgroup A of a topological group G will itself be a subgroup. If A is a normal subgroup in G, then $\overline{A}$ will also be a normal subgroup. If A is an Abelian subgroup, then $\overline{A}$ will also be an Abelian subgroup.

In fact, if $x, y \in \overline{A}$ and U is any neighbourhood of the element xy, then there exist neighbourhoods V of the element x and W of the element y such that $VW \subseteq U$. In addition, there exist elements $x', y' \in A$ such that $x' \in V$, $y' \in W$. The element $x'y'$ which belongs to the subgroup A is thus contained in U. This proves that $xy \in \overline{A}$.

Further, if $x \in \overline{A}$ and U is any neighbourhood of the element x^{-1}, then there exists a neighbourhood V of the element x such that $V^{-1} \subseteq U$. In addition, there exists an element $x' \in A$ such that $x' \in V$, and therefore the element x'^{-1} which belongs to the subgroup A is contained in U. This proves that $x^{-1} \in \overline{A}$. Thus $\overline{A}$ is a subgroup of the group G.

In addition, let A be a normal subgroup of the group G. If $x \in \overline{A}$, $g \in G$ and U is any neighbourhood of the element $g^{-1}xg$, then there exists a neighbourhood V of the element x such that $g^{-1}Vg \subseteq U$. In V we can find an element $x' \in A$, therefore the element $g^{-1}x'g \in g^{-1}Ag = A$ is contained in U. This proves that $g^{-1}xg \in \overline{A}$, i.e. $\overline{A}$ is a normal subgroup.

Finally, let the subgroup A be Abelian. If $x, y \in \overline{A}$ and U is an arbitrary neighbourhood of the element $x^{-1}y^{-1}xy$ — the *commutator* of the elements x and y—then from the continuity of the operations in the group G it follows easily that there exist neighbourhoods V of the element x and W of the element y such that $V^{-1}W^{-1}VW \subseteq U$. In addition, there exist elements $x', y' \in A$ such that $x' \in V, y' \in W$. Hence

$$1 = x'^{-1}y'^{-1}x'y' \in U,$$

i.e. every neighbourhood of the element $x^{-1}y^{-1}xy$ contains the identity, and therefore $x^{-1}y^{-1}xy = 1$, i.e. $xy = yx$. Thus the theorem has been proved.

Every open subgroup A of a topological group G is closed.

In fact, let $x \in \overline{A}$. The coset Ax contains x and, by VI.9.3, is open, and therefore it contains an element of the subgroup A. This is possible, however, only when $Ax = A$, whence $x \in A$, i.e. $\overline{A} = A$.

7. A homomorphism φ of the topological group G onto the topological group G' is called *continuous* if it satisfies any of the following conditions, whose equivalence can be verified without difficulty:

(1) for every subset A of G

$$\overline{A}\varphi \subseteq \overline{A\varphi};$$

(2) for every closed subset A' of G' its complete inverse image $A'\varphi^{-1}$ is closed in G;

(3) for every open subset A' of G' its complete inverse image $A'\varphi^{-1}$ is open in G;

(4) for every neighbourhood U' of the identity of the group G' its complete inverse image $U'\varphi^{-1}$ is open in G.

A continuous homomorphism φ of the topological group G onto the topological group G' is called *open* if it satisfies any of the following equivalent conditions:

(1′) for every open subset A of G its image $A\varphi$ is open in G';

(2′) for every neighbourhood U of the identity of the group G its image $U\varphi$ contains some neighbourhood U' of the identity of the group G'.

Finally, the topological groups G and G' are called *isomorphic* if there exists a one–one correspondence between them which is an isomorphism for G and G' both as groups (see II.4.1) and as topological spaces (see VI.7.8).

8. Let A be a closed subgroup of the topological group G, M the set of right cosets of the group G with respect to the subgroup A, φ the mapping of G onto M which carries every element $x \in G$ into the coset Ax, Σ a complete system of neighbourhoods of the space G, and $\Sigma\varphi$ the system of images of the neighbourhood in Σ under the mapping φ.

The set M can be regarded as a topological space with $\Sigma\varphi$ as a complete system of neighbourhoods.

To prove this it is sufficient to apply the criterion of VI.7.7. If $Ax \neq Ay$, then, since Ay is closed (see VI.9.3), there exists a neighbourhood U in Σ such that $x \in U$ and $U \cap Ay$ is empty. Then $U\varphi$ contains the coset Ax, but does not contain the coset Ay, i.e. condition (α) is satisfied.

Further, let the neighbourhoods U and V of Σ be such that $U\varphi \cap V\varphi$ contains the coset Ax. Because, by VI.9.3, the set aU is open for every $a \in A$, the product AU will also be open; the same is true for AV. The element x is contained in $AU \cap AV$ and, therefore, a neighbourhood W from Σ, containing x, is contained in this intersection. Because $(AU)\varphi = U\varphi$, $(AV)\varphi = V\varphi$, then $W\varphi \subseteq (U\varphi \cap V\varphi)$, where $Ax \in W\varphi$. This proves that condition (β) is also satisfied, i.e. the proof of the theorem is complete.

In the sense of the given topology we will speak of *the space of right* (or, similarly, *left*) *cosets* of a topological group with respect to a closed subgroup and, in particular, of *the topology in the factor-group of a topological group* with respect to a closed normal subgroup.

* The factor-group G/A of a topological group G with respect to a closed normal subgroup is a topological group, and the natural homomorphism of G onto G/A is an open homomorphism.

If φ is an open homomorphism of the topological group G onto the topological group G', then the kernel A of this homomorphism is a closed normal subgroup and there exists an isomorphic mapping ψ of the topological group G' onto the topological group G/A such that the product $\varphi\psi$ coincides with the natural homomorphism of G onto G/A.

The factor-group G/A of the topological group G is discrete if, and only if, the normal subgroup A is open.*

9. A topology of a group G is called *linear* (*completely linear*) if it can be given by a complete system of neighbourhoods of the identity consisting of subgroups (respectively, normal subgroups) of this group.

The discrete topology of every group will obviously be completely linear.

A system Σ of normal subgroups of the group G is a complete system of neighbourhoods of the identity for some (completely linear) topology of this group if, and only if,

(1′) *the intersection of all the normal subgroups in Σ only contains the identity of the group G;*

(2′) *the intersection of any two normal subgroups of Σ contains some third normal subgroup belonging to Σ.*

The necessity of the conditions (1′) and (2′) is obvious. On the other hand, if the system of normal subgroups Σ satisfies these conditions, then the system Σ_0 of all the cosets with respect to all the normal subgroups of Σ satisfies the conditions (α) and (β) of VI.7.7, i.e. it is a complete system of neighbourhoods for some topology in the set G. In fact, if $a, b \in G$, $a \neq b$, then, by (1′), we can find a normal subgroup A in Σ such that $a^{-1} b \notin A$, and then a and b lie in different cosets with respect to A. If, however, $a \in G$, $A, B \in \Sigma$, then, by (2′), Σ contains a normal subgroup C such that $C \subseteq A \cap B$, and then $aC \subseteq (aA \cap aB)$.

It remains to show that the operations of the group G are continuous in this topology (see VI.9.1). If $a, b \in G$, $A \in \Sigma$, then $aA \cdot bA = (ab)A$ which proves the continuity of multiplication; if $a \in G$, $A \in \Sigma$, then $(aA)^{-1} = a^{-1}A$, from which follows the continuity of the operation of taking the inverse element. Thus the theorem has been proved.

328   LECTURES IN GENERAL ALGEBRA

From this theorem it follows, in particular, that *every descending sequence of normal subgroups of a group G, whose intersection is equal to E, determines a complete linear topology of this group.*

10. *Every linearly topological group G is totally disconnected* (see VI. 8.6).

In fact, let the system of subgroups Σ be a complete system of neighbourhoods of the identity for the group G. If $a, b \in G$, $a \neq b$, then Σ contains a subgroup A such that $a^{-1}b \notin A$, i.e. $aA \neq bA$. By VI.9.3, every coset xA, including aA, is an open set. The set $G \backslash aA$ will also be open as the union of all the left cosets of the group G with respect to the subgroup A, distinct from aA. Thus we have obtained a decomposition of the group G into two non-intersecting open (closed) subsets, where $a \in aA$, $b \in G \backslash aA$.

* Every locally bicompact (see VI.8.4) totally disconnected topology of an arbitrary group is linear.

Every bicompact (see VI.8.3) totally disconnected topology of an arbitrary group is completely linear*.

§ 10. The connection between topologies and norms in rings and skew fields

1. A ring R is called a *topological ring* if a topology is given in the set R with respect to which the additive group of the ring R is a topological group, and the multiplicative groupoid of this ring is a topological groupoid (see VI.9.1).

An associative skew field K is called a *topological skew field* if a topology is given in K with respect to which it is a topological ring, and if, in addition, the operation of taking the inverse element is continuous in the sense of VI.9.1. The multiplicative group of a topological skew field will thus be a topological group. The definition of a topological skew field can easily be altered to a form in which it can be applied to non-associative skew fields or division rings.

The reader can formulate without difficulty the definition of isomorphism for topological rings. In general, many problems considered in the preceding paragraph for topological groups can also be considered for topological rings and skew fields. We will not, however, consider these now.

2. *Every pseudonormed ring R* (see VI.4.7) *with real-valued pseudonorm w(a) is a topological ring, and a complete system of neighbourhoods of zero is formed by the sets* U_α *(where α is any positive real number) of those elements a of R for which* $w(a) < \alpha$.

Proof. We know from VI.9.3 that if the additive group of the ring R is a topological group, then if U_α is open in it, so are all the sets of the form $a + U_\alpha$. We will show that the system of all such sets (for any $a \in R$ and any positive real α) is in fact a complete system of neighbourhoods for some topology in the set R (see VI.7.7).

Let $a, b \in R$, $a \neq b$. If $w(b - a) = \gamma$, then $\gamma > 0$. The set $a + U_\gamma$ contains the element a, because $0 \in U_\gamma$, but does not contain the element b, because $b - a \notin U_\gamma$.

On the other hand, let

$$a \in (b + U_\beta) \cap (c + U_\gamma).$$

Then $w(a - b) = \delta_1 < \beta$, $w(a - c) = \delta_2 < \gamma$. We set

$$\alpha = \min (\beta - \delta_1, \ \gamma - \delta_2).$$

If $x \in R$, $w(x) < \alpha$, then

$$a + x = b + (a - b) + x,$$

where

$$w[(a - b) + x] < \delta_1 + \alpha \leqslant \delta_1 + (\beta - \delta_1) = \beta.$$

This proves that $a + U_\alpha \subseteq b + U_\beta$. Similarly it follows that $a + U_\alpha \subseteq c + U_\gamma$.

We have obtained a topology in the set R, and we know that in every neighbourhood of the element $a \in R$ there is contained a neighbourhood of the form $a + U_\alpha$. We will now prove that the operations of the ring R are continuous in this topology.

Let $a, b \in R$ and $a + b + U_\gamma$ be a given neighbourhood of the element $a + b$. If $\delta = (1/2)\gamma$ and $x, y \in U_\delta$, then

$$w(x + y) \leqslant w(x) + w(y) < 2\delta = \gamma.$$

This proves that

$$(a + U_\delta) + (b + U_\delta) \subseteq a + b + U_\gamma,$$

i.e. it proves the continuity of addition.

In addition, let $a \in R$ and $-a + U_\alpha$ be a given neighbourhood of the element $-a$. If $x \in U_\alpha$, then, because $w(-x) = w(x)$, $-x \in U_\alpha$ also, and therefore

$$-(a + U_\alpha) \subseteq -a + U_\alpha.$$

This proves the continuity of the operation of taking the inverse element.

If, finally, $a, b \in R$, $w(a) = \alpha$, $w(b) = \beta$ and $ab + U_\gamma$ is a given neighbourhood of the element ab, then as δ we take a positive real number such that

$$\alpha\delta + \delta\beta + \delta^2 < \gamma.$$

If x, $y \in U_\delta$, then

$$w(ay + xb + xy) \leqslant w(a)w(y) + w(x)w(b) + w(x)w(y) < \gamma,$$

i.e.

$$(a + U_\delta)(b + U_\delta) \subseteq ab + U_\gamma,$$

which proves the continuity of the product. Thus the theorem has been proved.

3. *If a real-valued norm $w(a)$ is given in the associative skew field K (see VI.4.1), then in the topology defined in VI.10.2, K will be a topological skew field.*

We know already that K will be a topological ring, and therefore it only remains to prove the continuity of the operation of taking the inverse element.

We note first that from

$$w(a) = w(a \cdot 1) = w(a) \cdot w(1), \quad a \in K,$$

it follows that $w(1) = 1$. Therefore for $a \neq 0$, because

$$w(a) \cdot w(a^{-1}) = w(aa^{-1}) = w(1) = 1,$$

it follows that

$$w(a^{-1}) = [w(a)]^{-1}.$$

Now let $a \in K$, $a \neq 0$, $w(a) = \alpha$ and let $a^{-1} + U_\gamma$ be a given neighbourhood of the element a^{-1}. We set

$$\delta = \frac{\alpha\gamma}{\alpha^{-1} + \gamma}; \tag{1}$$

it is clear that $0 < \delta < \alpha$. Let $w(x) < \delta$. Then $a + x \neq 0$ and there exists a $y \in K$ such that

$$(a + x)^{-1} = a^{-1} + y.$$

Hence

$$y = (a + x)^{-1} - a^{-1} = a^{-1}[a - (a + x)](a + x)^{-1} =$$
$$a^{-1}(- x)(a + x)^{-1}.$$

However $w(a^{-1}) = \alpha^{-1}$, $w(- x) = w(x) < \delta$. In addition,

$$w(a) = w[(a + x) - x] \leqslant w(a + x) + w(x),$$

whence

$$w(a + x) \geqslant w(a) - w(x) > \alpha - \delta > 0,$$

and therefore

$$w[(a + x)^{-1}] = [w(a + x)]^{-1} < (\alpha - \delta)^{-1}.$$

Thus,

$$w(y) < \alpha^{-1}\delta(\alpha - \delta)^{-1},$$

which, after δ has been replaced by the expression (1), reduces to

$$w(y) < \gamma.$$

This proves that $(a + U_\delta)^{-1} \subseteq a^{-1} + U_\gamma$. Thus the theorem has been proved.

4. The usual norms of the field of real numbers and the field of complex numbers by means of absolute values (moduli) *induce* (in the sense of the theorem proved above) the usual topologies of these fields. The usual norm of the skew field of quaternions (see VI.4.1) induces a topology of this field which coincides on its additive group with the usual topology of four-dimensional Euclidean space (see VI.7.10). It is in fact these topologies of the given three skew fields which we shall have in mind when we speak of them as topological skew fields.

In the field of rational numbers and in the field of p-adic numbers (see III.3.12) their p-adic valuation (see VI.5.6 and VI.5.8) also induces a topology. This topology (and equally the topologies generated by it in the ring of p-adic integers and the additive groups of the given fields and ring) is called their *p-adic topology*. Because the p-adic valuation is integral-valued, the system of neighbourhoods of zero in this topology coincides with the set U_k (where k is any integer) of those numbers a (rational or p-adic) whose p-adic values are strictly *greater* than k.

5. Let K be an associative topological skew field. The element $a \in K$ is called *topologically nilpotent* if the sequence of its powers a^n, $n = 1, 2, \ldots$, converges to zero, i.e. any neighbourhood of zero U contains all these powers except, perhaps, a finite number of them. An element $a \in K$, $a \neq 0$, is called *neutral* if neither a nor a^{-1} is topologically nilpotent. Finally, the set $A, A \subset K$, is called *bounded on the right* if for any neighbourhood of zero U we can find neighbourhood of zero V such that $AV \subseteq U$.

We will prove the following theorem [Kaplansky, *Duke Math. J.* **14**, 527–541 (1947); for topological fields, with a somewhat different formulation—I. R. Shafarevich, *DAN SSSR* **40** 149–151 (1943)];

Let K be an associative topological skew field. The topology of this skew field is induced by a real-valued norm if, and only if, the following conditions are satisfied:

(1) *the set N of all the topologically nilpotent elements of the skew field K is open and bounded on the right;*

(2) *if the element a is topologically nilpotent, and the element b is topologically nilpotent or neutral, then the product ba is topologically nilpotent.*

6. The necessity of these conditions can be verified without difficulty. If the topology of the skew field K is induced by a real-valued norm $w(a)$, then the topological nilpotence of the element a is equivalent to the fact that $w(a) < 1$, and the neutrality of the element a to the fact that $w(a) = 1$. From this condition (2) follows at once. The fact that the set N is bounded on the right follows from the inclusion $NU_\gamma \subseteq U_\gamma$. Finally, the set N will also be open, because $N = U_1$.

7. We turn to the proof of the sufficiency of these conditions. We will show first that if $a \in N$ and $a \neq 0$, then $a^{-1} \notin N$. Suppose that this is not so and let U be an arbitrary neighbourhood of zero. Then, because of the equation $0 \cdot 0 = 0$ and because of the continuity of multiplication, there exist neighbourhoods of zero V and W such that $V \cdot W \subseteq U$. Because, for a sufficiently large natural number n, $a^n \in V$, $a^{-n} \in W$, then $1 \in U$, which is impossible, because U was an arbitrary neighbourhood of zero.

We denote by M the set of all neutral elements. Condition (2) of the theorem can now be written in the form

$$(N \cup M)N \subseteq N. \tag{2}$$

It is clear that $1 \in M$. From the definition of a neutral element it follows that if $a \in M$, then $a^{-1} \in M$. In addition, let $a, b \in M$. If $ab \in N$, then, by (2), $a^{-1}(ab) = b \in N$; if $(ab)^{-1} \in N$, then $b(ab)^{-1} = a^{-1} \in N$. Thus $ab \in M$, i.e.

$$MM \subseteq M. \tag{3}$$

Now let $a \in N$, $b \in M$. If $ab \in M$, then, by (3) and because $b^{-1} \in M$, $(ab)b^{-1} = a \in M$. If $(ab)^{-1} \in N$, then $b(ab)^{-1} = a^{-1} \in N$. Thus $ab \in N$, i.e.

$$NM \subseteq N. \tag{4}$$

From (2)–(4) it follows that

$$(N \cup M)(N \cup M) \subseteq (N \cup M). \tag{5}$$

In addition, let $a \in N$, and let x be an arbitrary element of the skew field K, distinct from zero. If U is a given neighbourhood of zero, then from $x^{-1} \cdot 0 \cdot x = 0$ and the continuity of multiplication it follows that there exists a neighbourhood of zero V such that $x^{-1}Vx \subseteq U$. Because $a^n \in V$ for a sufficiently large natural number n, then $x^{-1}a^n x = (x^{-1}ax)^n \in U$; hence $x^{-1}ax \in N$, i.e.

$$x^{-1}Nx \subseteq N. \tag{6}$$

If $a \in M$, $x \neq 0$, then $x^{-1}ax \in M$, because from $b = x^{-1}ax \in N$ it would follow, by (6), that $xbx^{-1} = a \in N$, and from $b^{-1} \in N$ it would follow that $a^{-1} \in N$. Thus

$$x^{-1}Mx \subseteq M. \tag{7}$$

8. From the results obtained, in particular from (3) and (7), it follows that M *will be a normal subgroup in the multiplicative group K^* of the elements of the skew field K distinct from zero.* We can thus consider the factor-group K^*/M. We note that this factor-group will be trivial if, and only if, N consists of zero alone, i.e., by condition (1), if the topology of the skew field K is discrete —it is necessary to take into account that the skew field K cannot contain *nilpotent* elements, i.e. elements a such that $a \neq 0$, but $a^n = 0$ for some natural n.

By (5) the set $N \cup M$ (without zero) can be decomposed into complete cosets with respect to M and these cosets form a subsemigroup in the factor-group K^*/M. It is easy to verify, by (6) and (7), the conditions (1)–(4) of VI.1.3, i.e. this subsemigroup will be the semigroup of positive elements for some linear ordering of the group K^*/M.

The ordering obtained is Archimedean (see VI.3.3). In fact, if a, $b \in K^*$ and the cosets aM and bM are strictly positive, then $a \in N$, $b \in N$. Let U be a given neighbourhood of zero; we can assume that $U \subseteq N$, because N is open. Because $0 \cdot b^{-1} = 0$, there exists a neighbourhood of zero V such that $Vb^{-1} \subseteq U$, and because from $a \in N$ there follows the existence of a natural number k such that $a^k \in V$, then $a^k b^{-1} \in U$ and therefore $a^k b^{-1} \in N$. From this it follows that in the ordered group K^*/M it will be true that $(aM)^k > bM$, i.e. we have proved that this group is Archimedean.

9. By Hölder's theorem (VI.3.4) the group K^*/M is isomorphic to a subgroup of the additive group of real numbers with its natural ordering. This determines a homomorphic mapping φ of the group K^* into the additive group of real numbers, where the elements of M are mapped into zero, and only they, and the images of the elements of N distinct from zero (and only these elements) are strictly positive. Let λ be some arbitrary positive real number. We set for $a \in K$

$$\left.\begin{array}{l} w(a) = 2^{-\lambda \cdot a\varphi}, \quad a \neq 0, \\ w(0) = 0. \end{array}\right\} \tag{8}$$

It is clear that conditions 1 and 2 of VI.4.1 are satisfied. Later we will show that it is possible to choose a λ for which condition 3 will also be satisfied.

From (8) it follows easily that $w(a) = 1$ if, and only if, $a \in M$, and $w(a) < 1$ if, and only if, $a \in N$. As in VI.10.2, we denote by U_α (where α is a positive real number) the set of those elements $a \in K$ for which $w(a) < \alpha$. If the topology of the skew field K is discrete, then when $\alpha < 1$ it will be true that $U_\alpha = 0$.

Let the topology of the skew field K be non-discrete. We consider an arbitrary U_α. In K there exists an element b such that $w(b) > \alpha^{-1}$. Because the set N is open, we can find a neighbourhood U of zero such that $bU \subseteq N = U_1$. Therefore $U \subseteq U_\alpha$.

Conversely, let U be an arbitrary neighbourhood of zero in the skew field K. Because the set N is bounded on the right and we have assumed that the skew field K is non-discrete, there exists a $c \neq 0$, such that $Nc \subseteq U$. From this it follows that if $\alpha = w(c)$, then $U_\alpha \subseteq U$, because $U_\alpha = U_1 c = Nc$.

Thus, *if λ is selected in such a way that $w(a)$ is a norm, then the topology induced by this norm in the sense of VI.10.2 will coincide with the original topology of the skew field K* (see the definition of the equivalence of systems of neighbourhoods in VI.7.8).

10. Still assuming that λ is arbitrary, we will prove the existence of a number l such that for all $a \in K$ the inequality

$$w(1 + a) \leqslant l(1 + w(a)) \qquad (9)$$

holds. In fact, if such a number l did not exist, then we could find a sequence of elements $a_n \in K$, $a_n \neq -1$, $n = 1, 2, \dots$, such that as $n \to \infty$,

$$\frac{1 + w(a_n)}{w(1 + a_n)} = \frac{1}{w(1 + a_n)} + \frac{w(a_n)}{w(1 + a_n)} \to 0,$$

i.e.

$$\frac{1}{w(1 + a_n)} = w((1 + a_n)^{-1}) \to 0,$$

$$\frac{w(a_n)}{w(1 + a_n)} = w(a_n(1 + a_n)^{-1}) \to 0.$$

From this it would follow, however, by the proof in the preceding section, that the sequences

$$(1 + a_n)^{-1} \quad \text{and} \quad a_n(1 + a_n)^{-1}, \quad n = 1, 2, \dots, \qquad (10)$$

would converge to zero in the topological skew field K, which is impossible, because addition in the skew field K is continuous, and the sum of the n-th terms of the sequences (10) is equal to 1.

From (9) it follows that if at least one of the elements $a, b \in K$ is distinct from zero, then

$$w(a + b) \leqslant l(w(a) + w(b)). \qquad (11)$$

In fact, if $a \neq 0$, then

$$w(a + b) = w[a(1 + a^{-1}b)] \leqslant$$
$$lw(a)[1 + w^{-1}(a)w(b)] = l(w(a) + w(b)).$$

It is clear that (11) is also valid for $a = b = 0$. From (11) it follows that

$$w(a+b) \leqslant 2l \max(w(a), w(b)).$$ (12)

11. There exists a positive real number v which is so small that $(2l)^v \leqslant 2$. We replace the number λ by the number λv in the definition (8). Because this raises the number $w(a)$ to the power v, then, by relating, at the same time, the symbol w to the new choice of the number λ, we obtain from (12)

$$w(a+b) \leqslant 2 \max(w(a), w(b)).$$ (13)

From this it easily follows for $k = 1, 2, \ldots$, that

$$w(a_1 + a_2 + \ldots + a_{2^k}) \leqslant 2^k \max_{1 \leqslant i \leqslant 2^k} w(a_i).$$ (14)

We will agree to denote by n the n-th multiple of the identity of the skew field K; this element will only appear under the sign w, and therefore there is no possibility of confusing it with the natural number n. We also note that K is not assumed to be of characteristic zero. From (14) it follows that

$$w(2^k) \leqslant 2^k, \quad k = 1, 2, \ldots$$ (15)

We will show that for any natural number n

$$w(n) \leqslant 2n.$$ (16)

In fact, let $2^k \leqslant n < 2^{k+1}$. We will prove (16) by induction with respect to k, because when $k = 0$ this assertion is true. Because $n = (n - 2^k) + 2^k$, then when $w(n - 2^k) \leqslant w(2^k)$ it follows from (13) and (15) that

$$w(n) \leqslant 2w(2^k) \leqslant 2 \cdot 2^k \leqslant 2n.$$

If $w(n - 2^k) \geqslant w(2^k)$, then, because $n - 2^k < 2^k$, by applying induction we find that

$$w(n) \leqslant 2w(n - 2^k) \leqslant 2 \cdot 2(n - 2^k) = 4n - 2^{k+2} < 2n.$$

12. Now we take an arbitrary element $a \in K$ and we apply (14) to the expansion of the element $(1 + a)^{n-1}$ in a binomial series, setting n equal to some power of the number 2. The binomial formula is applicable in the case under consideration, because the elements a and 1 commute. Because, by (16),

$$w(C_{n-1}^k) \leqslant 2C_{n-1}^k,$$

where C_{n-1}^k is the binomial coefficient, then

$$w((1 + a)^{n-1}) \leqslant n \max w(C_{n-1}^k a^k) = n \max [w(C_{n-1}^k)w(a)] \leqslant$$
$$2n \max (C_{n-1}^k w(a)) \leqslant 2n(1 + w(a))^{n-1}.$$

From this it follows that

$$[w(1 + a)]^{n-1} \leqslant 2n(1 + w(a))^{n-1},$$

and because n can be an arbitrarily large power of the number 2,

$$w(1 + a) \leqslant 1 + w(a).$$

The inequality 3_2 of VI.4.1 is equivalent, in the case we are considering (viz. that of a real-valued norm), to condition 3 of the definition of a norm — in fact, in this case $w(-1) = 1$ and therefore equation 3_1 of VI.4.1 is satisfied. Now 3_2 can be derived in the same way as (11) was derived from (9). The theorem of VI.10.5 has thus been proved.

* If an associative topological skew field is locally bicompact (see VI. 8.4), then its topology is induced by a real-valued norm [Kaplansky, *Duke Math. J.* **14**, 527–541 (1947)].

The field of real numbers, the field of complex numbers and the skew field of quaternions, considered with their natural topologies (see VI.10.4), are the only connected (see VI.8.6) locally bicompact associative topological skew fields [L. S. Pontrjagin, *Ann. of Math.* **33**, 163–174 (1932)].

Let F be a topological field. The topology of the field F is induced by a non-Archimedean valuation (see VI.4.3) with values in some linearly ordered group, with zero adjoined if, and only if: (1) in F there exists a neighbourhood of zero generated by a bounded additive subgroup; (2) if the subset $A \subset F$ does not intersect any neighbourhood of zero, then A^{-1} is bounded [Zelinsky, *Bull. Amer. math. Soc.* **54**, 1145–1150 (1948)].*

§ 11. Galois correspondences. The fundamental theorem of Galois theory

1. We say that between the partially ordered sets M and M' there is a *Galois correspondence* if we can find mappings $\varphi: M \to M'$ and $\psi: M' \to M$ which satisfy (for any $a, b \in M$, $a', b' \in M'$) the following requirements:

(α) if $a \leqslant b$, then $a\varphi \geqslant b\varphi$;
    if $a' \leqslant b'$, then $a'\psi \geqslant b'\psi$;
(β) $a\varphi\psi \geqslant a$, $a'\psi\varphi \geqslant a'$.

This concept is closely connected to the concept of closure in a partially ordered set (see VI.7.1):

If there is a Galois correspondence between the partially ordered sets M and M', then the equations

$$\bar{a} = a\varphi\psi, \ a \in M, \tag{1}$$

$$\bar{a}' = a'\psi\varphi, a' \in M',$$

define closure relations in M and M' respectively. If M_0 and M_0' are the systems of all elements of M and M' respectively, which are closed under these closures, then φ is an inverse isomorphism of M_0 onto M_0', and ψ is an inverse isomorphism of M_0' onto M_0 where on these sets the mappings φ and ψ are inverse to each other.

We will show that the equations (1) introduce a closure relation in the sets M and M'. It is clear that (β) immediately reduces to condition (1_0) of VI.7.1, and that condition (2_0) follows from (α). Further, from (β) there follows, because $a\varphi \in M'$, the inequality

$$a\varphi\psi\varphi \geqslant a\varphi,$$

and because, by (α), it follows from $a\varphi\psi \geqslant a$ that

$$a\varphi\psi\varphi \leqslant a\varphi,$$

then in fact

$$a\varphi\psi\varphi = a\varphi, \tag{2}$$

and therefore

$$a\varphi\psi\varphi\psi = a\varphi\psi, \ a \in M. \tag{3}$$

This proves that condition (3_0) of VI.7.1 is also satisfied.

The systems M_0 and M_0' of the elements closed in M and M' with respect to the closure which we have constructed consist respectively of the elements $a\varphi\psi$, where $a \in M$, and $a'\psi\varphi$, where $a' \in M'$. Equation (2), written in the form

$$(a\varphi)\psi\varphi = a\varphi,$$

shows that the image under φ of any element a of M is closed in M'. From this it follows that φ maps the system M_0 into the system M_0'. Similarly the mapping ψ maps M_0' into M_0.

From the validity of equation (3) and the similar equation

$$a'\psi\varphi\psi\varphi = a'\psi\varphi, \quad a' \in M',$$

it follows, however, that in fact φ and ψ, considered only on M_0 and M_0', will be one–one mappings inverse to one another. They are even inverse isomorphisms, as follows from (α). The theorem has thus been proved.

2. We will mention only one of the numerous applications of Galois correspondences in algebra. We consider a field K and a particular subfield P in it, and we denote by $G(K, P)$ the set of all automorphisms of the field K which leave every element of P fixed. This set will obviously be a group with respect to the multiplication of automorphisms. The group $G(K, P)$ is called the *Galois group* of the field K over the subfield P.

We denote by M the set of all subsets A of the field K which contain the subfield P,

$$P \subseteq A \subseteq K,$$

and by M' the set of all subsets A' of the group $G(K, P)$, where both these sets are considered with their set-theoretical partial ordering. For every $A \in M$ we denote by $A\varphi$ the set of the automorphisms of $G(K, P)$ which leave the set A fixed elementwise. In addition, for every $A' \in M'$ we denote by $A'\psi$ the set of all elements of the field K left invariant by all the automorphisms of A'.

It is clear that $A\varphi$ *will be a subgroup of the Galois group* $G(K, P)$ *and* $A'\psi$ *will be a subfield of the field* K, *containing* P. We can also verify at once that the mappings φ and ψ satisfy the conditions (α) and (β) of VI.11.1. Thus we have established a Galois correspondence between the sets M and M', which defines a closure in each of these two sets. Finally, *the mappings* φ *and* ψ *are inverse isomorphisms, inverse to each other, between the systems* $M_0 \subset M$ *and* $M_0' \subset M'$ *of closed elements, i.e. between some system of subfields of the field* K, *containing the subfield* P, *and some system of subgroups of the Galois group* $G(K, P)$.

3. Especially interesting are the cases when both all the subfields lying between P and K and also all the subgroups of the Galois group turn out to be closed, i.e. when the study of all the subfields of the field K containing the field P reduces to the study of all the subgroups of the group $G(K, P)$. We will consider one such case.

We will assume that only fields of characteristic zero are under consideration (see III.2.11). We will also assume that the reader is already familiar, from a course in higher algebra, with the fundamental algebra of polynomials over fields [see, for instance†, A. G. Kurosh, *A Course in Higher Algebra*, 6th ed., 1959, §§ 47–49; cited hereafter as *The Course*].

As above, let $P \subset K$. An element $\alpha \in K$ is called *algebraic* over the field P if it is a root of some polynomial from the ring $P[x]$ and, hence, a root of a uniquely determined irreducible polynomial $\varphi(x)$, whose leading coefficient is equal to one. The degree of this polynomial is called the *degree* of the element α and its roots, lying in the field K or in some extension of this field, are elements *conjugate* to α.

The field K is called an *algebraic extension* of the field P if every element of K is algebraic over P. The field K is a *finite extension* of the field P, and in fact an *extension of degree n*, if K is a finite-dimensional linear algebra over P (see V.6.6), which has dimension n. The degree of K over P will be denoted by the symbol $(K:P)$.

Every finite extension is an algebraic extension.

In fact, if $(K:P=n$, then every $n+1$ elements of K are linearly dependent over P. In particular, if $\alpha \in K$, then the elements $1, \alpha, \alpha^2, \ldots, \alpha^n$ are linearly dependent over P, and this means that α is the root of a polynomial of degree n from the ring $P[x]$.

4. The theorem of the primitive element. *If the field K of characteristic zero is an algebraic extension of the field P and is generated by adjoining a finite number of elements to P, then K is generated by adjoining a single element to P.*

It is sufficient to consider the case of adjoining two elements. Let

$$K = P(\alpha, \beta).$$

If $\varphi(x)$ and $\psi(x)$ are irreducible polynomials over P, which have as their roots α and β respectively, then there exists an extension L of the field K (for instance, the splitting field of the product $\varphi(x)\psi(x)$, see *The Course*, § 49‡) in which both these polynomials have all their roots.

Let

$$\alpha_1 = \alpha, \alpha_2, \ldots, \alpha_k$$

† See also Zariski and Samuel, *Commutative Algebra*, ch. II, vol. I, New York, 1958.

‡ See also Zariski and Samuel, *loc. cit.*, ch. II § 2.

be all the roots of the polynomial $\varphi(x)$ lying in L; they are distinct, because $\varphi(x)$ does not have multiple roots. Analogously

$$\beta_1 = \beta, \beta_2, \ldots, \beta_i$$

will be all the roots of the polynomial $\psi(x)$ lying in L. Because P, as a field of characteristic zero, is infinite, then we can find an element $c \in P$ such that

$$\alpha_i + c\beta_j \neq \alpha + c\beta, \tag{4}$$

if at least one of the indices i, j is distinct from 1.

We set

$$\gamma = \alpha + c\beta. \tag{5}$$

It is clear that $P(\gamma) \subseteq K$. Now we consider the polynomial

$$\overline{\varphi}(x) = \varphi(\gamma - cx)$$

with coefficients in the field $P(\gamma)$. Because, by (5),

$$\overline{\varphi}(\beta) = \varphi(\gamma - c\beta) = \varphi(\alpha) = 0$$

and, as we know, $\psi(\beta) = 0$, then the polynomials $\overline{\varphi}(x)$ and $\psi(x)$ have a common root β. This is their unique common root: if $\overline{\varphi}(\beta_j) = 0$, $j \neq 1$, then

$$\varphi(\gamma - c\beta_j) = 0,$$

i.e. $\gamma - c\beta_j$ is equal to some α_i, contrary to condition (4).

From this it follows that $x - \beta$ will be the greatest common divisor of the polynomials $\overline{\varphi}(x)$ and $\psi(x)$. The coefficients of these polynomials, and therefore also their greatest common divisor, lie in the field $P(\gamma)$, i.e. $\beta \in P(\gamma)$. Hence, by (5), $\alpha \in P(\gamma)$ also. Thus,

$$K = P(\alpha, \beta) = P(\gamma),$$

which is what we were required to prove.

5. An algebraic extension K of a field P is called a *normal extension* if every irreducible polynomial from the ring $P[x]$, which has at least one root in the field K, has all its roots in K, i.e. splits into linear factors over K.

* A field K will be a normal extension of its subfield P if, and only if, K is generated by adjoining to P all the roots of some set of polynomials from the ring $P[x]$.*

6. *If the field K of characteristic zero is of finite degree n and is a normal extension of its subfield P, then the Galois group $G(K, P)$ is finite and has order n.*

In fact, K is algebraic over P, by VI.11.3, and, by VI.11.4, has a primitive element,

$$K = P(\alpha).$$

Because $(K:P) = n$, then every element $\beta \in K$ can be expressed uniquely in the form

$$\beta = b_0 + b_1\alpha + b_2\alpha^2 + \ldots + b_{n-1}\alpha^{n-1}, \qquad (6)$$
$$b_0, b_1, b_2, \ldots, b_{n-1} \in P,$$

and therefore α has degree n over the field P. Because K is normal over P, the field K contains n distinct elements conjugate to α (because the field is of characteristic zero):

$$\alpha_1 = \alpha, \alpha_2, \ldots, \alpha_n. \qquad (7)$$

It is clear that

$$K = P(\alpha_i), \qquad i = 1, 2, \ldots, n.$$

As is well known (see† *The Course*, § 49), there exists a uniquely defined automorphism of the field K which leaves the elements of the field P fixed and carries α into α_i, $i = 1, 2, \ldots, n$, namely the automorphism φ_i which maps the element β of (6) into the element

$$\beta_i = b_0 + b_1\alpha_i + b_2\alpha_i^2 + \ldots + b_{n-1}\alpha_i^{n-1}.$$

This gives n elements of the Galois group $G(K, P)$. On the other hand, let φ be an arbitrary automorphism of the field K, belonging to $G(K, P)$, and let $\alpha\varphi = \alpha'$. If

$$f(x) = x^n + a_1 x^{n-1} + \ldots + a_n$$

is the irreducible polynomial from the ring $P[x]$, of which α is a root, then, because $a\varphi = a$ for all $a \in P$,

$$f(\alpha') = \alpha'^n + a_1\alpha'^{n-1} + \ldots + a_n =$$
$$(\alpha^n + a_1\alpha^{n-1} + \ldots + a_n)\varphi = [f(\alpha)]\varphi = 0\varphi = 0.$$

The element α' thus coincides with one of the elements α_i of (7), and therefore the automorphism φ coincides with the corresponding automorphism φ_i. The theorem has thus been proved.

---

† See Zariski and Samuel, Commutative Algebra, § 6, ch. II, vol. I.

7. It is clear that the fields Q which lie between P and K,

$$P \subseteq Q \subseteq K,$$

form a lattice with respect to set-theoretical inclusion. It is also clear that it follows from $K = P(\alpha)$ that $K = Q(\alpha)$ for every Q satisfying the inclusion (8).

If the field K is finite over the field P, then the intermediate field Q is finite over P, K is finite over Q and

$$(K : P) = (K : Q)(Q : P).$$

In fact, the finiteness of Q over P follows from the fact that Q is a subspace of the vector space K over the field P. The finiteness of K over Q follows from the fact that we obtain a basis of K over Q if, in the basis of K over P, we take a maximal subsystem, linearly independent over Q. Finally, let $\alpha_1, \alpha_2, ..., \alpha_k$ be a basis of K over Q, and $\beta_1, \beta_2, ..., \beta_l$ a basis of Q over P. Then for every $\gamma \in K$ it will be true that

$$\gamma = \sum_{i=1}^{k} b_i \alpha_i, \qquad b_i \in Q, \qquad i = 1, 2, ..., k, \qquad (9)$$

and because

$$b_i = \sum_{j=1}^{l} a_{ij} \beta_j, \qquad a_{ij} \in P, \qquad (10)$$

then

$$\gamma = \sum_{i=1}^{k} \sum_{j=1}^{l} a_{ij}(\alpha_i \beta_j). \qquad (11)$$

The linear independence over P of the system of kl elements $\alpha_i \beta_j$ follows from the fact that if the right-hand side of equation (11) were equal to zero, then it would follow, because of the linear independence of the system $\alpha_1, \alpha_2, ..., \alpha_k$ over Q, that the coefficients b_i in (9) were equal to zero, where the b_i have the form (10), and then, because the system $\beta_1, \beta_2, ..., \beta_l$ is linearly independent over P, all the coefficients a_{ij} would be equal to zero.

If the field K is normal over the field P, then it is also normal over every intermediate field Q.

In fact, let the polynomial $g(x)$ irreducible over Q have a root in K. The polynomial $f(x)$ irreducible over P, of which α is a root, has all its roots in K, and because $g(x)$ is a divisor of $f(x)$ in the ring $Q[x]$ (see *The Course*, § 48), then $g(x)$ also splits into linear factors over the field K.

8. The fundamental theorem of Galois theory. *If the field K of characteristic zero is a finite normal extension of the field P, then the correspondence which relates every intermediate field Q (see (8)) to the Galois group $G(K, Q)$ of the field K over this field Q is an inverse isomorphism between the lattice of all intermediate fields and the lattice of all subgroups of the Galois group $G(K, P)$.*

In fact, the mapping φ of the Galois correspondence considered in VI.11.2 relates every intermediate field Q to the subgroup of the group $G(K, P)$ which is the Galois group of K over Q,

$$Q\varphi = G(K, Q).$$

The fundamental theorem will thus be proved if we show that under the closures determined by the given Galois correspondences all the intermediate fields will be closed, and also all the subgroups of the Galois group.

If Q is an arbitrary intermediate field, then

$$Q\varphi = G(K, Q) = U \subseteq G(K, P),$$

$$U\psi = Q' = Q\varphi\psi,$$

$$Q'\varphi = G(K, Q') = U' = U\psi\varphi \subseteq G(K, P).$$

Therefore $Q \subseteq Q'$, $U \subseteq U'$. We denote by s and s' respectively the orders of the subgroups U and U'. Then

$$s \leqslant s'$$

and, by VI.11.7,

$$(K:Q) \geqslant (K:Q'). \tag{12}$$

However, by VI.11.6,

$$(K:Q) = s, \qquad (K:Q') = s'.$$

Therefore equality holds in (12), whence $Q' = Q$.

Now let U be an arbitrary subgroup of the group $G(K, P)$. We set

$$U\psi = Q,$$
$$Q\varphi = U\psi\varphi = U' \subseteq G(K, P). \tag{13}$$

Then $U \subseteq U'$, i.e., as above, $s \leqslant s'$. Suppose, however, that $K = Q(\alpha)$.
If

$$\varepsilon = \sigma_1, \sigma_2, \ldots \sigma_s \qquad (14)$$

are all the automorphisms, including the identity automorphism ε, forming the subgroup U, then α will be a root of the polynomial of degree s

$$f(x) = (x - \alpha\sigma_1)(x - \alpha\sigma_2) \ldots (x - \alpha\sigma_s).$$

The coefficients of this polynomial, written according to Vieta's formulae,† are left fixed by any of the automorphism (14)—the multiplication of all the elements of the group U on the right by one of its elements only permutes these elements. Therefore, by the definition of the mapping ψ and (13),

$$f(x) \in Q[x],$$

i.e. the degree of α over Q is not greater than s, whence

$$s' = (K:Q) \leqslant s.$$

Thus $s' = s$, i.e. $U' = U$. Thus the theorem has been proved.

From this theorem it follows, in particular, that *under the given conditions, the number of fields lying between P and K will be finite.*

* With the hypotheses of the fundamental theorem an intermediate field Q will be normal over the field P if, and only if, the corresponding subgroup $U = G(K, Q)$ is a normal subgroup of $G(K, P)$. The group $G(Q, P)$ is here isomorphic to the factor-group

$$G(K, P)/U.$$

In the case of fields of characteristic zero the finiteness and normality of K over P is not only sufficient, but also necessary for the validity of the assertion of the fundamental theorem.

If the field K of characteristic zero is an algebraic normal (but not necessarily finite) extension of the field P, then the correspondence

$$Q \to G(K, Q)$$

---

† i.e. the formulae for the coefficients of an equation in terms of its roots (Ed.).

is an inverse isomorphism between the lattice of all the subfields lying between P and K, and the lattice of all subgroups of the group $G(K, P)$, closed in the linear topology of this group (see VI.9.9), defined in the following way: a complete system of neighbourhoods of the identity is formed by the subgroups $G(K, Q_0)$, where Q_0 varies over all the subfields of the field K which are finite normal extensions of the field P [Krull, *Math. Ann.* **100**, 687–698 (1928)].*

BIBLIOGRAPHY

1. ALBERT A. A., *Modern Higher Algebra*, Chicago, 1937.
2. ALBERT A. A., *Structure of Algebras*, N. Y., 1939.
3. ALBERT A. A., *Fundamental Concepts of Higher Algebra*, Chicago, 1956 (reprinted, 1959).
4. ALEXANDROV P. S., *Introduction to the Theory of Groups*, Moscow, 1938, 2nd ed., Moscow, 1951; Rumanian transl., Bucharest, 1954; German transl., Berlin, 1954; Ukrainian transl., Kiev, 1955; Polish transl., Warsaw, 1956; English transl., London, 1959.
5. ALMEIDA COSTA A., *Abelian groups, noncommutative rings and ideals, hypercomplex systems and representation*, Lisbon, vol. 1, 1942; vol. 2, 1948.
6. ALMEIDA COSTA A., *Anéis associativos não comutativos*, Lisbon, 1955.
7. ANDREE R. V., *Selections from modern abstract algebra*, N. Y., 1958.
8. ARTIN E., *Galois theory*, Notre Dame, 1942; 2nd ed., 1946; Chinese transl., Shanghai, 1958.
9. ARTIN E., NESBITT C. J. and THRALL R. M., *Rings with minimum condition*, Ann Arbor, 1944.
10. ARTIN E., *Geometric algebra*, N. Y. – London, 1957.
11. AZUMAYA G., *The Algebraic Theory of Simple Rings*, (Japanese) Tokyo, 1951.
12. BAER R., *Linear algebra and projective geometry*, N. Y., 1952; Russian transl., Moscow, 1955.
13. BARBILIAN D., *Teoria aritmetica a idealelor (in inele necomutative)*, Bocharest, 1956.
14. BAUMGARTNER L., *Gruppentheorie*, 3rd ed., Berlin, 1958.
15. BIRKHOFF G., *Lattice theory*, N. Y., 1940; 2nd ed., 1948; Russian transl., *Theory of structures*, Moscow, 1952.
16. BIRKHOFF G. and MACLANE S., *A survey of modern algebra*, N. Y., 1941 (reprinted, 1944); 2nd ed., 1953.
17. BOERNER H., *Darstellungen von Gruppen*, Berlin – Göttingen – Heidelberg, 1955.
18. BOREVICH Z. I. and FADDEYEV D. K., *Homology theory of groups*, I, Vestn. Leningr. un-ta, 1956, No. 7, 3–39.
19. BORŮVKA O., *Úvod do theorie grup*, Prague, 1944; 2nd ed., 1952.
20. BOURBAKI N., *Éléments de mathématique*, Algèbre, ch. 1–8, Paris, 1942–1958.

21. BRUCK R. H., *A survey of binary systems*, Berlin, Göttingen, Heidelberg, 1958.
22. BURNSIDE W., *Theory of groups*, reprinted 2nd ed., N. Y., 1955.
23. CARTAN H. and EILENBERG S., *Homological algebra*, Princeton, 1956, Russian transl., Moscow, 1960.
24. CARMICHAEL R. D., *Introduction to the theory of groups of finite order*, Boston, 1937; reprinted, N. Y., 1956.
25. CHANG, HO-JUI, *Foundations of modern algebra* (Chinese), Shanghai, 1952.
26. CHATELET A., *Arithmétique et algèbre moderne*, t. 1 *(Notions fondamentales — Groupes)*, Paris, 1954; t. 2 *(Anneaux et corps, calcul algébrique, idéaux et divisibilité)*, Paris, 1956.
27. CHEBOTAREV N. G., *Foundations of Galois theory*, Pt. 1, Leningrad–Moscow, 1934; German transl., Groningen, 1950.
28. CHEBOTAREV N. G., *Galois theory*, Moscow, Leningrad, 1936.
29. CHEBOTAREV N. G., *Introduction to the theory of algebras*, Moscow–Leningrad, 1949; Chinese transl., Peking, 1954.
30. CHERNIKOV S. N., Finiteness conditions in the general theory of groups, *Uspekhi mat. nauk* **14**, No. 5, 45–96 (1959).
31. CHEVALLEY Cl., *Thèorie des groupes de Lie*, t. 3, *Théorèmes généraux sur les algèbres de Lie*, Paris, 1955; Russian transl., "Theory of Lie groups", III, Moscow, 1958.
32. CHEVALLEY Cl., *Fundamental concepts of algebra*, N. Y., 1956.
33. COXETER H. S. M. and MOSER W. O. J., *Generators and relations for discrete groups*, Berlin, Göttingen, Heidelberg, 1957.
34. DEURING M., *Algebren*, Berlin, 1935.
35. DICKSON L. E., *Linear groups* (reprinted), N. Y., 1958.
36. DUBREIL P., *Algèbre*, t. I, Paris, 1946; 2nd ed., 1954.
37. DUBREIL–JAÇOTIN M. L., LESIEUR L., CROISOT R., *Leçons sur la théorie des treillis, des structures algébriques ordonnées et des treillis géométriques*, Paris, 1953.
38. FUCHS L., *Abelian groups*, Budapest, 1958.
39. GLIVENKO V. I., *Théorie générale des structures*, Paris, 1938.
40. GLUSHKOV V. M., The structure of locally bicompact groups and the fifth problem of Hilbert, *Uspekhi mat. nauk* **12**, No. 2, 3–41 (1957).
41. GRAYEV M. I., The theory of topological groups, I, *Uspekhi mat. nauk* **5**, No. 2, 3–56 (1950).
42. HALL M., *Projective planes and related topics*, Calif. Inst. of Technol., 1954.
43. HALL M., *The theory of groups*, N. Y., 1959.
44. HAUPT O., *Einführung in die Algebra*, 2nd ed., Leipzig, 1952.
45. HERMES H., *Einführung in die Verbandstheorie*, Berlin, Göttingen, Heidelberg, 1955.
46. JACOBSON N., *Lectures in abstract algebra*, vol. 1, N. Y., 1951; vol. 2, 1952; Chinese transl., Peking, 1960; vol. 3, N.Y., 1964.

47. JACOBSON N., *Structure of rings*, N. Y., 1956; Russian transl., Moscow, 1961.
48. JACOBSON N., *The theory of rings*, N. Y., 1943; Russian transl., Moscow, 1947
49. JOHNSON R. E., *First course in abstract algebra*, N. Y., 1953.
50. JORDAN C., *Traité des substitutions et des équations algébriques*, Paris, 1957 (photostat).
51. KAPLANSKY I., *An introduction to differential algebra*, Paris, 1957; Russian transl., Moscow, 1959.
52. KAPLANSKY I., *Infinite abelian groups*, Ann Arbor, 1954 (reprinted, 1956).
53. KOCHENDÖRFFER R., *Einführung in die Algebra*, Berlin, 1955.
54. KRULL W., *Idealtheorie*, Berlin, 1953; reprinted, N. Y., 1948.
55. KUROSH A. G. and CHERNIKOV S. N., Soluble and nilpotent groups, *Uspekhi mat. nauk* 2, No. 3, 18–59 (1947); English transl., 1953.
56. KUROSH A. G., Methods of development and successive problems in the theory of infinite groups, *Uspekhi mat. nauk*. 3, 5–15 (1937).
57. KUROSH A. G., The present state of the theory of rings and algebras, *Uspekhi mat. nauk* 6, No. 2, 3–15 (1951).
58. KUROSH A. G., *The theory of groups*, Moscow–Leningrad, 1944; 2nd ed., Moscow, 1953; German transl., Berlin, 1953; Hungarian transl., Budapest, 1955; English transl., 2 vols., New York, 1955–1956; Rumanian transl., Bucharest, 1959; Japanese transl., 2 vols., Tokyo, 1960–1961.
59. LEDERMANN W., *Introduction to the theory of finite groups*, Edinburgh—London, 1949; 2nd ed., 1953; 3rd ed., 1957; Spanish transl., Madrid.
60. LENTIN A., RIVAUD J., *Éléments d'algèbre moderne*, Paris, 1956; 2nd ed., 1957.
61. LITTLEWOOD D. E., *The theory of group characters and matrix representations of groups*, 2nd ed., Oxford, 1950.
62. LOMONT J. S., *Applications of finite groups*, N. Y., 1959.
63. LUGOWSKI H., WEINERT J., *Grundzüge der Algebra*, Teil I, *Allgemeine Gruppentheorie*, Leipzig, 1957; Teil 2, *Allgemeine Ring- und Körpertheorie*, Leipzig, 1958.
64. LYAPIN E. S., *Semigroups*, Moscow, 1960. English transl., N.Y., 1963.
65. MAC DUFFEE C. C., *An introduction to abstract algebra*, N. Y., 1940.
66. McCOY N. H., *Rings and ideals*, Baltimore, 1948.
67. MILLER G. A., BLICHFELDT H. F. and DICKSON L. E., *Theory and application of finite groups*, N. Y., 2nd ed., 1938.
68. MILLER K. S., *Elements of modern abstract algebra*, N. Y., 1958.
69. MOISIL Gr. C., *Introducere in algebra*, I, *Inele şi ideale*, vol. 1, Bucharest, 1954.
70. MONTEIRO A. A., *Filtros e ideals*, Rio de Janeiro, 1955.
71. MONTGOMERY D. and ZIPPIN L., *Topological transformation groups*, N. Y., 1955.

72. MORGADO J., *Elementos de algebra moderna*: reticulados, sistemas parcialmente ordenados; vol. 1, Porto, 1956.

73. MURNAGHAN F. D., *The theory of group representations*, 1938; Russian transl., Moscow, 1950.

74. NAKAYAMA, *Algebra, II, Theory of rings* (Japanese), 1954.

75. NEUMANN J. VON, *Lectures on continuous geometries*, 2 vols., Princeton, 1936–1937.

76. NORTHCOTT D. G., *Ideal theory*, Cambridge, 1953.

77. OKUNEV L. Ya., *The elements of modern algebra*, Moscow, 1941.

78. OSIMA, *The theory of groups* (Japanese), 1954.

79. PICKERT G., *Einführung in die höhere Algebra*, Göttingen, 1951.

80. PICKERT G., *Projektive Ebenen*, Berlin, Göttingen, Heidelberg, 1955.

81. PLOTKIN B. I., Generalized soluble and generalized nilpotent groups, *Uspekhi mat. nauk* **13**, No. 4, 89–172 (1958).

82. PONTRYAGIN L. S., *Continuous groups*, Moscow, Leningrad, 1938; 2nd ed., 1954; English transl., Princeton, 1939; Rumanian transl., Bucharest, 1956; German transl., Leipzig, 1957.

83. POSTNIKOV M. M., Definite families of functions and algebras without divisors of zero over the field of real numbers, *Uspekhi mat. nauk* **9**, No. 2 67–104, (1954).

84. POSTNIKOV M. M., *Foundations of Galois theory*, Moscow, 1960; English transl. Oxford, 1962.

85. QUESANNE M., Delachet A., *L'algèbre moderne*, Paris, 1955; 2nd ed., 1957; Portugese transl., S. Paulo, 1956.

86. RÉDEI L., *Algebra*, vol. 1, Budapest, 1954; German transl., 1959; English translation in preparation by Pergamon Press.

87. REIDEMEISTER K., *Einführung in die kombinatorische Topologie*, Brunswick, 1932.

88. RITT J. F., *Differential algebra*, N. Y., 1950.

89. RITT J. F., *Differential equations from the algebraic standpoint*, N. Y., 1932; 2nd ed. 1947.

90. SAMUEL P., *Algèbre locale*, Paris, 1953.

91. SATO S., *The theory of groups* (Japanese); Chinese transl., Shanghai, 1934.

92. SCHILLING O. F. G., *The theory of valuations*, N. Y., 1950.

93. SCHMIDT O. Yu., *Abstract theory of groups*, 2nd ed., Moscow–Leningrad, 1933 (see also *Selected works of O. Yu. Schmidt, Mathematics*, Moscow, 1959).

94. SCORZA G., *Gruppi astratti*, Rome, 1942.

95. SHIRSHOV A. I., Some problems in the theory of rings which are nearly associative, *Uspekhi mat. nauk* **13**, No. 6, 3–20 (1958).

96. SHODA K., *General algebra* (Japanese), Tokyo, 1947.

97. SKORNYAKOV L. A., Projective planes, *Uspekhi mat. nauk* **6**, No. 6, 112–154 (1951); English transl., 1953.

98. SPECHT W., *Gruppentheorie*, Berlin, Göttingen, Heidelberg, 1956.
99. SPEISER A., *Die Theorie der Gruppen von endlicher Ordnung*, 3rd ed., 1937; 4th ed., Basel, Stuttgart, 1956; English reprint., 1945.
100. SUSHKEVICH A. K., *The theory of generalized groups*, Kharkov, Kiev, 1937.
101. SUZUKI M., *Structure of a group and the structure of its lattice of subgroups*, Berlin, Göttingen, Heidelberg, 1956; Russian transl., Moscow, 1960.
102. TANNAKA T., *The principle of duality* (Japanese), Tokyo, 1951, 1954; Chinese transl., Ughan, 1943.
103. VAN DER WAERDEN B. L., *Gruppen von linearen Transformationen*, Berlin 1935.
104. VAN DER WAERDEN B. L., *Moderne Algebra*, 2 vols., 1930, 1931; 2nd ed., 1937, 1940; 3rd ed., 1950; 4th ed., *Algebra*, 1955; Russian transl., 1934, 1937; 2nd Russian transl., Moscow, Leningrad, 1947; English translation, N. Y., 1949; Portuguese transl., Lisbon, 1954.
105. VASILACHE S., *Elemente de teoria multimilor şi a structurilor algebrice*, Bocharest, 1956.
106. VILENKIN N. Ya., The theory of topological groups, II, *Uspekhi mat. nauk 5*, No. 4, 19–74 (1950).
107. WEIL A., *L'intégration dans les groupes topologiques et ses applications*. Paris, 1940; Russian transl., Moscow, 1950.
108. WEYL H., *The classical groups, their invariants and representations*, Princeton, 1939; 2nd ed., 1946; Russian transl., Moscow, 1947.
109. WOLF P., *Algebraische Theorie der Galoisschen Algebren*, Berlin, 1956.
110. ZAPPA G., *Gruppi, corpi, equazioni*, 2nd ed., Naples, 1954.
111. ZARISKI O. and SAMUEL P., *Commutative algebra*, vol. 1, Princeton, 1958; vol. 2, 1960.
112. ZASSENHAUS H., *Lehrbuch der Gruppentheorie*, Bd. I, Leipzig—Berlin, 1937; English transl., N. Y., 1949; 2nd ed. English transl., 1958.

INDEX

Isomorphism (*cont.*)
  of rings 39
  of sets with closure 315
  of topological
    groups 326
    spaces 315
  of universal algebras of the same
    type 93
  of vector spaces 216
  operator
    of groupoids 202
    of rings 205
Isotope, principal 55
Isotopy
  of groupoids 53
  of rings 56

Join of equivalence relations 8
Jordan ring 28

Kernel of a homomorphism 102

Lattice 161
  Boolean (= Boolean algebra) 198
  complete 166
  distributive 170, 196
  free 165
  modular (= Dedekind) 170
  of equivalence relations 166
  of sets 196
    Boolean 199
  of subalgebras 162
  of subgroups 162
  of subrings 162
  of subsets 162
Laurent power series 52
Law
  anti-commutative 27
  associative 20
  cancellation 21, 44
  commutative 21
  distributive 25
Left
  annihilator
    of a ring 65
    of a subset of a ring 227
  coset 58
  ideal 65
  multiplication 205
Left-sided partition of a group 58

Lemma
  Gauss's 77
  Schur's 231
  Zassenhaus's 120
Length of a normal series 122
Lie ring 27
  of endomorphisms of an Abelian
    group 265
Limit element of a well-ordered set
  15
Linear
  algebra (= algebra over a field)
    235
  dependence 218
  subspace 216
  topology 327
  transformation 221
    of finite rank 228
  vector space 216
Linearly ordered
  groupoid 272
  ring 278
  set 10
Locally bicompact space 320
Logarithmic norm 297
Loop 53
Lower
  bound 15
  central chain 129

Maximal
  chain 16
  element 15
  ideal 82
Minimal element 11
Models 6
Modular (= Dedekind) lattice 170
Module (= Abelian group with ring
    of operators) 203
  free 209
  unital 204
Monotonic
  homomorphism 285
  mapping 168
  transformation 273
Multi-operators 97
Multiplication 20
Multiplicative
  group
    of a skew field 33
    of roots of unity 24
  groupoid of a ring 26
  semigroup of an associative ring
    26

Mutual commutator
in a group 125
in an Ω-group 125
Mutually prime elements of a semigroup 70

n-ary
algebraic operation 91
relation 6
Natural
homomorphism 96
mapping 9
Neighbourhood 313
Neutral element 332
Nilpotent Ω-group 129
Non-Archimedean norm 295
Norm 292
Archimedean 295
logarithmic 297
non-Archimedean 295
Normal
extension of a field 341
series
of a lattice 173
of an Ω-group 122
space 319
subgroup 58
Normed
algebra 304
ring 292
Null ideal 64
Nullary algebraic operation 91

One-sided ideal 65
Open
homomorphism 326
subset 313
Operator 201
automorphism 202
endomorphism 202
group 201
groupoid 201
homomorphism
of groupoids 202
of rings 205
isomorphism
of groupoids 202
of rings 205
ring 206
with ring of operators 207
Order
of a group 24
of an element 35

Ordered
ring 278
set 10

p-adic
number 115
topology 331
valuation 302
Partial
algebraic operation 91
ordering 10
Partially ordered
groupoid 272
ring 278
set 10
Partition of a set into classes 7
Periodic
group 36
part of a group 215
Permutation 25
Polynomial 30
Power
of a set 6
of an element 35
series 31
Primary
cyclic group 211
group 215
Prime
element (of a semigroup) 68
ideal 82
subfield 102
Primitive
class of algebras 138
polynomial 76
Principal
derived operation 136
fractional ideal 84
ideal 74
isotope 55
right ideal 209
series
of a lattice 174
of an Ω-group 124
Product
of binary relations 4
of ideals 81
of mappings 2
Pseudonorm 297
Pseudonormed algebra 304

Quasi-field 52
Quasi-group 52
Quaternion 239
Quotient-set 9

OTHER TITLES IN THE SERIES IN PURE
AND APPLIED MATHEMATICS